Adele ♡
Saccarelli
Cavallaro

Searching for Oz

By Adele Saccarelli-Cavallaro
with Michael Cavallaro

First Edition
2 3 4 5 6 7 8 9 10

ISBN

978-0-9973988-5-4
0-9973988-5-X

Credits

Cover Design: Prodesign

Hibernian Publishing
Brick, New Jersey

Dedication

To Michael (Marvel), an individual who has loved purely from his heart, has modeled self-love and shared with me a way to love myself. I was able to become who I truly am because his love allowed me to discover my own.

To the world: With my love, I have created this book (and a workbook to follow) with the intent of bringing a deeper awareness of abuse in all its forms to light with the hope of making real change.

Where there is abuse, there is no chance for love.

Acknowledgements

To Mike and Gail O'Connell who have made the publishing of this book possible!

To Nick Salamone, who has connected me to these wonderful people from Hibernian Publishing.

To Phyllis VanDerVoort, Gail Kerschner, Pat Kilgannon, Barb Wallace, Deb Wolk, Lynn Sharer, Rachael Simms, Mary Herald, Amy Kruzic, Mike Camoin, Barbara Ann Valinotti, Shinjini Bakshi, Catia Whitmore, Rose Cavallaro, Jordan Oliver, Nancy Baker, and Annmarie Serratore, all who have listened to me through the struggles of every aspect in writing this book.

To my beautiful stepchildren, Lissy, Cassie, Timmy and Joey who have shown me the meaning of being connected and truly loving unconditionally. To my darling birth children, Michelle and Kaitlyn, who have shown me nothing but support through-out this entire process and have taken this beautiful unconditional love that they have learned from the others and have sprinkled it like fairy dust everywhere they go.

To all of my advisors/friends: Linda (G-linda) Urie, Leslie (Good Witch) McMichaels, Kathy (Turn the Channel) O'Connell, Maureen (Is this experiment over yet) Watson.

To Kerri Joy, who shared with me, tips on storytelling, giving a renewed vitality to my story.

CHAPTER 1

Breathe, Dottie. Look around.

I seem to be inside my car. How did I get here? Why am I here?

It figures, more of not knowing where I am or how I got there, just like the rest of my life.

Oh my god! I really did sleep in my car.

I quickly look around to see if anyone has noticed that someone passed out in their car in some random parking lot.

Aaah, no one around! Well for at least this moment I am safe.

Then suddenly, I realize that this particular parking lot was not so random. I am parked at my grade school, St. Daniel's!

This has happened before. Not the place, but the feeling.

I seem to be doing this everywhere. Sometimes I wonder how I am able to function.

The last thing I remember, I was driving through my hometown, desperately seeking the same feeling of home that I once had as a little girl — when I was Dorothy.

It is hard to remember that feeling — that feeling of relaxed contentment seems to be gone forever. Since then, I have never felt that feeling — the feeling that most call love. Yet, there is something more that I can't put my finger on, something that seems quite tangible. I know that I will never be at peace until I find that feeling again.

I feel strange today. I look around. It feels as if my body and mind are colliding. It's like I am just landing in my body for the very first time. The emotional tornado that ripped through me last night, took over my mind. As my body separated from my mind, my emotions placed me in an alternate reality that most call sleep. That was when I must have pulled over and passed out.

Safety first...everything under control...that's me!

All my life I had done everything like a tornado.

Last night during the drive, the memories came like a thunderstorm. A thunderstorm is the first thing that is needed for a tornado to begin, and that can't be good. Memories of saying yes instead of no, of guilt, of insecurity — all tore through me. The feelings were so intense that I just let go of my control. My mind took over while my body blindly followed.

I have never been able to sit still long enough to feel things. I still don't understand. As I look out my window, my car is not parked between the lines. My car is diagonal across four spaces!

Figures, a good representation of my life.

I didn't know what enticed me to turn into this particular parking lot. When I left my house the night before, I was searching for something that was missing; little did I know that this would be a turning point in my life. That turn would completely alter my path.

Less than two years ago, I moved back to Pennsylvania from Kansas which seems to coincide with all the changes that are currently taking place. A year and a half ago, I began taking Adderall, a prescribed medication for my inability to focus. That is what the little pill was supposed to do, but as my body adjusted to the drug, it did so much more.

Every action, thought and feeling seemed to become clearer. It was sometimes difficult to ignore those things that I kept hidden inside of me. One of those secrets was the fact that my marriage had been over for quite some time.

As my emotions took a turn, I began to reflect on my life. In my career, the drug assisted me in going from last in sales to the top sales person in my company. It allowed me to do the logical thinking that was required. I worked and worked and worked. My bosses couldn't believe the transformation. Neither could I.

Before the medication, my life moved at mock speed with no direction. I was distracted by everything which caused me to fall behind when I was in school. I struggled with understanding the words of others as well as misunderstanding many conversations. I understood the words singularly, but when spoken together, and so quickly, it made my mind spin. Confusion was like a game that couldn't win.

8

My hyperactivity and attention problems caused me to miss blocks of information. I had difficulty with sustaining my focus, It interfered with my reading, understanding and decision making skills. Communication pained me. I still experience that pain and tension within me.

At times, I seemed spaced out and had difficulty with spacial awareness – bumping into things and perception difficulties. Standing or sitting still seemed impossible and there was no way to channel off this frustrated or backed-up energy. Sports helped me on some level, as it allowed me to channel some of the excess energy, but never resolved the problem.

Today, since I have been on the Adderall, life has been much smoother, especially when it comes to such things as organization, being on time and listening and understanding more. To many, that is a miracle in and of itself.

However, it also fills my every waking hour with tasks such as sorting, organizing and categorizing. It is like I can't stop. I find very little time to eat. My children think I have gone mad. Everything I touch or see has to be put in some kind of order, even human lives. My mind is out of control with detailed, yet hyper-focused thoughts, feelings and memories.

Nevertheless, the medication creates focus and productivity. It gives me a chance to catch up mentally. I know that I am far behind, so I read everything I can get my hands on. I focus on the reality of my new found knowledge, but not the creativity that I had always loved. It is great for my mind, but not so much for my heart. No one realizes that the medication masks these unresolved emotions and yes, these unresolved emotions still exist. I can still feel them, burning underneath my skin. I have lost weight along with my intuitive instincts. As a result, I now live my life in my mind and almost not at all in my heart.

The benefit of this new focused mind is that for once, reading is magical; almost a trade-off. I tell others about my new discovery and how reading is like watching a movie and how I can hear the whole story all the way — from beginning to end — sometimes in one sitting! No one seems to understand when I passionately explain my new discoveries but I don't care. I finally can read the way I have imagined others did!

With this new found skill, I can attend to most conversations and understand them clearly. My life is completely changed. A new door to new dimensions has opened. This door has magnificent experiences flowing through it. They are so wondrous and all-inspiring.

For the past year and a half while on this medication, my life has fallen in place. Everything in my life was in order — work, my house, bills and my kids' schedules. The blue pill I chose shifted my perspective on life. Life was fluid and truly enjoyable for the first time. This was the answer to all my challenges.

But was it? No, not at all. The intense feelings are getting more and more difficult to fight off.

This week I was forced to be with myself. I was without anything to do or accomplish or goal to reach. This shifted my focus — no kids, no work and no distractions. I looked for something to organize. When I was alone last night, before the drive, I naturally shifted my focus to these intense feelings. I said to myself, could I organize these feelings like I did with my external world?

"For true freedom, Dorothy, you will have to resolve these internal feelings and get your past in order."

When I was very little, I would often hear these voices quite clearly, but as I grew older, they became fuzzy and unrecognizable.

My thoughts stop. I look around. Chirping birds outside the car bring me back to the present. I move around in my seat, glancing up at the school.

Why now? Am I ready? Do I even want to open that can of worms again? These feelings suck. I know there's no hope in getting rid of such feelings. Already tried.

I glance at the steering wheel. The voice comes again. *"For true freedom, Dorothy, you will have to resolve these internal feelings and get your past in order."*

Yesterday, my three kids left to be with their dad for an entire week. My kids' dad and now my ex, was another one of the big changes that happened to me after my clarity appeared. Don and I never had the type of relationship where we bantered back and forth with blame and accusation. We were more like buddies, so the divorce was pretty smooth. We had each other's back and we didn't ruffle each other's feathers. So, when I asked him to take them for longer than a weekend and a couple hours after school, he naturally complied.

Don was safe. I understood him and it seemed that he understood me. He didn't force me to change or force me to do anything for that matter. He understood my background and I understood his. Our past wounds allowed us to not put pressure on each other, even if it would have possibly led to our growth in the relationship or growth as individuals. Could we have worked out the problems in our relationship on our own? I don't think so. And the two therapists sucked.

Things remained the same during the separation and divorce. Not much was said. Not much was forced. No pressure. Living our lives and having to feel our pasts were pressure in itself.

I move around again in my seat, while I press down on the lever to move my seat back. I know that spending time alone, without the kids this week, is what I need right now. This week there will be no distractions that will keep me from focusing on my feelings. I have an opportunity for self-discovery and resolution.

I have become numb in my life. It has been my survival mechanism. The feelings of not being good enough, the shame, the guilt and the abuse are now beginning to seep into my conscious mind more and more every day. All the things in my life that I have tried to forget, ignore and suppress are now becoming more intense.

This Adderall seems to bring everything to focus, to light. All the memories that were once so easily suppressed and carefully hidden are now knocking at my door asking for forgiveness and resolution. All of the emotions that I didn't know what to do with are now dancing before my eyes in neon lights. I can no longer turn them off. They are frightening, yet appealing. They are appealing because if I can resolve these feelings, this can of worms, maybe just maybe, I can get beyond it and feel the love that I once knew — the love that I felt when I was a little girl. Does it still exist?

I turn on the ignition, moving the windshield wipers to their proper place. I take another deep breath. I sit still, feeling my body against the seat of my car. It is as if it is the first time. I feel my body and am aware of all of its sensations.

Maybe I should go in?

I turn in my seat, looking back at the Catholic school's large doors. The realization hit me as hard as a flying window coming off its hinges hurled by a powerful wind of a twister. At this moment, I realize why my car is parked at my grade school. It is time to literally revisit my past.

I open my purse and find my blue Adderall and red Swedish fish out of their bottle and bag. They are all mixed up.

Damn.

I look up and roll my eyes.

How ironic. Swedish fish. A representation of calm creatures swimming in the ocean and Adderall, a blue prescription pill to chill down a fast mind.

I pop an Adderall into my mouth.

I turn off the ignition and open the car door. I feel the warm golden shower of sunlight on my face and the cool crisp autumn air fully bringing me back to the present; a new state of awareness as I get out of the car. I look ahead at the recess yard which brings a smile to my face. Memories surface and bring me back in time, feeling each one of my schoolmates, in observation of all of them. They all surround me. I can feel their presence as if they are here.

~

Oh, how I loved that part of my life. The recess yard was my domain. I was certainly not an outcast there like some of my peers. It was the only thing that I could hold onto in order to be able to survive in all the other areas of my life. I watched some of my peers feeling bad after being chosen last in the recess yard games. But oh, how I felt and understood the pain of those feelings of incompetency and shame when recess was over when we had to return to that building. Once inside the building, all of my learning challenges and the pain sprung back to life. A building whose dull colored walls and fluorescent lighting made me spin. Being in the building was like being in a tornado. My head spun, my emotions spun and my thoughts were in disarray. School work always reminded me of my struggles and how broken I perceived myself to be.

I wonder if my mom and dad struggled in school because they always seemed to understand that part of me. My mom and dad never seemed to care about the grades as long as I made an effort.

~

I continue to walk towards the building. I suddenly stop and drop my head down remembering how difficult it was to get good grades and believing that my brain was not like everyone else's. My reality is placed back again to the past.

~

I was not like the other kids in the school especially when it came time for testing or responding to a question. It seemed so effortless for most of those kids. My school environment was filled with distractions. The piercing florescent lights seemed to make the desks and even the words on the chalkboard move around. It was quite distracting and made it literally impossible to conform to the stillness that was required by the Catholic grade school rigidity.

~

I continue to walk on the brick path that has been restored. Almost at the door, I stop to notice the faded yellow chalk on the brick path. It lost its sparkle. The few clouds left over from the storm still appeared traumatized due to the tornado that had passed through this town just a few days ago.

I reach out with both hands and pull the handles on the thick heavy school doors.

Locked out.

I still don't belong. I didn't fit in then and I don't fit in now.

Maybe I just don't belong in this world...

I begin to lose all sense of focus as to why I am here, almost as though I am lost in the twister again until suddenly my mind and body stop. A few clouds in the sky kindly move aside to let the sun shine, taking center stage in the spotlight for a brief moment. The autumn sun reveals itself again, lighting up the entire recess yard. In this spotlight, a van appears. The woman driving gives me a wave as she pulls into a school parking space.

I wave back and stop for the van.

I hear a little voice inside saying,

Follow your heart. Follow the road of yellow brick, Dorothy!

Seriously?

I turn my head and gaze over at the rest of the faded yellow chalk. I look at where the brick road will lead me. I take this as a sign to not go back to my car and not run from the opportunity that had presented itself. I follow the brick road around to the other entrance of the school to see if there is another way to get in. As I walk I drift off again into that same reality of my past.

~

I knew that something was wrong with me, not being able to read. I just didn't know the name of what was causing my mind to move like a tornado. The tornado in MY brain touched down and raced across the earth causing problems for everyone else. It moved at warp speed knocking over everything in its path — spinning around with no self-control, no self-awareness, and no awareness of others. Then when it touched down, it usually caused real disaster, like a disruption in a classroom or maybe at home disturbing a dad who needed stillness. When the tornado was exhausted it removed itself from the ground, bringing all the baggage and weight with it. Now the tornado owned these items for a while to remind us of the chaos that it had caused. Eventually the tornado would let go of those things, but did it REALLY release them? No, of course not! They stayed with the tornado only to cause more anxiety and more movement, not to mention the poor tornado's overwhelming sense of wrongness for causing all of this.

~

Whew!

I arrive at the other entrance, my head slowly coming out of my alternate reality. I realize that even a blue pill will not stop these memories and intense feelings.

Maybe I am ready.

My thoughts become a little bit clearer, my heart still far away, but my courage still willing to participate.

Take that leap.

I ring the bell.

CHAPTER 2

No More Hiding From The Twister

Who rang that bell?

It is as if the gatekeeper of Oz himself is inside my head.

What is wrong with me?

The happy little birds singing behind me bring me back to the present. The sound and the vibration pass through me at all levels. I feel the change, a hint of courage in my heart — but don't quite understand; I know the feelings are a marker to continue on.

"Go ahead, bluebirds," I say out loud as I peer in through the glass doors. "Go tell the sun to bring me back a rainbow!" My eyes catch sight of the four words written on the wall above the opening of the foyer, Our Lady of Angels.

What is this? Where the hell is St. Daniel's?

I am confused, yet curious, as I start knocking on the door.

Try the door!

I try the door and it opens! There's a woman who appears inside the door. She has blonde hair that is almost white. It shines.

"Did you ring the bell?" she asks. "We usually can't hear if you just knock."

"I thought this was St. Daniel's," I tell her.

"Yes, it is. St. Daniel's is down at the other end of the school. This side is Our Lady of Angels, a school for children with Invisible Challenges."

"Are you kidding?" I ask, somewhat confused.

"No, why would I kid?"

Well, she certainly didn't look like she spent much time kidding.

"Invisible Challenges?" I turn around again and say, "Don't bother, little bluebirds, the rainbow has already arrived."

"Excuse me, Miss?" the woman asks, somewhat confused.

OMG! This woman thinks I'm crazy.

"Would you like to come in this way?" she asks, looking cautiously at me. "You can walk through here to get to St. Daniel's."

"It would be much more appropriate for me to walk through a door that leads to possible answers for Invisible Challenges," I say and then look at her glowing smile.

She definitely thinks I'm nuts. Am I? I don't even remember driving here, for God's sake.

"Yes, please. I think that I would much rather come through this entrance."

The woman looks a little muddled but pushes the door open for me, enough so I can grasp the heavy old door and swing it fully open.

I open the door to great change, to bright colors! It is no longer black and white, but emerald green walls and yellow paths guiding the way to unknown worlds. Everything is newly painted and the emerald green walls are soothing and almost healing in a way which makes this place feel like a sanctuary as opposed to the prison that I remember. The non-fluorescent LED lighting made sure to show themselves off to me: bright but not distracting.

I stand in the high ceiling foyer, spin around slowly and then turn towards the glass doors where I find the sun waiting for me, shining in through the windows. The solar light comes in seemingly penetrating my soul and awakening something much like the sound of the birds but yet more powerful than I can understand. In that moment, I know that something has changed forever. The outside seems so dull now.

Maybe what they say is true. The beauty really does lie within.

The woman's eyes join mine at the window. "Well, what do you know, the sun finally decided to grace us with its presence. It's about time!"

"Yeah," I tell her. "Isn't it great?" As I turn towards the woman, I notice that the woman's hair is still shining. Actually, her face has got a bright glow to her as well.

The woman, still looking outside, says, "Look at all those bluebirds? And is that a rainbow?"

I look out the window more closely. "Yes, it looks like a little one…starting to form," I answer.

"No, look over there."

"Oh, yes…wow!" I notice a fully developed rainbow.

The lady turns towards me and says, "So, I didn't catch your name, Miss?"

No answer.

Speak, Dottie! I say to myself as I continue to stare out the window.

"Excuse me, Miss. Was there something that I can help you with?"

I turn around slowly, and say, "My name is Dottie. And I would like to see the principal of St. Daniel's."

"Do you have an appointment?" she inquires, somehow managing to look upon me from her smaller stature. Her blue eyes are now twinkling and have a softness to them that is indescribable.

"I don't," I answer, "but I used to go here."

"Oh really? Well okay then!" she says with a smile, "Come on in! Right this way, ma'am." She motions me with her arm that is enveloped by a white delicate long sleeve which is made of silk. It seems to dance on her arm as it moves.

I begin to follow this radiant white-haired woman who's wearing white sandals and sparkly silver nail polish.

As I join her and begin to walk next to her, I hear the clicking of the front door getting ready to close.

*Boom…*went the doors.

It startles me a bit. The calm woman continues to walk, as I turn around at the distraction.

I walk through the hallway, in awe of the changes that are made, as she directs me down to the main office. I whisper under my breath, "We are not in Saint Daniel's anymore."

I hear laughter coming from the first classroom and unidentified sounds and tones from the second classroom. There is a teacher in the front of the room and computer monitors to her right. There are wires to the left of her and speakers to the back of the room.

The children are looking at the monitors and laughing as the teacher speaks to them turning their heads towards the screens and then back to the teacher. I stop at the classroom to watch the activity that seems so out of place for a classroom.

"What kind of classrooms are these?" I inquire, looking around.

"By the expression on your face, I am assuming that you have never seen anything like this before."

I nod.

The woman says, "Multi-level classrooms; the students are graded by how much information that they can absorb. The project is in its second year. These types of kids have a talent for multi-sensory learning, but let's face it, every kid has the potential."

"True." I continue to follow her.

The woman and I reach our destination, the office, and then she motions me to sit and wait for the vice principal to get off the phone. She whispers some words as she walks out the door, "Are you hear to see the Wizard?"

"What?" I say looking up at her.

The woman vanishes out the door...

Suddenly, I realize that this used to be my third-grade classroom. I look over at where I used to sit. The memory of that time triggers a vision of the moment, a hologram of my past.

~

"What's this?" I remember saying to my third-grade teacher.

Sister handed me a piece of paper with a picture of Lion from the book *The Wonderful Wizard of Oz* on it.

"The Lion represents the name of your reading group for the year, Dorothy," she had said.

"Oh really, Sister? The Cowardly Lion? The one that thinks of himself as a failure; the one who is fearful of life or of making a mistake?" I whispered to myself. "That figures!"

When we had joined our teams, according to character, I noticed that all the slow readers were on my team!

"That was 'no' big surprise," I whispered under my breath. Of course, I hadn't said this directly to Sister.

It had been only a few weeks before my reading partner moved to the Tin Woodman Team.

"Wow, he must have learned how to be brave in our Lion's group. I guess he is ready to learn how the heart works now."

"What's wrong with me? Why can't I get this?"

I continued to try my hardest to understand what was being taught.

"Teachers! Wake up sleepyheads! Let me make things easy for you. It might help me and be easier for you if you would just send me straight to the Scarecrow Team to find out how my brain operates. I already get this courage thing. I play sports! I understand that in order to accomplish anything, one needs strength, self-discipline and perseverance. I understand that in order to move to the next step, you need confidence! No fear! I'm ready, people!"

But still there is no movement. I stayed in the Cowardly Lion group struggling the whole year.

~

"Hello, Miss, can I help you?" the nun says while hanging up the phone. I look up at Sister. No words come out.

Bluebirds, the rainbow, the wizard, my reading groups…weird.

19

"Are you okay?" she asks.

"Yeah," I respond.

I think I am.

I open my mouth, this time surer of my response.

"My name is Dottie and I'm writing a book about children with challenges, such as auditory processing disorder, ADHD and dyslexia. Helping them to become their own self-advocates."

Huh! I'm writing what? When did that happen?

"I figured that it would be helpful if I could walk through the school so I could remember some things about my childhood challenges. Would you mind?"

Gosh, that was easy, lying to a nun.

Did I have a choice? The other option could have been, "Well, you see, Sister, I just wanted to revisit the place that caused me so much pain and humiliation. Do you mind?"

Jesus!

"How did you get in the school?" the nun asks.

"Some woman," I say. The nun looks at me confused. "She had blonde hair," hoping to jog her memory.

"Okay," she shrugs her shoulders like I lied and made the woman up. "Never mind that. It would be my pleasure to walk you around!" She touches my shoulder gently and motions me to get up. "And how about the Multi-Sensory School?"

I nod and follow her to the door.

The nun says with excitement, "I think it's wonderful!"

The nun introduces herself as Sister Emily, but insists that most of the students call her Sister Em.

So, for one hour, I pretend that I am a passionate writer.

Hey, maybe, I'll take some notes and really look like a professional writer. Just take me through Oz!

She introduces me to all the teachers, repeating the lie over and over again. She announces to almost everyone in the school that I am going to write a book about my experiences at St. Daniel's School. She lets me walk into the classrooms and stay as long as I want.

"Dottie, are you finished here?" Sister Em taps me lightly on the shoulder again. "I would suggest visiting the upper school, which consists of the fourth to eighth grades. Are you up for it, today?"

I nod, following Sister back to the office, still in another reality. *Not STILL, never still. I am just in another reality.*

Sister makes a phone call to the upper school for me, continuing the lie. I exit the building through the *more appropriate* doors and find the sun and those happy little bluebirds waiting for me. They chirp and fly about from tree to tree. I follow the path of yellow brick over to the other school, noticing the warmth of the bright sun, the smell of the green grass and the violets. What a great day it turns out to be!

I spin around walking backwards facing the wonderful new school and notice the solar panels that are on the roof.

Wow, really progressive.

I turn around continuing to walk as I brush my hand up against the fence. The fence surrounds the hearty garden of vegetables such as cabbage and brussel sprouts that are apparently maintained by the kids or even maybe the nuns from the convent.

The convent, what a place! Our class would go there periodically. I don't remember much about the convent except getting my period there in the seventh grade.

How ironic that was!

I seriously did not know what the hell my period was then. I excused myself and then stuffed some tissues in my underwear until I got home. My sister noticed the bloody tissues in the bathroom and told my mom. Of course, my mom was so excited that I got my period. It would have been nice if she had been excited to tell me about my period prior to me getting it. She felt so happy that her last child finally got her period and said that it was a special day. It

21

would have been more special if I had known that one day I would be bleeding out of a hole that I didn't know that I had.

The bus ride home was hell that day; although there was a realization for me about the book *Are You There, God, It's Me Margaret?* by Judy Blume that kept getting passed around at my school. My classmate, Katie, constantly talked about that book throughout my sixth-grade year and I never understood what she was talking about. Well, it finally made sense that day. I would have picked up the book that day to learn all about the reproduction system, if I could attend long enough to read it.

Instead, I asked my older teenage sister who was a nurse's aide to tell me about it. She was very blunt to say the least. "Listen, here's a tampon. You have a hole right there, where eventually a baby will pass through. Blood will come out every month, trust me, it's a good thing. If the blood doesn't come out that will mean you're pregnant. You don't want to be pregnant. You fuck around, you're gonna get pregnant. Just stick the tampon up there to stop the blood from leaking and staining all your underwear. It's really easy."

I smile at the memory. I get to the crosswalk where I hear from a distance a slam of a door, the lady from the van. There she is again. The lady who taught kids how to read from her mobile reading van. I have another grade school memory of my difficulties reading in the van.

~

"No, Dottie, this is a 'g' sound, not a 'k' sound. 'G'. Do you hear it now?"

"They sound the same to me. The information that you're giving me lady doesn't seem to be going in properly. Therefore, there is either something wrong with your information or something wrong with my brain. I presume that it has to do with the latter of the two, because everyone else seems to be getting it."

~

I smile at my hostile thoughts.

I reach the traffic light where I need to walk across the street to the St. Daniel's Upper School. I look up at the flashing sign that reads *Walk*. I slip into another memory.

Father Rich and I are walking across the street and he is smiling at me. Smiling, always smiling at me. All the girls used to say that he was so cute. He WAS cute and sweet too, one of those touchy-feely guys.

I come to. I look up and notice on the side of the building that reads "Baum." St. Daniel's building was dedicated to a Monsignor Baum? How come I never noticed that name before?

Maybe because you were checked out, Dottie, that's why.

Isn't Baum the author of *The Wonderful Wizard of Oz*? The one and only L. Frank Baum!

What the hell?

The book *The Wonderful Wizard of Oz* is forever present today. I take another deep breath. I cross the street and walk towards the entrance. The office buzzes me in. I let myself in, stand in the foyer and look up towards the stairs. Before proceeding, I take a right and peek into the room that saved my life, the gymnasium. Memories begin to surface again.

~

"Dorothy, we're going to make you the setter in volleyball. The setter must touch the ball every time. This way you won't get distracted and bored in this sport," Coach Bob said.

~

"Concentrate, Dorothy. I know that you've pitched a million balls already today, but go throw twenty more. Do you want to be a great pitcher or an average pitcher?" Coach Patterson prodded.

~

"Dorothy, who cares if you are the only sixth grader trying out, you can run circles around those seventh and eighth grade girls. Come on, Dorothy, try out! Come on, you chicken shit!" said Katrina.

~

23

"I hope that I don't look like a boy playing on the boys' soccer team. I just wish that there was a girls' soccer team," I said.

"Well, there isn't one. You don't look like a boy," Leo said. "Don't quit, Dorothy. The guys need you."

"I know. I just wish that there was at least one other girl on the team," I said.

"When you get to high school, there will be plenty of girls to play soccer with. And who cares...you love the sport, right?" Leo asked.

~

I come out of the memory and proceed up the stairs, slowly walking away from all the good memories. I am confronted with what seems like a dark forest on the walls in the school hallway. Some artwork of lions, tigers and bears — *oh why* — are hanging up for the Halloween holiday display.

Really?

I continue through the forest and run up the last set of stairs grabbing the end of the railing, like I did as a sixth grader. I catch my breath, walk towards the office and peek in. I notice that the room I had spent the most amount of time in, the office, is completely the same.

A priest approaches me, smiling, and calmly says, "Hello, I hear that you are writing a book."

"Yes," I say and wonder if they do confessions on Thursday so that I can be absolved from my sins and lies today.

"Would you like to sit here and talk?" he implores, looking closely at me.

"No, I just want to walk around," I mutter, feeling out of place.

"Walk around?" He inquires, "Where?"

"Everywhere...anywhere...I don't care," I say.

"Well, do you want to sit here first to ask me any questions?"

"No...I pretty much just want to walk around," I state again, hoping he would get the point.

"Why don't you sit here? I will be right back."

I laugh at the fact that he just wants me to "sit here," with Jesus staring back at me on his cross.

"Jesus," I whisper, roll my eyes and then give Jesus a quick smile.

Hello, Jesus, still here? You must be sick of staring at the same old couch and tile on the floor since the '70s.

I run my fingers across the couch material and my foot across the tile. I look up at the opposite wall.

Oh, what is this? Something that was added to the wall; new stenciling, I see. The question is does the new stenciled fence and flowers mean that everyone here is fenced in more than ever before or does it mean that there is a new opening of gates to communication? I am sure it's not the latter of the two.

I chuckle at my judgmental thoughts, then my eyes take note of the many patterns on the floor taking me away to another place again, sixth grade, on this very same couch.

~

"We are so caught! Brian, I told you not to say that I signed it," I whined, squirming around.

"I had to. They made me," Brian said simply, as if that was the only reason.

"Why didn't you say that YOU signed your detention slip?" I countered, knowing the answer already.

He smiled wryly, "They would have known I was lying."

"No, they wouldn't have! You didn't use your head." I stomped my foot.

"Dorothy, you spelled my dad's name Brain, instead of Brian."

"Brian, I'm in so much trouble. My mom is gonna be so mad at me. Why do I always do this?!"

"We'll get out of it." Of course, Brian was always the optimistic one. But only because his parents were a bunch of liberal hippies and didn't believe in discipline.

"How?"

"I don't know, we always do," he shrugged.

"Yeah, right. YOU always do!"

"Brian, what's wrong? Why are you turning three shades of red?"

"You might be right, Dorothy...look..." Brian points up to our moms. "Hi, Mom. Hi, Mrs. Cavarelli," Brian says.

The voices fade...

"They should have known I was dyslexic then," I mumble to myself.

"You're dyslexic? Is that what your book is about?" asks the same blonde woman who had greeted me at the entrance of the other school.

"Hey, you," I say. "You do exist? I didn't make you up. The nun didn't know who you were."

"Yes, I do exist," she says looking at me funny. "My name is Glenda."

"Really? Glinda? Like the witch, Glinda, in the book *The Wonderful Wizard of Oz?*"

"Yes, I am Glenda. Although my name is spelled with an 'e,' not like that awesome Glinda the witch in that amazing story. Why?"

"Never mind," I answer.

"Are you okay? Your face is flushed," says Glenda.

"I'm fine."

"Now, where is it that you want to go, my dear?" asks Glenda as she drifts out through the office door. "You said that you wanted to walk around."

"Oh, yes, maybe the second floor, Mr. Marvel's room."

"Oh, is that where he taught?"

"You heard of him?" I say. "That was a long time ago."

"Heard of him?! I know him now. As a matter of fact, he will be here later today! At least that's what they are saying in there." She points to the office.

"No way. He was my seventh-grade teacher!"

As I continue to talk, Glenda directs me to the stairwell leading me to the steps which lead up to Mr. Marvel's classroom.

"He was the only teacher who understood how I learned. I remember the year he taught me was his very first year of teaching. He was intrigued about the way I learned. I certainly wasn't," I explain.

"Really?"

"Yes. He always would ask me questions about how I figured out a word problem or how I saw a word or what did I really see. He used to talk about how the brain worked. He told me that he learned about all this cool stuff during his student teaching in Europe with a guy named Terry from England."

I suddenly stop.

"What is it?"

"I'm just remembering when Mr. Marvel's dad died. I was standing right here on these steps when I told him that I could help him," I say patting the railing.

"Really, I didn't know that. You told him that you could help him?" said Glenda.

"Yeah, I know. Why would a seventh grader give advice to her teacher?" I answer. "My dad died that year as well."

"Oh, I see," Glenda compassionately says.

We lock eyes for a moment. I notice her hair is still shining.

"So you had trouble learning?" she says to me. "You did mention that you are dyslexic. It's funny how things work out, isn't it?"

"What things?" I ask.

"It's just kind of interesting, don't ya think, that he was teaching you then and now you come here to where he is creating it?" says Glenda.

27

"Creating what?" I inquire.

"The St. Daniel's Multi-Level School! Mr. Marvel is creating this part of the school for children who have Invisible Challenges. In fact, he just flew in last week. He finally found a house in town."

"Really?" I say.

The two of us pass my old sixth-grade classroom. Glenda steps aside giving me some room to reflect.

I drop my head down, feeling a sense of "not good enough" again.

"What is it?" Glenda responds.

"Oh, sorry, just remembering stuff," I say.

I grab my pen and notebook pretending to write about my findings for this book that I am supposedly writing.

Glenda smiles.

I switch the subject and say, "Do you know that once Mr. Marvel insisted that I play the witch in the school play? Other teachers said that I couldn't do it, and I really didn't believe that I could do it either, remembering the lines and all. Mr. Marvel said, 'Nope. She's right for the job,'" I say, as I exaggerate a little. "We did the stage play of *The Wonderful Wizard of Oz!* OMG! That's right! We did that play! There it is again."

"What is again?" Glenda asks.

"Oh, *The Wonderful Wizard of Oz*. I can't seem to get away from that story this morning. It's making me a bit crazy. It's a long story. Don't ask."

"But I want to ask. What a great story it was! It's one of my favorites! I tell that story all the time."

"Really?" I question.

"If I must admit, I did write the most awesome report on the story once. It's kind of like a story about human behavior. A story about the triumph of good over evil," Glenda explains with her bright eyes and becomes dramatic with her arms as she continues to walk me down the hall. "It's an extraordinary story with beautiful colors, amazing characters in contrast to her gray tornado-like world. It's about this little girl named Dorothy who was basically stuck, but she used her creative energy to get herself unstuck. I could go on and on about that story. By the way, is your real name Dorothy, Dottie!?" Glenda inquires and giggles.

"Yes, it is," I answer giggling along.

Glenda might be a little crazy herself.

I smile at how cute Glenda is. We reach the room where I had spent seventh grade with Mr. Marvel. The room is empty. The students must be down in the gym or cafeteria. I am glad for this because it gives me a change to go in and remember my past without any interruptions.

"Yep, this is it!" I say starting to fade again into the old memories. I attempt to bring myself back with some words to Glenda. "Thanks so much."

"Oh, you're very welcome!" Glenda exclaims as she begins to walk away. "Good luck with your book," she says.

"I am not really writing a book," I confess.

"Well maybe you should, my dear," Glenda winks and suddenly looks down at her watch. "Oh, heavens, I must go, Dorothy. Have fun. Hope you find what you are looking for."

Glenda disappears in a flash.

People go and come so quickly around here.

CHAPTER 3

I Am Not A Crystal Ball, Marvel!

Almost there.

After checking out some of the classrooms, I head down the stairs to the gymnasium and find that the doors are locked.

Yet another barrier.

This is the place that I want to wander through and feel those feelings again; there is no place like this place. There is no place like home. This is at least close to the home that I had been seeking last night! I stand here thinking that there has to be some way to get past the barrier. This was the only area in the building that I would never be locked out of or ever feel like an outcast.

I stand in front of the doors, trying to fight the urge to kick down the door, but suddenly, a faint echoing sound rings in my head. Turning around, I see a man walking towards me. The gentleman, who is dressed like a janitor, motions to the gym doors and asks, "Do ya wanna get in there?"

"Yes, will you let me in?" I hold my breath, waiting for the answer that I want, as well as trying to hide my desperation.

The janitor taps on his pants pockets. "Sorry, ma'am. Keys are upstairs and I am on my way out the door."

Of course.

"However, if you really want to get in there you could go through those doors," pointing to the double doors just up the first flight of stairs. "You will have to go through the band room, down to the stage and then that will plop you right down to the gym floor. Just know that you have to go back the same way, because the gym doors will be locked." He points again at the locks on the doors.

Stuttering out a thank you, the janitor disappears before I could make a coherent sentence. Finally — alone, I bolt through the double doors, my body in the band room and my mind already in the gym. My body stops suddenly to identify a particular feeling that occurred right in front of this old piano that I played in the third grade. When my mind is conscious of my body, or I should say when my mind is "still" enough to feel my body, I am able to remember some of my piano teacher's words that went along with those feelings.

~

"Dorothy, turn the page," Sister Marietta would say. "Are you reading this music or did you just memorize the notes again? It sounds good and the rhythm is perfect, but it's important to be able to read the music as you play."

~

I remember some more thoughts and feelings about my piano teacher, Sister Marietta. I look up and start to feel and hear her kind voice from my past seeping through the walls.

~

"Do you understand, sweetie?" she says.

I then remember my angry thoughts. "Sister, if only I could focus long enough, I could learn to read the damn music."

~

Of course, I wouldn't have ever said that to Sister. I was only in the third grade, but I probably should have. Sister was very patient. She also had that look like she knew things about me that I hadn't even discovered yet for myself or didn't want to admit about myself quite yet.

Sister Marietta was the type who participated in life. She had a presence about her like "I see you and I will let you know what I see" kind of presence. She kind of scared me a bit but I found her to be interesting and brave, like nothing had to be kept a secret, like anything was safe to say; but *I never share secrets.*

Sister seemed to not only understand me but understood my family situation. I learned this when I overheard my mother on the phone saying that Sister Marietta told my dad that he needs to go easier on me and that he seemed to make me nervous. Of course, that information was never repeated back to me directly. Communication about emotions or feelings was not a top priority of the Cavarelli family.

Dad was very upset when he heard about Sister's comments. It was probably the day that I was asked to wait outside after I had finished my piano lesson. It was also the day that dad just stared at me the whole way home and felt completely different. That day I felt love in his eyes, or maybe it was guilt? It was also the same week that dad followed me halfway up to the softball field to tell me that he was so sorry for yelling at me in the car before practice and wanted to make sure that I was okay. He didn't feel like Dad that week. I knew something was up.

I tap lightly on the piano keys.

It meant so much to me that I could feel his love — feel him — the real him that day. I didn't have many days like those. I knew that was the kind of love that was hidden and very seldom expressed in him, in my family or, for that matter, the human race. Was this kind of love really possible?

As a child, I was very clear on this kind of love. It was pure. I knew when someone's words were spoken from love, from their heart. It was very easy for me to identify this kind of expression. When I would feel this love, their bodies seemed transparent and I could barely see their physical forms clearly when looking at them. They felt so light, almost as if their bodies would vanish right before my very eyes. It was sometimes difficult to stay focused as their bodies seemed to move around like a flickering light bulb does when it's about to go out.

It's kind of difficult to allow that love to come through when there is so much guilt and shame in the world that blocks this kind of love.

Does everyone see and feel this? I wouldn't know because I never share such secrets with anyone.

Today, I find it much more complicated to understand people. A lot of times, I can hear two different versions of what others are saying. People's words, intentions and feelings seem to get all jumbled up. It's almost as if everything is overlapping and twisted like a tornado.

I can't seem to sort it out these days; it felt easier when there were fewer responsibilities and fewer people in my life. Today I am very unclear about this pure love and if it even still exists.

My fingers dance and start to play a major scale.

As a grown woman, I hang on to these pleasant memories of pure love, of Dad's display of love on the softball field because if I didn't, I would only be left with Dad memories of nerves, disruptions and annoyances.

It wasn't always easy back then. My dad was different than other dads. He always was.

My dad's white blood cells were not like every other dad's. Nope. Dad's cells didn't grow and divide in an orderly way, as the body needs them to. The doctors labeled these unorderly cells, leukemia. The label didn't make it any better because the suffering started when I was in the second grade until February of my seventh-grade year when the disease took his life. I thought that the reason for my dad's frustration and outbursts was simply because I was in his way.

I wasn't informed that the true reason for my dad's frustration was because of the chemo that was swirling through his bloodstream, probably like a tornado. The chemo was supposed to slow down the growth of his cancer cells but, only caused him to have great anxiety, depression, swollen hands and feet, not to mention a loss of appetite, nausea, vomiting, and very painful mouth sores.

My dad's transition was commonly called death, but I knew that there was no such thing as death and that humans only travel from one form of existence to another, contrary to my Catholic upbringing. I could feel the other side like they were right in front of me. Even the Blessed Mother would make herself known when I was forced to stay still in church. I knew that they were only just a veil away. I would always look around to see if anyone else saw that Mother Mary floated back and forth from her statue to the pews.

~

Even though I know the facts today about my dad, there are still those feelings of sadness that I had been in his way and that my hyperactivity caused him pain.

If I would have known he was sick, I would have taken care of him, or not have been such a nuisance. Well, at least I would have tried to be "still."

Memories of my hyperactivity and annoyances continue to swirl around my mind like a tornado as I make my way towards the gym. Suddenly, I regain an awareness of where I am and find myself walking along the same path of the stage where I played the Wicked Witch of the West in seventh grade.

33

I walk towards the middle of the curtain parting it open just enough to squeeze through. I jump down from the stage, landing on a platform that feels like home — the basketball court. I grab the basketball that was left next to the foul line and turn to shoot. I get balanced, put the elbow in and aim the ball. My body stops again. The body is completely still. My mind, however, is running.

Playing basketball with girls in this gym, what an adjustment that was! Before the sixth grade, I only played sports with a bunch of guys, the five guys in my neighborhood. Playing football with a bunch of guys was somewhat awkward, but so much fun! It made up for all those other feelings of not being good enough. I always felt so good about myself when playing football. I was on top of my game.

Absentmindedly, I begin to bounce the ball.

Down, up.

Back then, I really did know how to communicate better with boys. They treated me like one of the guys. "Dorothy, get your little girly ass over here. Let's play." They were direct.

My attitude with them was "This is where I stand." I may at times have seemed a little bossy. They didn't seem to mind though. Guys were plain and simple, right to the point. Most of the times, they said what they meant. If I was getting on their nerves they would just tell me to "shut up" or "knock it off." It was straightforward. Communication wasn't as complicated with guys as it was with the girls. I had some girlfriends, but I really didn't like doing "girl" things. I tried liking them, but I just didn't get it.

Up, down.

Sports just came easy to me. I loved playing basketball, soccer and my favorite, football, right across the street from my house! The guys accepted me. Yes, every once in a while, they would bust me about being a girl, but it didn't bother me. I could overlook those comments because I knew they liked me. It was during these times that I felt better about myself.

I would do anything to feel better about myself.

I loved watching the guys excel in their skill. Leo, my closest friend, would try to strategize during the football games, the way a real quarterback would run his team in the NFL.

Oh, how he lit up when he created the plays and directed the team. It seemed to give him such satisfaction. I so loved watching the intensity on his face when he would lay out the play in the dirt, and even more, watching the twinkle in his eyes when one of his plays led to a touchdown. I could see that love again, that love inside of him, that love for life, at least for that moment on the football field.

Down, up.

I remember that I had to make some adjustment when playing basketball with girls, transitioning challenges at its best, nothing like playing soccer on the boys' team. There were times when I started to stand out in girls' basketball; receiving more compliments from the coaches. I didn't want anyone to feel the way I felt in the classroom, incompetent or not good enough. I would slow down and try to help the girls, purposely not playing to my potential. I didn't want them to feel bad.

I always seemed to put other people first. Ever since I can remember, it seemed to be the only way to survive. I excelled in sports and it made me stand out. Standing out in a positive way was not all that it was cracked up to be. It felt good to be noticed, but it also created resentment from others — envy and disappointment.

Up, down.

I would feel what seemed like jealousy from the other girls. This was when I would hear two different versions; one part was what was spoken, and the other was what they were really feeling.

"Oh, that was good, Dorothy," with a smile, and then the other version, "Show-off!" I remembered feeling that judgment from others.

After a while, I started to get the hang of looking and feeling like the other girls after joining softball, volleyball and track. I learned words like "It is not about winning, it's about how you play the game. If it wasn't for the whole team effort, we wouldn't have won. The closeness of the girls is what it's really about."

Staying even with my peers so no one would feel bad worked for me. I fit in until that day of the eighth-grade awards ceremony at St. Daniel's. I received the Most Valuable Player award for basketball. I remember looking around to feel if the others were judging me and the feelings of not fitting in. Each year, I got more and more effective at shutting down my feelings so I wouldn't have to feel others.

~

Down, up.

With a basketball, still in my hands, I get ready to shoot the ball, and then suddenly I notice the clearing of someone's throat.

It sounds like it is coming from behind the curtain on the stage.

It startles me at first. "Hello, is someone there?"

No answer.

"Who's behind that curtain?!"

"Hello," the voice responds from behind the curtain.

Putting a face to the voice, a tall man with big brown eyes, brown hair, and with a grin on his face, parts the curtain. There he was, Mr. Marvel!

"Mr. Marvel?!" I gasp.

"Ms. Dorothy Cavarelli!" he sarcastically says as he squints his eyes, curls his nose and upper lip.

Still standing at the foul line, I say, "Hi."

"Hi!" he answers back.

"You look exactly the same," I say still holding the basketball. "Y-you … w-well, your face, you feel the same?"

"That's because I never age," Marvel pesters me like he did as a seventh-grade teacher. "But you seemed to have gotten older. Funny, I remember you being shorter and smaller and much smarter. Guess it's all perspective."

We stare at one another locking eyes until it becomes weird for me. Something about his eyes; there is a presence that is unmistakable.

Was that presence there before?

His presence is like Sister Marietta's! It's kind of like a "Here I am" kind of presence.

Well, it makes me uncomfortable.

Yet, he is not in my face; he is in his own space. He doesn't feel like he is hiding secrets like most people do. I am starting to wonder if both Sister Marietta and Mr. Marvel went to the same school. The "no hidden secrets" school. I laugh at my thoughts.

*Wait! I want to go to that school. Well, maybe not revealing **all** my secrets.*

"I see you are still consumed by thoughts, Miss Dorothy?"

I break the stare, and Mr. Marvel's face starts to become clear again.

"Yeah," I chuckle. "I guess so. People call me Dottie now."

"How old are you now, Miss Dottie?"

"Thirty-four."

"How old are you, Mr. Marvel?"

"Forty-three. Why don't you call me Michael?"

"Michael?" I ask.

"Sure, that IS my name," Michael grins.

"Michael," I say out loud. *Weird.*

"It's just a title, right?" he asks to make a point rather than to elicit an answer. "Do names really matter anyway?"

Still weird as ever.

I nod, remembering how odd he was. I find it difficult staring for too long into his big light brown eyes. They beam. When I look into most people's eyes I seldom feel that love and kindness right at the surface. I usually have to look deeper. But with Mr. Marvel, you can just feel the love by being in his presence. When you look into his eyes, the feeling is so intense.

Typically, I can't feel that loving feeling in people. It's as if they are covered with this invisible film that separates them from others, like a form of protection; but not with Mr. Marvel.

Oh my, how should I behave? It's as if this feeling vibrates every cell in my being. I don't remember his eyes being that bright and transparent. Then again, it was twenty years ago.

"There it is! I am glad that I came back here," Mr. Marvel says reaching for his jacket. "I thought I lost it," he says with relief as he looks up at me again.

I return to my stare. A vision appears of a St. Daniel's stairwell near the seventh-grade classroom.

~

"You look so sad, Mr. Marvel. Is there anything that I can do?"

"No, but thank you, Dorothy."

"I can just listen. I know what it's like to lose a parent, so I know how it feels losing someone close to me."

"Thank you, Dorothy."

"Well, if you ever want to talk, I'll be here, okay, Mr. Marvel?"

"You are sweet, Dorothy, I'll be there in a minute; go back to the classroom, okay?"

"Okay."

~

"Hello, Dottie! Are you there?"

"Yeah," I respond but not quite yet back in my body.

And then right back in my head again.

"Did you ever marry?" I ask.

"Yes, I did."

"Kids?"

"Yes. Four."

"How old are they?"

"Eleven, seventeen, twenty-one, and twenty-two."

"Are you still married?" I point to his bare ring finger.

"Divorced."

"Did you ever marry again?"

"No." Marvel chuckles as he puts his jacket on. "This feels like an interrogation."

"Why didn't you?" I persist.

Mr. Marvel answers, "I guess I have been too busy creating the school."

"I heard that you just bought a house."

"Yep, I did," he answers with a grin.

I switch the subject and say, "Do you remember when you insisted that I play the witch in the school play? I really didn't believe that I could remember the lines."

"Yep! I told them you were the girl for the job. The play *The Wonderful Wizard of Oz*, right?" Marvel remembers. "That was fun, wasn't it?"

"It was," I say. I always liked Marvel for his kind gentle manner and for his clarity.

"You know I did see that school you're creating. That's pretty cool," I say with a smile. "Hey, maybe we could talk sometime. I am really interested in that kind of stuff. In fact, I am studying to be an ADD coach. I want to help people with ADD."

"How can you help people with ADD, when you are not well yourself?"

I freeze.

"Don't worry about others right now," Marvel said. "You might want to focus on yourself and understand that mental spinning of yours. It's time to go within and love yourself, Dottie."

Marvel looks at me, waiting for a response.

Nothing.

"But can you? That is the real question, Dottie? Lots of aspects that you might want to figure out, to find that freedom you're looking for, ay?"

Still. Nothing.

I feel my palms starting to sweat while still holding the basketball, as well as my breath.

"Home is where the rainbow lies, right, Miss Wicked Witch of the West?" Marvel laughs and points to the stage where our class performed *The Wonderful Wizard of Oz,* oblivious to the fact that he just insulted me just moments ago.

You are not well yourself.

I repeat the words over and over in my head.

You are not well yourself.

"Hey, did you see that Broadway show *Wicked*? How about that? What a perspective on the Wicked Witch of the West."

Still no words from me.

I know that Marvel has always been direct. He is talking to me like nothing happened; like he didn't insult me just now. There is so much film around me that I can't even see his light brown eyes anymore.

Marvel never said anything that he didn't mean, even though I didn't always understand what he meant.

Did Marvel even know any other way to communicate?

Marvel looks at his watch, squints his eyes and glints his teeth. "I really have to run."

Marvel, in his bright Hawaiian shirt, starts to walk back towards the band room. Midway he turns around and points to the curtain, motioning to the basketball court in the gym and says, "Bet you feel right at home in this gym," and winks.

I snarl but no words are released from my mouth.

"Okay, then, good to see you, Dottie!" Marvel smiles.

Poof.

Marvel is gone!

I put the ball down and walk over to the stage. I pull myself up onto the stage and start to walk back towards the band room. I stop, turn around, re-open the curtain once more, stare at the rectangular tape outlining the space that I once loved, the basketball court, and whisper the words that I needed to hear at that moment, "home."

There is no place like home.

CHAPTER 4

Why, Oh Why, Can't I Fly Over the Rainbow?

Tap, tap, tap.

I wait impatiently. I click my shoe against the café counter waiting for my coffee. To say that I am a little riled up after the curtain incident is an understatement.

Tap, tap, tap.

I feel like a kid. I am thirty-four years old now. I will not let another person get to me like this.

Tap, tap.

"Coffee's up!" *Tap.*

Finally!

I frantically, rumble through my purse looking for my phone.

Wait! I don't need my phone.

Putting my purse down on the counter, I look around to make sure no one saw this episode of looking through my purse like a mad woman. I am in this space of embarrassment and wrongness again. Marvel's harsh words linger over me like clouds right before a storm.

What gave him the right to say that I was not well myself? I know that I am having a difficult time lately, but he had no right to say it. He doesn't even know me.

Keep no secrets — especially to yourself — they separate and destroy. Be honest and truthful of how you are feeling. I remember Marvel's words in class.

"Oh shut up!" I snarl, talking back to my thoughts.

The only feelings that I want to admit is the fact that Marvel made me so mad today. I feel the humiliation start to kick in. I am determined to figure this out. I take the coffee from the server who asks if I am okay.

"I'm fine, thanks, and the 'shut up' wasn't meant for you." I apologize as I make my way to a table. I decide to sit inside instead of going back to my car. Perhaps I need people around me right now.

Back in the seventh grade Marvel was the only person that believed me, when I told him that the words moved around the page and that's why it was easier to read a page while moving around. "Hell, if the words are moving, you should be allowed to move, Dorothy," Marvel had said. He placed me in the back of the classroom so I could move and I wouldn't disturb the others, but didn't forget about me like most of the other teachers did.

I just don't understand why *I am so mad.*

Marvel knew how to keep me on task, which was a great challenge for me. They seemed to get so frustrated with me and gave up so easily. But what they weren't doing was putting the responsibility back on me. He always made me accountable and I respected that. I would listen because I respected him. I sensed his kindness and his truth. I felt his integrity.

So why am I so mad right now?

I reach in my purse again, but this time for some paper to write down my "mixed up" feelings. Marvel's words about "feeling at home" on the basketball court were really sweet, but he said I was broken, not well. Why didn't I tell him to go to hell?!

I don't have that skill to say what is on my mind especially when it comes to my emotions. I sit with the pen in my hand and nothing comes.

Tap, tap, tap...with the pen.

I wait. I wait some more. Suddenly the words show their presence and come straight towards me like a tornado that is travelling too fast to stop.

My mind that was once clear on suppressing unwanted feelings — if not suppressed, it could lead to socially unacceptable outcomes now clouding with thoughts and emotions of anger, embarrassment, judgment and hurt.

My mind starts to spin; internally vomiting everything that was learned about the brain at my ADHD coaching academy.

My emotions are activating my anterior insula and the anterior cingulate cortex which is beginning to interfere with my prefrontal cortex which is supposed to be for executive functioning, more knowledge learned from the academy.

Get out of your head! Write your emotions.

Why would I feel rejected? I just wanted to tell him what I was doing these days and the least he could do is accept me.

I look up.

Gosh! Do I need acceptance that bad? My brain always gets me in trouble. Ugh, this brain of mine.

I guess the consequences of possibly throwing one's shoes at someone else's new house would definitely not be pleasant.

I laugh to myself as I look down at my red Converses, and have a vision of throwing my red sneakers at Marvel's new house.

Tap, tap, tap.

I cannot understand why this is getting to me. I write:

Why can't I just fly over the rainbow so I don't have to feel this?

That is a little corny. What is it, Dottie? What is wrong?

I haven't felt like this for the past year and half — since I started the medication. These emotions and feelings have overridden that little pill today. They are way stronger and more powerful than any pill. It was only a stimulant anyway.

I continue to write.

My brain…

My writing is interrupted by laughter that penetrates through the doorway of the quiet coffee shop. The laughing is so loud that the noise has everyone's focus in the place, including the employees.

But I know that laughter. I look up and to my surprise, it's the kids.

"Hi, Mom," three little pint-sized munchkins yell from across the café; each showing off their beautiful personalities that always brings a smile to my face.

44

My oldest son, Christopher, who always would smile and say "busy" when I would ask him to do something for me, darts towards me and says, "What's up, Mom?" My oldest girl, Megan, who will turn nine soon, floats in behind Chris with a smile. She tells me of the activities that she will be involved in, down to the very last detail. My youngest girl, Kacey, in that tiny little body of hers, would make certain everything that was not said or talked about would be mentioned out loud.

"How are you guys? I miss you guys already." I feel the glow coming to my face as I reach up to playfully ruffle my son's hair.

My ex, Don, making a connection with me, strolls in behind them with Kacey, by his side. Kacey, our little entrepreneur, tugs my ex's arm and says, "Hey, Dad, we're hungry! Dad, why don't you just give me the money? I can take care of it," she playfully demands. Of course, he hands the money over to her without hesitation; exchanging a familiar smile with me that we have done millions of times since Kacey was as young as two. She was only six but always ready to keep up with her siblings.

Megan, with her cautious eyes, checks to see if I am visibly upset. Not seeing anything to concern herself with, she leans into my shoulder, wraps her arm around me, then gazes around to see if she knows anyone at the café.

Christopher, almost eleven years old, waves to one of his friends over in the corner, but sits across from me at the table. "What's up, Mom? What have you been doing with your time — rearranging our closets or putting away my cups that I left on the kitchen table?"

My ex smiles at me and we both watch the mixed emotions of everyone in the family unit. Don and I turn to Kacey as she drops some of the coins on the floor. As Kacey picks up the coins, she then turns to me. "How ya doing, Madre? We were at the bank today and we got lollipops."

As Kacey picks up the last coin from the floor, I pull her close to me, her face full of life. It shines. Her eyes so ever present. She, unlike her mom and older sister, is not a fan of floating out of her body, and going with the flow. She always seems to be right there in the moment.

They purchase their drinks and we all make our way to the door. The kids follow me to my car and my ex makes his way to his. The kids give me a group hug and one at a time, I kiss them all on their foreheads, just like I did when they were babies.

"Love you guys," I whisper.

I feel the love that wraps around me, feeling the love in their eyes for me, but don't soak it in fully. Instead I start to fill the space with unimportant chatter and details.

"I love you, Mom," each one of them expresses. They walk towards their father who is almost at his car.

As the distance between us grows, my ex calls out from his car. "So, you will get them after school on Tuesday on the twelfth? That's a little over a week, right?" he says.

Right. Back to business.

"Right," I reply and wave. I attempt to push the pain down a little further not to feel it. It still feels awkward knowing that I am the reason for his pain. What I do know that it was the right decision, but that doesn't make the pain go away.

Will it ever go away?

I wish them farewell and walk toward my car, remembering that I am still wearing the clothes that I had on yesterday.

It was time to go home.

~

I turn around to head towards my car, and before I take a step, a face suddenly appears — a face I never thought I would see again.

There she is, Elizabeth.

Elizabeth, a girl that I haven't seen since I disappointed her so.

"You don't remember me, do you, Dorothy?" she asks. Her face seems to be unsure.

"Of course, I remember you, Elizabeth," I murmur. "People call me Dottie now."

"Are you back from Kansas?" Elizabeth continues, making no acknowledgment of my preferred name. "I saw on Facebook that you were living in Kansas."

Ah, Facebook. Made stalking legal since 2005. Whatever, Dottie. Answer her!
"Yes, I am," I answer.

Elizabeth and I continue to chat about family, kids and career. Just five minutes, and our worlds are caught up. No more, no less.

"Bye, Dorothy!"

"Bye, Elizabeth."

I finish up with Elizabeth, get in my car and sink into the driver's seat, resting my head on the steering wheel. I need to write this down and I need to somehow get over all this guilt — my husband and now — Elizabeth. But how? I grab the blank paper from the passenger seat and start to write:

In ninth grade, I had become friends with Elizabeth who started confiding in me quickly after we met. One day I received a letter from her in my first period class. Elizabeth writes to me that her brother was molesting her little sister and mentions that he used to abuse her, too. I was shocked by the letter.

By seventh-period English class, I couldn't contain myself any longer. I decided to open the letter and write back to her. For those moments while I was writing, I became this person that I never knew was inside of me. In detail, I told her that she must tell and do this and do that.

While writing this I also shared some personal feelings. I went on and on about my feelings about life and some other things that we discussed — things like I don't care if I smoke or drink anymore. Who cares anyway? What does it matter? I was hyperfocused like I never had been before.

Being hyperfocused allowed me to block out everyone and every sound — everything around me. That is why I didn't immediately notice the teacher standing right beside me saying, "Dorothy, can you hear me? What are you writing? That doesn't look like the English assignment." My heart raced as I watched the paper leave my desk into the teacher's hands.

No!

The next several months of school were hell.

The authorities at my school spent the first couple days probing me about who this person was and how important it was for this family to get the help they needed. I kept saying that I would handle it. If I would have known then how they were going to handle it, I would have lied. I would have said that my

47

writing simply was created from my unbelievable imagination and I made the whole thing up.

But nope, naïve little me gave in. I caved under the pressure of the adults, who by the way, were interrogating a naïve little girl who was not in the presence of a guardian. In the back of my young mind, I was thinking and hoping that they could do something about it. Elizabeth was harassed and it didn't let up until she called her mother. They tortured her and handled it so poorly. In the end, their priority was to keep this hush, hush, and make it go away.

They never even told my mother!

The fact that they lied to me, betrayed my trust and never helped Elizabeth's family was so disheartening and disappointing. This created challenges for me and doubt in the Catholic Church, authority, adults, and anyone for that matter. I knew that those in authority could not be trusted, and if you ever wanted something done, you had to rely on yourself.

Elizabeth and I remained friends throughout high school, but I always felt this guilt for having exposed her and never truly being able to help.

Years later, Elizabeth asked me to be in her wedding. She asked me and I couldn't go. I just couldn't face them. I just couldn't relive that mistake again: the guilt, and the fact that I didn't help her family. Father Rich even called me to say that he couldn't believe that I wasn't able to make the wedding. He said, "This is just not right, Dorothy." Father Rich married Elizabeth and her husband and later married Don and me.

I loved her. I still love her. The friendship eventually faded; just another casualty from one's past.

I better get home before I meet anyone else from my past. I return home, only to find my house in disarray. The kids had messed up the kitchen, left the lights on and the Wii game "Portal" blasting on the TV. The kids were not supposed to be there.

Typical. How frustrating!

I find a note from the kids that read:

Where ARE you, Mom?! Your beautiful, adorable, awesome children are HERE! We decided to come here before going to Dad's house. Love, Megan, Kacey and Christopher.
My feelings of frustration instantly changed after feeling the love of the note.

I'm a sucker.

The kids could always count on me being home, doing laundry, reorganizing their rooms, or helping them with an emotional or social issue. Although when it came to homework, that was their dad's department. He was just so smart — one of his many hidden talents. He always seems to keep his amazing abilities under wraps — along with many other things.

I was blessed to work from home after reaching number one in my company. The kids liked the fact that I worked out of the house and that I was easily assessable to lend an ear or help finish a project.

Things did change after I started taking Adderall though. They told me that I seem more focused, and they weren't sure if they liked it. With this newly developed focus, they would say that they now had to deal with a mom that made more sense. A mom with more clarity who would put more responsibility back on them which was made clear "not so great for them."

Marvel lingers back into my thoughts as I walk in the living room to the sofa.

I notice how tired I am as I make my way to the couch. I grab a pen attempt to write some more but sleep slowly takes over.

Tap, tap…Down went the pen.

CHAPTER 5

It's A Twister. It's A Twister

3am

I open my eyes. The red letters of the television clock glare at me from my spot on the couch.

It doesn't take me long to remember what occurred yesterday — the school, Marvel and Elizabeth. I begin to feel the guilt again. I can't go back to sleep, and I can't turn off my brain. I manage to pull myself off the couch just enough to reach in the cabinet and take out my high school scrapbook and reminisce about the good times in high school.

Each page that I turn brings up tons of good memories! Basketball, volleyball and soccer championships; special notes from friends of the past. I suddenly stop and read a note from Father Rich. A sweet note congratulating me about how I played and how special I was. Why was I so special? More importantly, why was I so special to him? Weird. As an adult reading this letter, it seems a bit odd more than endearing or heartfelt. I remember receiving it as a teen and thinking that it was so sweet. "Be sure to come see me," the note read. "Remember our pact."

What pact?

I close the scrapbook and attempt to switch the gears in my brain. I search for something pleasant.

Nothing.

My mind can't help but trail back to Elizabeth.

Ugh, I am so sorry, Elizabeth. The letter was taken away from me. Elizabeth! I know. I shouldn't have had it out.

Ugh.

I make another attempt to switch all the guilt, fear and mistrust to something better. I begin to stir. The stir stimulates other memories inside of me. I feel a tornado nearby; although this type of twister feels like it's been brewing for quite some time.

Grabbing the closest pen, I begin to scribble some words:

I was sixteen years old and I was driving home from school. I was in a great mood, feeling amazing because I had just gotten my driver's license. My grandmom, Lulu, had just died a couple weeks back. I could feel her, just a veil away. I felt her with me and it felt good. But suddenly there it was — as clear as day — I remembered. No, Grandmom, take it back. Take back the memory. "But you already see it. Take it," Grandmom says.

I stop writing and look up. I can't believe I am going to write this on paper.

I place my pen on the paper again and start to write:

That day when I was sixteen, memories came flooding in the car like a dam that just burst. Flashes of pictures and memories instantly became so clear. I wondered how my mind kept them hidden for so long. Memories that I hid so far down for so long that they didn't even feel real or belong to me. I hid them, lied to myself but really knew that they were there and they were mine.

What the hell?! I want to bury these memories again. I am feeling like my thoughts are now controlled by a powerful unstoppable twister.

"That was me in those memories — me — from such a long time ago," I say in the car.

I pulled the car over. This happened to that girl, and her family; not to me.

Oh my god, it happened to me!

It happened to me; it happened to me. It happened to me!

I just keep saying it over and over in the car as I cried. I cried in the car for what seemed like an hour. The tears just poured down my cheeks and my heart ached.

Why then? When I was sixteen years old? Why at that very moment — when everything was going great? "You will know what to do with them. It's a gift! I love you," Grandmom says.

My whole life had changed in a heartbeat and there was nothing I could do about it. The flood had arrived. Damn, I couldn't take it back. The damage was done.

It shattered my entire life. Nothing was ever the same.

I stop writing. Tears fall.

Tap, tap, tap.

My pen has its own beat.

I look up at the clock in the kitchen. It's 3:30am? The pen joins the paper again as if they were always connected and never had any trouble writing and forming words.

Since my teens, I never understood why people would tell me about their abuse. It was like I had something on my forehead that said, "Please tell me your stories of how you were sexually abused. Tell me how much it sucked living with this confusing feeling and how it had ruined your life."

It wasn't until later, that I realized that they were the ones with the "invisible sign" on their forehead. I would feel it in them and on them. Then I would end up getting to personally know them. I would be talking to them and poof — out it would come, all the gory ugly painful details.

Tap, tap, tap.

My foot seems to ponder the situation with me.

Girls, boys, women or men. It didn't matter. I have heard so many stories over the years.

Today, I can look at someone and I just know. I see it and feel it on them. I can see when and where it happened or is still happening. It's a very strange gift. Sometimes I also see the abusers not just the abused. I can see their own abuse, what happened to them as children, before they actually abused anyone else.

It's frustrating sometimes…

I have to watch these parents, grandparents and relatives cheering on their kids from the bleachers. At the parent-teacher conferences I can't say a word. If it was physical, yes, I would have the right, but not this, not something that is invisible, not something that I can feel that is going on behind the scenes, not something that is private, not something that is a family matter.

I look up remembering more. I place my pen down on the paper.

My heart hurts…

My mind, eyes and writing hand tire, but my body races. I grab all my journaling and walk up to the bedroom to move around this stirring body. I flop on the bed with my tired mind overriding the rest of my body. I place the papers on my dresser and fade away and fall into a deep sleep.

I awake, but this time find I am snuggled under a blanket in my own bed, cuddled and cradled by its six inches of memory foam. A part of me wishes I could place these memories deep within the foam.

I glance at my journaling on the dresser. In that moment I have a revelation that I have some of my secrets written down for someone to find. My mind races as I jump off the bed and grab the papers and lock them in my safe in the closet.

I can't discern if yesterday was real or just another dream.

Did I really run into Elizabeth and allow those feelings to surface again? Did I really write all those feelings from my past? Was I really ready for all these memories to surface again?

Did I really see Marvel, and did he really say those words?

The lines between reality and dream state are beginning to blur for me. I can never tell which ones are which, yet everything feels real. I plop back onto my bed.

I lightly bite the memory foam quilt. A shot of energy swirls through me like a bolt of lightning. I sit up, feeling present in my eyes and decide that I will spend the day writing.

I move my body and head downstairs. I head for the kitchen. I hold up an almost empty coffee cup. I look around for my purse, sun glasses and keys. They all are on the floor next to the couch where I flopped myself down last night. I have no plans for the day and with my kids away the house seems too quiet for me. I need a place where there is movement. I can think better where there is movement. I can find a café where I can take my laptop and write some more.

I grab my laptop and leave the house.

CHAPTER 6

I Am Not In Kansas Anymore

"Dorothy Cavarelli?" shouts a familiar voice. I press regular at the gas pump and glance over at the driver's seat of the car.

"Hey, Brain. Oops, I mean Brian, is that you?" I tease, as I look up while I pump gas in my car.

"Whatcha doin'?" Brian asks from the window of his car.

"Pumping gas," I tease again. "And after, I was gonna try and find a café. I'm doing some writing. I'm free from the children today. My ex has them."

That was an overshare!

Brian smiles. He parks his car in a nearby parking space. He gets out of his car and walks over towards me.

"What have you been up to?" I say.

Let him talk, Dottie.

"You remember my new age upbringing? My crazy parents."

"Yes, they were total hippies," I respond quickly.

"After my parents died, my sister and I opened a new-age shop, ya know, vitamins, healthy food, crystals, dream-catchers, and that kind of stuff."

I nod, biting my lip not to interrupt him.

"We were just barely paying the bills, ya know how it is. But I am starting to change all that. It's all good. Now the shop is picking up, and I am starting to use this brain of mine. Ha!"

I smile, trying to be in the moment. Trying not to fill the space with chatter instead of just silence.

Nope, I can't stay quiet.

"I am so sorry about your parents. When did you lose them?"

"Well, ya know, they finally stopped the heavy partying a few years after I graduated high school. They were doing great for like ten years, working on their crystal and dreamcatcher business, and only smoking pot. Then the cops busted them for friggin' growing marijuana. It was so dumb. They never sold it. They just shared it with the people who lived in our house. Anyway, one thing led to another and they got involved with this protest group to express how they felt about legalizing marijuana. On their way to one of the protests, a drunk driver hit them head on. It was awful. It was about eight years ago. It sucked for a while. I learned a lot from that experience, which really led me to cleaning up my act."

"Well, I am really sorry for your loss, Brian."

"Thank you, Dorothy," Brian says.

"People call me, Dottie, now."

"Okay, Dottie, you should drop by the café!"

"Your new age place is a café too?"

"No. Leo's café!"

"Leo?! You still keep in touch with him? Where is it?"

"Leo's dad's old place!"

"That's still around? I thought that was going out of business."

"It did. And it sat there forever. After Leo's dad died, Leo finally decided to do something about it! He was a chicken shit. He wasn't brave enough to put it in to action, until now!"

"Awwww, his dad died? Is Leo okay?"

"He's okay. He worked through a lot with Michael. Actually, so did I! I could have never done what I did with my family and used this brain of mine the way I do now if it wasn't for Marvel."

"What are you talking about? You are the smartest guy I know! And who helped you? Did you say, Marvel?" I add.

Brian doesn't answer me because he has his head turned away from me, being distracted by another car pulling into the parking lot.

"No way! It can't be. Dorothy!" Tim rolls down his window as he pulls right next to us into the gas station.

"It is!" said Brian. "She goes by Dottie. I was just telling her about how much we learned from Marvel."

"Still learning, right, Brian?" Tim adds.

"Absolutely!" Brian answers.

"I am learning how to open up this heart of mine. Michael changed my life," Tim shares.

"Open up your heart? What? You were the most sensitive heartfelt guy I knew!" I respond. "And who? Did you guys say, Marvel? As in Mr. Marvel?"

"Yes, that's the man!" Tim confirms.

"I saw Mr. Marvel yesterday," I answer.

Tim and Brian look at each other, snickering at what I called him.

"What's so funny?"

"It's funny that you still call him Mr. Marvel, that's all." Tim giggles, as he gets out of his car and opens his gas tank, and places the nozzle into the hole.

"Why? What do you call him?"

"Marvel," Brian answers.

"Michael," Tim adds.

"A pain in our ass, sometimes," Brian jokes.

"Now that sounds more accurate! Well, I think that he is kind of obnoxious, don't you agree?"

"Well, I wouldn't say obnoxious," Tim joins in.

"Obnoxious? Meaning, extremely unpleasant? I wouldn't use that word," Brian adds.

"I would say," Tim says and glances at Brian, "pushing us to grow and work through our issues, yes."

"He's a fuck-head sometimes, I know," Brian adds. They both chuckle.

"Actually, it's all in how you perceive him and how loaded you are with shit!" Brian chuckles again.

"Or how deep you are in your shit! Ha!" Tim adds.

"He's just direct," Brian informs.

"If you can't handle 'direct' then don't talk to Michael," Tim says as he looks at Brian.

Brian asks, "So ya coming?"

"Coming over to the café? Like now?" I question.

"Yeah," said Brian. "Like now!"

"I can't wait to see Leo's face, when he sees you," Tim says as he places the level back in the gas pump.

Brian adds, "It's like 'The Team' is getting back together again. Remember, The Team and the four of us with our desks pushed up against the wall. What was that, second grade?"

"Yes, I do remember and it WAS second grade. It traumatized me, being singled out like that," I growl and move to another conversation. "So Leo is at the café now?"

"Yeah, he's always there," Brian answers.

"Okay, then, I'm in!"

I get into my car and follow Brian. I feel the anxiety rumbling. I start to spin. I drop into another memory.

~

"Concentrate, Dorothy!" Words that I heard over and over again and that I tried so hard to forget.

"Sit still, Dorothy! Stop fidgeting! Why are you so hyper? What did you eat this morning?" It was such an effort to stay focused. Everything distracted me; the coughs, the kids, the shuffling of papers. Even the things that were supposed to be "still" were moving around, like the chalk on the board, or the desks that we sat in. I couldn't keep the black print on the white paper still.

I found it best to move with it. Although how can this be done when "stillness" was the norm in this building? It was like those items that were picked up by the tornado. They had no choice but to move.

I just wanted to blend with everyone else!

One day in school, I moved my body way too fast, faster than normal. I needed to move!

Ohhh, I was moved all right. My second-grade teacher, Mrs. Eastwick, made some drastic changes. The one change that occurred immediately was the location of my desk. My seat went from being in the cast to being an outcast! But there was good news — I had company! I joined the guys that were already against the wall.

Brian Spear, Tim Mann, Leo Strong, and I were against the wall for the rest of the year.

Oh, THAT was a good idea. Now I'll REALLY learn!

So, now I had an official label. Not only was I the kid who couldn't stay "still" and couldn't read, but I was also labeled as having a behavior problem.

Mrs. Eastwick was wicked. I told Leo that I wished someone would drop a house on her.

Weeks passed, and still, there was no movement of our seats. So, I decided that Brian, Tim, Leo, and I needed to form our own team! It took some time for them to fully accept me being the girl and all.

Each one of us possessed special talents. Brian was pretty much the smartest person I've ever met. He was brilliant. When a situation surfaced that required brains to analyze, it was always Brian who assisted the team. He had this hidden knowledge that no one was aware of. I guess his flakiness stopped everyone from noticing his brilliance. Actually, I don't think that he was aware of it either. But it certainly surfaced when it came time to figure out our team's moves and countermoves. He made our assignments fun. He would have rap songs for our times tables and certain techniques to remember our spelling words.

We were pretty much on our own, with our desks up against the wall.

Tim had a heart of gold. He empathized with how isolated we all felt and always knew the right things to say to make us feel better when one of us was having a bad day.

When courage was needed to fight an enemy, or to set up some boundaries, it was Leo who had plenty of it. He had courage beyond belief. Oh, and he was oh so funny. That's what I loved about him. Anytime, anyone of us became too serious and stress about being up against the wall, he always knew how to lighten it up with one of his funny jokes.

The bond continued to grow stronger throughout the year. Our loyalty to one another was unbreakable. This teacher did us a favor. We were learning the skills of life!

Every couple of weeks, I would write a note to "The Team." It would say something like this:

Brain, (he loved when I misspelled his name), Tim, and Leo,

Alright, guys, how are we gonna get our desks back in line with everyone in this classroom?

Dorothy

One day, Leo told us that his father was coming to school for a parent-teacher conference. He was so scared of his dad. I never knew why. I just knew that his hands would start to shake when he would talk about his dad. Brian would talk him down so he could relax. "No worries, Leo," he would say. He had this way of calming down any situation. Brian wasn't afraid of anyone or anything, well, except for fire. He is certainly not calm near fire. He literally shakes. His house burn to the ground, when he was young, during one of his parents' wild parties. They had to build a new house from scratch.

Anyway, I convinced the boys that moving our desks in a row was now more important than ever. WE needed to make it appear to his dad that we were just like everyone else in this classroom. It would require some quick strategic planning. I emphasized that teamwork was crucial at this time. We needed to stick together.

During this process of slowly but carefully moving our desks to form some sort of row, it was Jackie Gulch who would throw a broomstick in our plan. She raised her hand, informing Mrs. Eastwick that we were trying to move our desks back into a row because Leo's father was visiting the school. She must have overheard us.

All of us stopped suddenly, faces frozen, except for Leo, of course. He threw Jackie a nasty look while she made her way to the water fountain and then a growl that caused her to stop walking. Then he whispered to the team, "I wished that I could squirt water on that girl," hoping that she would melt. Leo had a way of scaring the crap out of you if he had to.

Mrs. Eastwick, catching the gist of what was going on, looked over at our team. I watched Mrs. Eastwick's face, waiting to see what she would do. Her reputation was on the line.

What would she do?

What kind of person was she really?

I stared at her, attempting to telepathically speak to her. "Haven't we suffered enough, Mrs. Eastwick? What's it gonna be, Mrs. Eastwick?"

Then she uttered the words that I'll never forget. "Mind your own business, Jackie."

YES! We completed the row and held each other's hands under the desks. The plan was a success! That day, I was recognized as the leader. What a day!

We were a team back then.

I pull in behind the boys at the café. We all get out of our cars and walk into the café. Tim and Brian place their hands on my shoulders and give me a shove and yell across the café.

"Look who we found pumping gas, Leo!" Brian brags about finding me. He acts as if he had just won an Oscar.

"Dorothy? No way!" Leo howls. "Put 'em up, put 'em up, tough girl. Wow, the football girl turned out just fine. You look like a lady!"

I begin to blush after the lady comment.

"How the hell are you?!" Leo asks as he grabs me, picking me up and spinning me around like old times.

"Well, first, I don't go by Dorothy anymore. It's Dottie, now," I say.

"What if I still want to call you Dorothy, Dottie. Will that be okay?" Leo teases.

"Not if you want me to answer you," I tease back.

"Alrighty then, how the hell are you, Dottie?" Leo asks again.

"I'm good, and how are you, Leo?" I ask as Leo finally, gently puts me down.

"Well, what do you think?" Leo asks spreads out his arms and spins around one hundred and eighty degrees.

"Finally got the courage, Dottie!" Leo says with excitement. "Yes. I am officially the owner of this place. I had to wait for my dad to die in order to get some balls. You remember my dad, yes?"

"I do," I say. "I am so sorry about that."

"Well, I am bringing his restaurant to the next level!" Leo says. "For years I worked for him and not a word. I couldn't speak up, couldn't tell him my ideas. I was such a mess. Michael helped me through it."

I take a breath.

"He should be here very soon," Leo says as he goes behind the counter to grab a drink.

"Michael, as in Mr. Marvel?" I say and turn to the other guys.

"Yeah, why?" Leo asks unaware, with his face under the counter.

"Ahh, just wondering." I quickly add, "I better be going anyway."

"You just got here," Tim says.

"But I have stuff to do," I answer.

"You said that you were looking for a café, remember? Well, here it is!" Brian says. "We won't bother you. Come on, stay."

Overshare; gets you every time.

"I know. I just remembered that I have to talk to one of the kids about her piano practice."

"Didn't you say that your ex is taking care of all that?" Tim asks.

Again, T-M-I always seems to bite you in the ass.

"Yes, but I should double check." I start to walk backwards as I talk. "I just really should check," I say getting closer to the door so I will miss Marvel. "You can never rely on my ex with these types of things." I yell louder so they can hear me from across the room almost at the door. As I back up, I am stopped by a stern body that blocks my backward movement. I turn around, my eyes parallel to Mr. Marvel's chest.

"Hello again, Dottie," Marvel says.

"Hello," I say sheepishly. I gasp inside.

"Whatcha doing?" Marvel asks.

"Oh nothing," I chatter with my head down. "I just saw these guys at the gas station and then I wanted to see Leo's café, so I followed them and here I am!"

My eyes become still as I lock into Marvel's presence. I look in his eyes for a brief moment.

Grrrr... I am not well enough, huh!

"Hey, there you are," Marvel says as he looks at me.

"Yep, here I am," I stumble with my words as I look down.

I begin to swirl in my head, almost like a tornado; hot air from my anger and cold air that wants to give him the cold shoulder. I feel the force coming.

I look up at him again. He is still and steady. The thunderstorm blows over. I feel still.

Here goes!

"So, I've been talking to these guys about how you have helped them. I probably could use a little help. Ya know, since I AM NOT WELL," I say with a smile, "and it's time for me to focus on ME right now; go within, or whatever you said."

"Ugh!" Marvel asks, "Shit. I insulted you, didn't I?"

Stumbling on my words again, I admit, "I guess that I have been really struggling lately. Maybe I could use some help."

"Well okay then, follow me." Marvel places his hands on my shoulders, turning them to direct me back towards the table. "You couldn't have picked a better time."

"Hey guys, this girl wants to do some work on herself. Anyone interested in helping?"

All three guys raise their hands and say together, "We're in!"

I stand there surrounded by this feeling of pressure, yet this amazing feeling of connectedness.

Tim asks, "So you don't have to go?"

"I can stay," I say with a smile.

Looks like I am not in Kansas anymore.

CHAPTER 7

I Am Definitely Not In Kansas Anymore

I stare at Marvel's back as he approaches the café counter. I turn around and there they are, three grown men staring at me. They still feel like the three boys that I once formed a bond with in the second grade while our desks were up against the wall. I can't help but see them as second graders in adult bodies. The three of them have the innocence and the wonderment of young children. The excitement emanating from their faces is so innocent and loving. I can feel their readiness to teach me what they have discovered.

Three boys that I once had taught the concept of teamwork now seem to know more than me.

Brian, who I called "Brain" all throughout grade school, was this free-spirited dude who had hippie parents that he just adored. He talked about his parents like they were long time buddies. He was medium height and skinny, even thinner than 'skinny' almost scrawny. He wore his hair long. He didn't care if the other boys would call him a girl back then. He was confident being a male. He also had no reservations when it came to talking about his female side.

"Everyone has a male and female side, ya know?" he would say to the other kids. Most kids didn't understand most of the words that he used, but he didn't care. He was always so relaxed, although he was always known for not using his brain — the way most people expected to use his brain. Most teachers did not like his unorthodox ways, always going against the grain. I guess his type of mind was not really conducive to the Catholic school ways of conforming. His academic intelligence wasn't quite there. I, on the other hand, absolutely loved his mind. He always had something inspirational to share with me just when I needed it. I always admired him for his delivery, the timing of his words with people. He could feel just what they needed to hear when they needed to hear it. I was intrigued by his mind and how he thought. It was fascinating to me, but to everyone else, it was quite annoying.

Tim was a different story. He stood rigid, medium stature, fair skin with blond hair and blue eyes. He was heavily built and wore glasses. He was extremely smart academically. He was very logical, although he would hide his emotions. He knew how to talk his way out of feeling anything. Nobody was getting through that dense armor. He would sometimes reveal his true feelings to me but it was never too deep.

Leo was in a class all by himself. He was strong, thick and stubborn. He was quite short with dark hair and a stocky build. He appeared so proud of himself; pride at its best. He was considered a behavior problem in school and basically pretty much considered a coward by most of his peers. All talk, no action. I didn't see it that way. He always encouraged me to try new things and go after what I wanted. I could see his bravery when no one else could.

"Ya ready?" Leo asks as his face becomes clearer and everything else appears transparent in the café.

"I guess," I answer.

"Where shall we begin?" asks Tim looking at the other two.

"It's always best to start at the beginning," I answer, as my smile tickles my face.

They laugh at my comment, but I just imagine Glenda's face and her sparkly wand pointing down toward the beginning of the road of yellow brick.

Brian says, "Alright Dottie. It's about living your life free from limitations while becoming a conscious human being. It's about understanding how human life works on multiple levels. When you truly get this, you will begin living it fully yourself while experiencing, creating and remembering your multidimensional life. You will begin to see that there are new ways of seeing and experiencing things — in fact everything, while being human."

Leo slaps Brian on the back of his head and said, "Dottie, don't listen to him. Use your brain, Brian. That stuff is too 'out there.' Bring it down to earth for God's sake! Remember Brian, you are no longer a hippie. You are not having some new age fluffy, airy fairy conversation with your cosmic cowboy friends."

Brian punches Leo on the arm. "Oh, shut up, Leo." They both chuckle and put the focus back on me. I notice that Leo's body doesn't even move after the punch. Leo looks at his arm and laughs again then glances at Brian. "Really, Brian? Is that all ya got?"

Marvel glides past the table and says, "Do you have it covered guys? Can you handle her?"

The guys give a wave to Marvel as he exits the café.

Brian continues, "I was very much limited by the way I was raised. My parents were old hippies and easy going. They were free and whimsical. They never taught me about structure, organization or how to motivate myself to get things done. They were kind of the 'if it was meant to be here, it would be here' type of folks. They were sometimes a little flaky."

"Ya think?" Leo jokes. I laugh at Leo as I glance out the window watching Marvel get into his car.

"They always relied on one another to finish each other's sentences. They completed things in their own time and very rarely seem to be able to work with a schedule for time management. So, I naturally picked up some of those behaviors and habits. I find out later what would seem to be really cool for me as a teenager, actually created many difficulties and challenges for me as an adult.

"You see, Dottie, when you grow up with your family and you don't know anything different, you assume this type of behavior is normal and believe that it's just the way the world works. Until I met Marvel, I had no idea there were other ways of being or interacting with the world. My family pretty much just stayed to themselves. I had no idea that I could actually be different and change all the things that made my life difficult, mostly because I had no idea that the way I grew up was dysfunctional."

Leo leans his body in front of Brian at the table and says, "Okay, Dottie. Ya gotta be brave and strong like me." He smiles at Brian and then continues. "My parents taught me how to be strong, follow directions and stand up for what I want. They taught me structure and how to get things done, which allowed me to excel in sports. Because I was so good at doing what I was told I became an excellent athlete. I actually thought that I was pretty much perfect until I later realized I had so much anger about authority and being told what to do. When I was told what to do, I felt like a child being bossed around and not in charge of my own life. I was afraid to question authority. If I questioned the authority in my house I was mentally bullied or even sometimes hit by my father, whereas Mom was passive-aggressive when I disagreed with her. She would withdraw her love from me so I would always chase her for her approval. This kind of upbringing also created an inability for me to think outside the box or be creative. I was so used to being told what to do; I never relied on my original thought or my own imagination. It was so important to be a good boy and do what I was told. This all bled through into my adult life. I didn't realize how much my parents affected me until I learned this new perspective of being."

Brian concludes, "Hey Dottie, don't you want to make your journey home a little easier?"

"There ya go again, Brain. The road home? Are you serious? Where's home, dude? Do you have a map?!" Leo chuckles. "What 'home' are you actually referring to, Brian?"

"Well ..." Brian starts to continue but Leo interrupts.

"Brian wait. Let ME explain. I don't think you are actually capable. 'Home' means..." Leo patted his chest referring to his heart, "inside here. Your heart, self-love, your essence, YOUR love that is inside of you, ya know, like having a heart, unlike Tim here." Leo pauses, smiles and then says, "Just kidding Timmy-boy. You know I love ya."

Brian smiles and Tim chuckles.

Brian joins Leo, taps on his chest and says, "The connection to the inner part of you, the place inside that has all of your answers."

I lean over and tell Tim that he is full of heart.

"Dottie, we are just playing," he says back. "That's what we do here, play. You'll get used to it!"

"Well for me, Dottie, it's all about the heart," Tim says smiling and looking up at Leo out of the corner of his eye. "And how I feel inside, how much I love myself and am connected to my own soul. The issue for me was that my parents never taught me to understand what living through the heart really meant.

"Most people don't know this. You see, I was a very sensitive child. I was greatly affected by my environment and the people around me. I felt everything! I am talking every noise in my environment. It was completely distracting. Because of this, I became very mental and tried to manipulate my world and others in order to survive. My mom was very controlling and wanted everything her way which was very confusing to me as a child. I thought I had to please her. I felt like I was a victim to my mom's needs. My mom never touched me and so I was always craving to be touched and caressed."

Leo and Brian reach over to touch Tim. They push and pat him everywhere, including lightly slapping his face, causing Tim to smile. Tim laughs and says, "Real funny, guys." Tim holds his face up waiting for the guys to be done, closing his eyes, but barely flinching.

"Are you finished, guys?" Tim asks then continues. "Anyway, I felt so disconnected from everyone in my family and yet so hypersensitive to everything they did. My mom was always in her mind thinking, worrying, and planning and making up stories. My dad was kind of creepy and he always felt like he was eyeing the girls. He was really disconnected from my mom, which is probably why she was so crazy sometimes. She was pretty much unpredictable in her behavior. You never knew when she was going to start screaming or yelling. My dad, on the other hand, was pretty quiet, but just plain weird. He would bully me by the way he talked to me and said things that caused me to feel like I was worthless or not good enough to be loved. These things created all kinds of anxiety for me. Because I was thinking so much, I often miscommunicated or didn't finish listening to other people when they were talking, which caused a whole lot of problems for me. I felt like I should always do what people wanted so they would like me. I developed problems with communication, intimacy and touch which caused me great challenges with relationships. I had no idea that this wasn't normal, or the way the rest of the world lived, at least until I met that 'obnoxious' guy, Marvel," Tim expresses, blurting out a laugh as he looks at me.

"Ha, Tim," I respond.

"Okay, are you finished, Tim?" Brian says, almost not being able to contain himself. "If it bothers you, it's your issue. That's a basic one, but it's a good one! Like if someone is annoying you, I guarantee you that you have behaved this way some time in your life. It proves to be true to me every time. Actually, sometimes it's quite annoying to admit."

"True!" Leo and Tim agree.

"For best results, receive the information, understand it, feel it in your heart, then discern what resonates with you and is useful for your own journey," Tim says.

"You sound like a robot, Timmy. 'For best results?'" Brian says making fun of Tim. "Listen, Dottie. Keep your heart open and receive the information — being open to what you hear."

Leo adds, "So take it from a guy who had to learn how to keep his heart open. That was tough, right, Timmy-boy?" Tim wraps his arm around Leo.

A smile suddenly tickles my face again — I start to feel that I almost had something to do with these three guys getting together. When we found ourselves against the wall in second grade, I talked about how important it was to accept each person on our team. Leo was a jock, who never would have associated himself with a guy like Brian, let alone, hang out with a softie like Tim.

"Some people are like robots," Tim says and smiles. "They follow anyone who is an authority and do anything an authority says. The key here is being your own authority. Question everything and then make your own decision."

Brian adds, "There are concepts that Marvel has written that are extremely helpful. They are straightforward."

"They are really helpful," Leo agrees and switches to another concept.

"Here's another one, Dottie. If you are behaving in a certain way, it's because you are benefitting from it in some way, positively or negatively."

I interrupt, "Leo, I just want to feel better! Maybe clear up some of these emotions that are haunting me. I just can't ignore them anymore."

"This is usually what happens with people," Brian responds. "They reach a point where the pain and discomfort of the way they are living exceeds their desire to remain unaware. The pain of their patterns outweighs the joy in their life and they come to a crossroads where they decide to change. This is basically where you choose the right or left hand path."

"Whoa, that was deep but good, Brian," Leo smiles then continues. "Basically people become split or polarized and they have to choose between living from their heart or living the typical normal life with secrets, fears and pain. This sometimes occurs between the ages of forty or fifty, that 'mid-life crisis' thing. This was tough for me because you all know how much I love pain. No pain, no gain." Leo laughs and raises his arms, showing off his biceps.

Brian leans into Tim and responds. "Still the same old Leo, but ya gotta love him."

Leo asks, "What's not to love?"

Brian rolls his eyes and continues to talk. "You should do sessions with Marvel."

"Do you want the 4-1-1 on how to make the sessions easier with Marvel?" Leo asks.

"Sure," I say.

Wait! I will be doing sessions with Michael?

"Don't fight him when he says things," Leo puts up his fists and smiles.

Brian adds, "That means don't argue, justify, accuse, or resist mentally or emotionally. This will make it easier for you."

Brian raises his hands up and shows the quotes symbol with his fingers. "Always remember that any information you come across is simply that. It's just information."

Tim continues, "All information that you receive should be felt, understood and discerned carefully to see if it is something that assists you on your journey. You really should do this with anyone that you connect with."

Brian adds, "When you hear something that doesn't feel right to you, avoid judging it. Wait to form an opinion until you have heard what he has said. This stops any judgment which will prevent you from getting as much from this information as possible."

Leo put up his hands in quotes imitating Brian. "You are going overboard with this new brain of yours, Brian."

Brian gives Leo the evil eye, lovingly, of course.

"Alright, Brian. I am just trying to make it fun." Leo laughs. "My apologies! I'll be serious now."

"Always apply what you know!" Tim says.

Brian moves on. "Knowledge is wonderful but it is not wisdom. Wisdom only comes through experience. Life could be enjoyable if you understand that all experience leads to wisdom."

"Here's another one that I love! You know how we humans love to have opinions and judge everything?" Leo adds, "That would be me, in case you didn't know!"

"Yes. Definitely him!" Tim agrees as he smiles touching my shoulder. "When you judge something, it blinds you from the truth in your experience because you are viewing your experience based on your thoughts and beliefs. While these thoughts and beliefs are true for you because it is what you have experienced, it is not true for everything or everyone. When you judge something, your judgment is based on what you personally believe to be true."

Brian says, "The same thing can happen when you blindly follow authority. You are not paying attention to your own truth and so you follow their truth because they are 'the authority.'"

"Take it all in, then decide if it's good for you or not," Tim says holding his hand to his heart. "Keep your heart open!"

"When I have my heart open it always seems to get hurt," I say.

"Another concept … 'hurt is not getting what you want,'" Leo chimes in.

"The cause of your hurt is unfulfilled expectations and the lack of acceptance of what is. The expectation can be anything: expecting to be loved or approved of, getting a new toy, or even getting a new job," Brian explains.

"Anytime that we don't like something or we get hurt by something, it's because we have chosen not to accept what is. That would make sense, right?" Leo chimes in.

"When you truly get this, you won't be hurt. You will be able to keep your heart open," Tim adds.

"My heart open?" I ask. "What does that even mean?"

Tim continues. "Most people think that an open heart means you open your heart to the world and it opens outward, but the truth is, your heart opens inward to reveal your true self and your own inner connection that makes living life more beautiful."

Brian finishes up. "It is the love within your own heart that holds your joy, not just loving others. True joy comes from the love within you."

I smile while feeling this love swirl around us. Again, everything else becomes transparent and the only thing that exists is the four of us. I switch those feelings to thoughts, and say, "So, is this how you guys are going to teach me? You will all finish each other's thoughts and sentences. You guys crack me up. If you are going to take this journey with me, as you would say…" I smile and make "air" quotes with my fingers. "It's hard for me to grasp all that you are saying. You might want to slow down and work at my pace. Imagine that I am an infant just learning to walk. You guys go way too fast! It's like putting an infant on a skateboard and pushing him downhill."

"We will work at your pace, no skateboards, not yet," Brian said. "We will meet you where you are at and slow down the pace. Does that work?"

I nod.

Leo adds, "Think of us as your 'spotters' while you are weight lifting," Leo holds up his arm making a muscle again.

I reach up and gently pull down Leo's arm. "Take it easy, big guy. We're not working out right now, although I do miss playing football with all the guys from the old neighborhood."

"We should get the team back together," Leo jokes, knowing that the other guys would never play football with him anymore, let alone even hang with him."

"We should! Do you still know or hang with them anymore?" I say.

"No. They think I am an asshole," Leo states.

"How do you know?" I ask.

"They came right out and told me," Leo informs.

"Really? All our football buddies? Seriously? They said that?" I inquire.

"They said I am too intense. They just can't handle my strong personality — unlike these two awesome guys!" Leo says as he pats Tim and Brian on their shoulders.

"Do you still watch football?" I ask, changing what seems like a touchy subject.

"Duh … of course I do," Leo teases.

"We watch it here, every Sunday!" Tim shouts out.

"Well, let's be clear. I don't watch it." Brian looks at Leo wanting to continue and says, "Soooo, can I continue, guys?"

"Sure!" Leo chuckles.

"So, your answers must be found and remembered by you," Brian says. "It is the only way that they permanently become yours because up until now, all of the answers that you thought were yours were actually something you heard from others like mom, dad, your family, your teachers, etc.

"And you assumed they were yours. You have to figure out what's yours, not only your thoughts and beliefs but your responses in life as well. This was tough for me to understand. Sometimes the things that you feel are not even yours. They are your family behavior patterns, hence, my hippie dad and flower child mom," Brian says.

Tim jumps in, "These patterns come from your family belief systems, your core programs, that you were taught consciously and unconsciously as a child and you had no idea you were being taught."

"Consciously and unconsciously?" I ask.

Brian answers. "Yes. Conscious things were things that you openly talked about and these were known and accepted. Like for example, when your parents deliberately bullied or maybe made you feel guilty to make you do something that you did not want to do or it felt wrong to do. You saw it, heard it and experienced it; therefore, it was a conscious experience. Consciously you knew what they were doing and somewhere began to believe that bullying or making somebody feel guilty was the way you got your way."

"Unconscious belief systems can come as easily as watching your family behave, interact with others and make choices," Leo joins in.

"Whether conscious or unconscious, most of the time, you assume these things could be true and voilà, a belief system is created," Tim says exaggerating the 'voilà.'

"For example, let's say when you were a child you watched your father always do the opposite of what your mother asked or told him to do and now you as an adult do the opposite of what people ask or tell you to do. You may feel controlled or manipulated when this happens, so you resist. This would be an example of having issues with authority figures or being controlled. What you did not know was that your father had a very controlling mother and after that saw all women or people who asked or told him what to do as authorities trying to control him. And now, voila, you are repeating his pattern unconsciously. Make sense?"

"Yes, I think so," I say with a bit of hesitancy.

Brian continues. "Here's another one. If you depend on answers from anyone else, it is simply repeating another's answers and discoveries. It is like being a parrot with no inner wisdom. The best you can hope for on this journey is information that will give you guidelines and direction for your own inner memory and then the discovery of your own answers."

73

"This may take some time to sink in. It's definitely a process," Tim says. "It took me awhile. My head was like a tin can, echoing everyone else's words. It took some time to feel it for myself."

Leo jumps in. "Very true, Tim, but how about Brian here? His head is like a black hole in space, anything that goes near it gets sucked into the vast emptiness. Everything that went in got lost in the cosmos." Leo chuckles as he taps on Brian's soft knit hat hanging down over his shoulders to his butt.

Brian corrects Leo. "A black hole is a place in space where gravity pulls so much that even light cannot get out, let alone anything being sucked in." Brian then turns to Tim, "Tim, did you know that? The gravity is so damn strong because matter has been squeezed into a tiny space. Because no light can get out, people can't even see black holes. They are invisible!"

"Actually, Brian, space telescopes with special tools can help find black holes. The special tools can see how stars that are very close to black holes act differently than other stars," Tim informs.

"OMG! Whatever, you two! Do you see what I have to deal with, Dottie? They are a bunch of nerds," Leo says.

"But they are cute nerds, though, right?" I tell him.

"I wouldn't call them cute. Maybe really smart! Anyway, the fact remains is that it took forever for Brian to start using that brain of his. Isn't that right Brian?" Leo kids and shoves Brian. "On the other hand, he does have such a beautiful loving heart for a nerd!"

Brian smiles at Leo, taking off his hat.

Tim adds, "He did not have the mental awareness of how the world works or how to completely understand or even verbalize that heart piece to someone, so it was difficult for him."

Brian interrupts, "That's very true, Dottie. Okay, let's talk about Leo now, the guy who was the worst at getting this process."

"The worst? I don't think so," Leo interrupts.

"Come on, Leo, you were a little thick and stubborn at getting all this," Brian challenges.

Leo leans in to me. "I was just questioning a lot. Aren't we supposed to question everything?" He then turns to Brian.

"Question everything, yes. Fight and defend every one of your actions before listening to a possible solution? No," Brian answers. "You were born into that prideful, egotistical family. It was bound to happen."

Leo jumps in. "And what I learned about being prideful is this. With pride comes shame." Leo continues, "And shame is something I don't ever want to feel again if I don't have to."

"You can say that again!" Brian said.

"Shame is something I don't ever want to feel again if I don't have to," Tim repeats while smiling.

Leo smiles at Tim and says, "So basically, I was the bully and yet the coward of the group. I felt that strong pride like a lion, and then felt the shame later. It was not a picnic, believe me."

Tim informs, "Pride is a cover up for shameful feelings. Underneath the pride is shame. There always seems to be prideful feelings when trying to cover up shame. Pride protects people from being shameful. These two feelings are polar opposites."

Brian jokes, "Well that makes sense because, Leo, you are a little bipolar!"

"Imagine that?" Leo says.

Tim adds, "Ya see, Dottie, let me explain a little bit about Leo. He worked for his dad all these years. He wanted to leave, but he was too afraid to start anything on his own. He took the coward's way out. Sorry, Leo, but it's true," Tim says as he smiles. "He waited until his dad died. He did not have the courage to say what he really wanted and lived in fear of rejection. So he really turned the abuse that he received as a child, inward, by living in fear, turning away from himself."

"Giving myself up to the fear," Leo adds.

"Oh," I say giving Leo a compassionate smile. "And sorry to hear about your dad, Leo." I make my way over to Leo, invisibly checking to see if it's still a touchy subject.

Wow, this is just what my oldest daughter does to people...checking people's temperature.

"No need to be sorry. I forgave my dad after he died, but it was a process. It was the toughest thing I ever had to do because I was so pissed at him. More importantly, I forgave myself for accepting the way my dad treated me all those years. I wasted a lot of my life in fear, anger, wrongfulness and guilt because I accepted that abuse. I allowed it," Leo says as he pats on his bulky chest.

Brian adds, "Today, with this new awareness he no longer lives in the past and is able to see this experience as benign."

"What do you mean?" I ask. "Benign?"

"Neutral, not charged, not upset at all by the situation," Leo answers. "As long as we hold onto the pain it continues. There is a reason we continue to hold on to it. We think we see a benefit to continuing the pain. There are many reasons we choose to continue. In my case I held onto the fear believing I needed to remember it so I could stay on guard. I kept me from getting 'hurt' but that didn't serve me very well, although it seemed like the only choice I had at the time."

"Really?" I ask, not really expecting a response.

"You will better understand this as you go through some of your own stuff," Tim replies.

Leo continues, "But I know that when I completely realized that the past is no longer relevant to my present experience, I decided that I wanted to live fully in the moment. I then said to myself, 'Oh, it is time for me to see this differently.' Sometimes during this process, though ..." Leo stops and looks up as more customers enter his café. "Hello," he says to them.

Tim continues. "Sometimes during this process, it is quite difficult not to judge yourself for all the silly and stupid choices you have made."

"And keep in mind that judgment will just slow you down. It will slow the process down," Brian concludes. "Leo was too scared to pursue anything while his dad was here on earth, but look at him today. Leo is responsible for this café and he is kicking butt!" Brian holds his hand up for a high five that Leo slaps.

Tim then adds again, "Okay, let's do Mr. Brian, or Brain, as you would say, Dottie."

I smile.

Brian says, "Okay, here's my story. I was so connected to my heart and soul. I lived primarily by feeling. I still do. That's who my family was as a unit. It was awesome, yet not so great at the same time. I didn't really participate in the world. I disregarded my outer world. I disregarded my brain, mind and communication, for that matter. I felt like, why did it matter? I knew who I was. My family was so telepathically connected that we finished each other's sentences. We were one and had such cohesiveness that the outside world didn't really matter to us. So today, among this group, I am the feeler and at times have no forethought. I live moment to moment. I live by feeling."

"That would explain a lot when we were in the second grade. You were so damn easy-going," I add.

"Now I am beginning to see the importance of being separate and being responsible for me. I have discovered that the skills of the mind work very well in the human world. These skills are required for me to communicate clearly and function in a world where people mostly use their mind and quite often are not connected to their heart, their intuition and that telepathic skill. Bottom line is that to live in the world with people you need both a functional mind and a connection to your heart," Brian informs.

Tim takes over. "Then there is me. I am the mentalist. Sometimes I have trouble getting out of my head."

"Sometimes?" Leo asks.

"All right, a lot of times, but my mind was what got me through."

"Through what?" I inquire.

"Through the pain," Tim answers.

"What pain?" I ask.

"The pain of feeling unwanted, unloved, not heard and being abandoned emotionally," Tim tells me. "Of course, most of this pain was based on misunderstandings of what I thought was happening and what I understood as a truth from the view of a child. However, my mother leaving was not a misunderstanding. She did, in fact, leave us. Why she left was misunderstood by me. I have spent most of my life in my thoughts not to feel the pain. Dottie, being in my thoughts I believed was safer than feeling. I could rely on my thoughts and what I perceived to be true to keep me from feeling. These past couple years, I have made my way to those feelings. I won't lie to you, Dottie. It wasn't easy, revisiting the past and feeling the pain."

Tim continues, "I had to feel in order to work my way back to this core belief, 'I am unwanted, unlovable.' I was torn in opposite directions. On one hand, in order to feel wanted and loved I stopped making my own decisions. Instead, my life didn't feel like it was mine because I felt obligated to other people. I dropped everything for them and they thought I was wonderful because I was always there for them. It gave me self-worth and made me feel loved. But the flip side was that in order to do this, I sacrificed my own happiness so that I didn't have to feel that I was not loved and I could avoid seeing myself. I became bitter and resentful and felt burdened by this identity. There was a catch though. Even though I did all these things to feel loved, I was prepared to be unloved because somewhere deep down I truly believed I was not lovable or wanted."

Brian interrupts, "Once you wake up, you begin to understand that most of what you thought was true was in fact a misperception seen through the eyes of a child and then you recognize that you grew up to be an adult believing what you thought was true as a child."

Tim exclaims, "What a realization that was! What an awakening! And boy how it changes everything. You will eventually see that everything you have experienced has led you to this point. All of your actions and choices have brought you something valuable…your wisdom."

"Hey, Dottie, are you there?" Leo stops and stares at me.

"Earth to Dottie!" Brian asks while feeling me mentally drift off.

"Oh, yes," I answer. "It's just a lot of information. In fact, I didn't follow half of what you guys just said. I kind of got lost."

"Aren't you always getting lost? It's like back in grade school," Leo says joking.

"On your return to your awakening, you must choose the road of balance, leading you to unity, like the road of yellow brick, the road that I helped put together in our grade school play. But you wouldn't know anything about that, Miss Wicked Witch of the West. You were too busy being a witch. Ha!" Leo says laughing.

"Or maybe the road of yellow brick needs to be gold." Brian adds, "Gold is the highest form of consciousness."

"Figures you would know that," Leo says.

Tim brings us back to seriousness again. "I know this is a lot of information. Just absorb it. Don't try to hold onto the words."

"Okay, I have had enough. I am famished. Can I eat now?" I joke but am completely serious.

Leo stands up and says, "What can I get you, my lady? Anything you want. It's on the house." Leo takes my order and heads back to the kitchen while Tim continues to talk about another concept.

On his way to the kitchen Leo comments, "She is full, Tim. I don't think that she can absorb any more information. She not only said that she was full, but she feels full. Hello, Timmy boy! Can't you feel it? Feel, Tim." Leo places his hands on either sides of his mouth and shouts out, "Obviously, Tim is still working on awareness and sensing, well actually, feeling. Yes, there is a heart in there somewhere, Tim. I just know it."

Brian senses the customers nearby focusing on their group and shushes Leo with his pointer finger over his mouth.

Tim chuckles.

Brian instructs, "Dottie, here are some exercises that you can work on before we meet again." Brian hands me a folder with some exercises enclosed as well as everyone's contact information.

Brian adds, "Call us when you are ready."

"Seriously, there's homework. What did I get myself into?" I joke. "And ready for what?"

"For more!" Leo says as he walks back to the table with my drink.

I take a deep breath.

Tim grabs the paper and circles the words "Be kind in all things."

"All things," he says. "That includes being kind to yourself, Dottie."

I smile.

We eat and stay at the café talking about old times. I leave the café completely full from food, but more importantly, with some really important wisdom that I cannot yet identify or explain. But it's a start.

~

I arrive home, make it to the couch again and open up the folder. It reads:

"Anything that bothers you is your issue."

Really? Anything?

I begin to write things that bother me:

My mom, sisters, children, my ex, fellow employees, and Mr. Marvel.

I put the pen down and read:

"People are your mirrors and teachers."

Hmmmmm

"Be kind in all things."

I am kind! Am I kind to myself? What does that even mean?

"People don't do things to you, they do things for themselves."

Seriously?

Turning the page, I see more questions.

Enough of this.

I toss the notes aside and walk upstairs to my bedroom and plop on my memory foam mattress. My head is swirling like a tornado trying to absorb everything the guys said today. The room continues to spin until I close my eyes. After a significant amount of rumination, the thoughts gradually slow down which puts me in a deep sleep.

DREAM:

"Where am I?" I look around and see that I am in Marvel's old classroom, but he is nowhere to be found. Suddenly, Glenda, the woman from the school, appears at the door.

"Dorothy, you look lost. Are you trying to find your way home?" Glenda inquires with a twinkle in her eye. "There is no place like home, ya know?"

I sit bolt upright in my bed in a state of panic. I try to remember my dream, but I am too exhausted to care. I collapse back onto my pillow and fall back into a sound sleep.

CHAPTER 8

If I Only Had A Brain

My eyelids open slightly, just enough so that I can observe where I am. I shift my eyes from left to right, not quite sure if I want to re-enter this existence. Then I remember what was said to me yesterday. I feel different but don't know quite how. Something has changed. I start to feel my heart.

Open? Not quite sure if that is where my heart is. Is it weird? Yes, it's weird.

I want to say it's expanded. I always used to think that if my heart was open, it would feel amazing and freeing. It doesn't… *far from it.*

This is quite uncomfortable and certainly not familiar. I don't have any thoughts, which is unusual for me at this time of the morning. I remember what they said about absorbing through the heart and not the brain. Again, what did that even mean?

I lean over and grab the folder that was given to me. I find the second set of questions and start to read:

What childhood beliefs do you live today and still perceive or believe? Write as much as you can.

I grab the pen to write, hesitant to write the following words:

I am bad, dirty and icky.

As my eyes tear up and memories surface, I quickly choke it right back down. I then feel the anger creeping up, a feeling of heat flashes across my face. This is clearly the anger that I am never allowed to feel, always silenced. My anger becomes a thunderstorm, the force that will start a possible inner tornado that is out of control. I fight it at first. I attempt to silence it and go in and look at those tears, memories and anger.

Instead, I decide to join my inner tornado. Thoughts make their way in.

Gosh, I wonder what the kids are doing today? Maybe I will give them a call or clean up a little downstairs.

I get dressed, look at my closet and start to rearrange it. I walk downstairs, pick things up along the way and rearrange my antiques on the living room shelves.

I shouldn't bother the kids. It's Dad's weekend. Ugh!

I stand in the kitchen looking for something else to do.

What the hell am I looking for? Relax.

I go back up the stairs and plop on the bed. I open the folder where I find Brian's cell number on the inside cover. I take a deep breath, grab my cell and dial.

"Hello."

"Hey, Brian. I think I need some help. I am stirring."

"Where do you want to meet?"

"I don't care! Anywhere! It doesn't matter to me," I respond desperately.

"Come on over to my house. It's right outside of town, not too far from Leo's café." He then describes where he lives. "Turn right then left. It's the white farmhouse up on the hill. There's a scarecrow right in the front yard as you come up the long driveway."

I arrive at his house in about twenty-five minutes.

"Damn, girl, you got here fast!" Brian chuckles after opening his front door.

I step through the doorway and say, "Having some trouble with never-ending thoughts. I can't seem to stop the thoughts. I can't stop ruminating."

"Aaah, Dottie, thoughts. I get you. Most people get lost in their thoughts to avoid emotions. Are your thoughts moving so fast, almost like a tornado, from one subject to another?"

"Yes, they are, like a tornado," I tell him and laugh.

"I should start you at the very beginning. Are you ready?"

"Sure, absolutely," I respond.

"Okay then, get out of your thoughts and follow me." Brian leads me down the hall to a room that smells like incense. He motions me to sit in one of his tie-dye chairs. I take a seat and look around at the shelves loaded with crystals, dream-catchers, new-age books and rocks.

"I know, Dottie," Brian chuckles. "After my parents died I just couldn't get rid of this stuff. It was so precious to them. They were such awesome people."

I nod while looking around at everything.

"The people that I grew up with were so into what they felt, rather than what they thought. People are more than their thoughts. They are the creators of their thoughts. Our thoughts come from our beliefs. So, beliefs eventually turn into belief systems. A belief system is often a complex design of multiple beliefs creating an entire system. We can talk in detail about our belief systems later. You can talk about that with Marvel later when you work with him."

"Okay," I respond.

"Thoughts come from the belief systems that an individual has created or decided to accept as their own and are even sometimes brought into their lifetime as a way for them to internally work through certain lessons they have come to experience."

"So what you're saying is that I chose this?" I ask.

"Well, yes, in a way. You are here having experiences, and the experiences you are creating for yourself are based on your belief systems — what you believe to be true about yourself and your world. One of the biggest challenges is that you believe that your beliefs are real and in a sense, they are, because they are based on what you have experienced in your life. Just because you have experienced it, and it is your truth, doesn't make it true for everyone everywhere."

"It just makes it true for you?"

"Yes," he answers.

"Give me an example of what you believe is true," Brian says.

"I believe that it is clearly not safe to give information to an authority, especially a catholic authority, if you want something to be resolved."

"That was your experience from...?"

"The Catholic school authority disappointed me with something."

"Okay. It is not true for all of authority."
"My trust was betrayed," I say.

"But not every authority figure is untrustworthy. You see, while you experienced betrayal with authority, not all authority will betray you. But that's what you experienced so you believed that to be true.

"These decisions can be made either consciously or unconsciously and you might not even be aware of what you chose. It is not the belief itself, but the attachment to a belief that makes it yours. Once the belief is yours, it allows you to unconsciously run your life on autopilot so to speak. Believing that the belief is true allows the belief to attach to you almost like a piece of Velcro. And once it is stuck to you, it becomes part of your life and you run your life with this belief attached. Most of the time this happens unconsciously and you are not even aware you are living your life with this autopilot. Just imagine how many beliefs a one-year-old experiences or even before one, when they haven't even words yet."

"Yeah, I can see that. So, my beliefs about authority are attached to me. Is it my beliefs and thoughts that caused this?"

"Yes, because you believe your beliefs and thoughts are real, they become your reality. So, everything you do, the way you behave and the choices you make will all be based on your reality. Your life experiences will play out these patterns. Sometimes beliefs and thoughts are the same. Beliefs are often deeper than thoughts. Often our thoughts are a result of what we believe. In your example, where you spoke of your belief about authority, especially Catholic authority. You believe authority cannot be trusted. Because you believe this, any thoughts you have about authority will be influenced by your belief. This can play out many ways in your life — such as avoiding authority figures completely — refusing an authority figure's help; defensive anytime you are around an authority figure, or maybe refusing to be in a authority role. These are just a few examples. Once you have created beliefs, you are always creating experiences to support these beliefs and you are no longer present and living 'in the moment' with the 'innocence of a child.'"

I nod.

"Dottie, how much time do you spend living in the moment?"

"Well, I am not too sure what that even means, living in the moment." I laugh.

"How much time do you spend thinking about the past or the future?" Brian asks.

"Well, a lot," I answer. "I never really am without a thought.

"That's what it means to not live in the moment," Brian informs.

"See, thoughts and beliefs create judgments. In your example, you judge authority as being untrustworthy which comes from your beliefs about authority that are based on your past experience with authority," Brian says.

"Oh, yeah. I can see why that would be true. When my dad had cancer, I was the cause of his frustration because I felt like I was always getting in his way. He would yell at me all the time."

"Do you hear how you are judging yourself? How much time do you spend judging yourself? Don't answer that. I already know or I can guess. A lot, right?" Brian continues, "Judgments are the source of almost all pain and difficulties.

"For instance, when you said your dad yelled at you when he was sick, you created the belief that your dad was upset with you because how you were acting was annoying to him but the reality was, he could have been upset or angry for many reasons. He could have just been not feeling well or he was afraid of dying or any other reason. Instead of asking, you assumed you were the cause of his anger and your beliefs and judgments were created," Brian explains.

I say, "I might have asked him as to why he felt so frustrated if I knew he was sick. It might have been different if I knew he was sick."

"So write this down. Your homework will be writing down everything that you believe about yourself and this world up until now, okay? And I mean everything; nothing is too small or insignificant."

I nod and jot it down.

"As human beings, we get our identity from how we act or how we behave, judge ourselves from these actions and then judge ourselves based on our actions by the way the world responds to us. But you are not your thoughts or your behaviors. You select behaviors, either deliberately or not."

Brian continues. "These judgments get cemented in place because the more thoughts occur and are repeated, the stronger they become. Although you can't see thoughts or feelings, they are real. Anything that exists has substance even if you can't see it. Thoughts exist as a substance called energy. While you can't see it, this energy has a charge much like an electric current. Your thoughts have a charge and, when repeated, the charge gets stronger creating energy patterns that affect the nerve pathways in the brain. This energy pattern eventually becomes beliefs if they aren't already supporting an existing belief. Our beliefs and thoughts are energy, and the energy of each belief or thought has a specific frequency, much like the frequency on a radio. Just like a magnet these frequencies will attract other frequencies in the form of people, places and things, and we will have experiences where our frequency matches theirs. These frequencies or 'energy waves' have different vibrations that create many patterns that weave and overlap forming a complex pattern we call a matrix that can sometimes make it difficult to move or make changes in our lives. Am I losing you?"

I shrug my shoulders.

"All right, the movie *The Matrix* is a perfect example of how these interwoven frequencies keep us trapped by our thoughts and beliefs."

"The *Matrix*? The one with Keanu Reeves? I saw it," I reply and look at him like he's crazy.

"Watch it again after today."

I nod.

"Can you see how these woven patterns play such a huge part in making change difficult for us? Because so much energy is given to continuing these patterns over time, breaking them can be a real challenge. Are you able to see after a while thoughts and beliefs make it a little more difficult to change? If the thought has turned into a belief, it makes it even a little more difficult to change."

I nod.

"A good example of this is during Catholic Mass every Sunday. Remember that line that we repeated out loud. 'Lord I am not worthy to receive you, but only say the word and I shall be healed.' Like how many times did we say that?"

"Every single Sunday before communion," I reply.

"After enough repetition at mass we really believed what we were saying. After a certain amount of time passes, the belief starts to sink in."

"Yes, I remember."

"I am not worthy? You are worthy. You are a beautiful being that is worthy, always. You are everything. You are love. You are a part of Source or God. You are a participant of your healing process. You are responsible for your own life. You are not a victim to your life. You are your own healer. Thoughts and beliefs affect the etheric, astral, and mental planes, which can be felt in our

87

physical world by someone who is sensitive."

"What?" I ask.

"Oooops, I am being 'cosmic' again. Sorry Dottie. Anyway, look those up later," said Brian. "The words: etheric, astral and mental planes. On second thought, don't. That is 'out there' stuff," he says looking not quite sure. "Leo would be busting me right now."

I scrunch my eyebrows. "So Marvel taught you all this?"

"Yeah, why?" Brian ignores my inquiry.

I shrug my shoulders. "Just wondering."

"He did. For so long I never thought that I was smart. What I mean by that is intellectually smart. Yes, I have depth in my thoughts. I always have. It's more about the book smart thing — like I didn't have a brain. Marvel has explained to me that I had it in me all the time; I just wasn't accessing it!

"Remember I told you about your thought patterns and frequencies interweaving and connecting? Well, in order to change these beliefs, you have to unwind or untie the knots of these beliefs for you to find the root or source where it started to really change. For instance, you shared about your difficulty with authority. It is not enough to just be aware that you have a problem with authority. You have to 'dig deeper' and ask yourself why you have that belief and where did it come from. You don't just wake up one day and start believing you don't trust authority figures. You have to untie the knots and trail back to where they came from.

"So the root of a pattern must shift for the thinking to shift. Ultimately the belief behind the thought must change for the process to permanently change. Sometimes you may change one pattern or set of thoughts and later do something that looks like the one you just shifted. While these changes are important, ALL connected patterns or the roots of the patterns must change for the thinking to shift. This is important to know. The root of the pattern must be shifted. Again, the more often you think the thoughts and the more emotion and feeling that's put into them, the stronger they are and the more difficult they are to change. These are the secrets of being human that no one

88

speaks of."

"I would like to shift a few things permanently," I say.

"You have to understand that it's a process, Dottie," Brian informs. "Human beliefs can be quite complex."

"I would like to have some of my memories just go away, ya know?"

"Your memories just don't go away, but they can certainly be benign or feel neutral. When they become wisdom, they have no feeling. All that is left is what you have learned."

"Okay," I tell him.

"So, I can't make the memories of my past go away, but I can resolve the feelings and beliefs about what I believed about my past. For instance, Dottie, my parents were friggin' crazy as humans. I remember people walking around here naked. Multiple people have had sex in this very room."

Really?

"Now as an adult, I know that they are called orgies. Jesus, it was ridiculous what I thought was normal."

What?

"Yeah, you heard me correctly. Friggin' orgies. Can you believe it?" Brian expresses. "Anyway, so let's talk more about thoughts."

"What? I'm still recovering from the orgy story. Jesus, Brian. I knew your parents were liberal, but OMG!"

Brian smiles and says, "Yep. That was my life. One naked person after another. There was always someone on top of someone doing something and I would walk by like I was walking down the street like it was nothing."

"I just can't believe it. That must have really screwed up your mind."

"You bet it did! I was all distorted with crazy ideas and behaviors I thought were normal that freaked everyone out. Our family was connected and we knew love, but it was all twisted up by distorted lust and sex. I could deeply love and was not afraid to feel or be intimate with others, but the sex part was totally distorted. It got in the way of me having any real intimate relationships. In fact, sex was awesome, but it was like a mental experience, not a love-felt connection. When I realized this, I thought: 'Wow, I am just like a dog.' I could hump anything, get off and feel so detached afterwards. Sex was like washing your hands and not even noticing the soap or water. So, when I was with someone, I was so into the sexual feeling I never really connected with them. I could have just had sex with myself!"

"Now I understand and feel so much more. Like how it molded my personality and affected my life in sooo many ways; in fact, in every way." Brian adds, "Hey, one good thing that I got out of it was I am comfortable with my body, and other people's bodies."

Brian laughs out loud.

"Yeah, I guess so," I replied. "Unlike me."

"That's something you really need to work through with Marvel. You can feel safe with him. Trust me, I know the difference between sincere people and one's that are not; after the hundreds of people who went through my house. I can tell who is who."

"Okay, thanks."

"Okay. Back to some basic understandings."

"Whew, Brian."

"Thoughts are drawn from a pool of existing thoughts that exist in the universe. All thoughts that ever will be thought have already been thought. There are probably no new thoughts just variations…"

"Okay, you lost me dude," I say.

"Too much information? I just always feel that everyone should have the foundation of how this all works; I can never quite tell when enough is enough. Leo would be having a field day right now," Brian comments and laughs.

"That's okay, Brian. You are sometimes airy fairy and I can't get out of my head. I have so many thoughts in this head of mine — twirling around like a tornado."

"Being in our thoughts is something we commonly do. Unfortunately, when this happens we direct our life with thoughts which are based on our beliefs. Our beliefs are based on our experiences, so while true for us, they are not always accurate. When we direct our life through our thoughts, it is not possible to be who we truly are and live life through our heart or true self. Living life without thoughts, what Marvel refers to as thoughtlessness, allows us to be in a state of neutrality, free of judgment. We all have the ability to be in any experience without attaching to it. Thoughtlessness in its highest form is pure awareness.

"In your example, Dottie, being in a state of thoughtlessness, having no thoughts, about authority figures, frees you to have an experience with authority figures without judgment. Imagine how your life would change if the things that caused you the most difficulty were just neutral experiences in your life," Brian suggested with a smile.

"That would be awesome!" I reflected. "But it seems like I always attract this stuff in my life that things cling to me like static electricity."

"Well, in a sense that's what's happening. As I said earlier, thoughts are energy, and this energy has a frequency or vibration like radio waves."

"It reminds me of the old expression 'birds of a feather flock together.' Kind of explains why groups like gangs come about," I mused.

"Exactly!" Brian shouts triumphantly. "Now you're getting it! These energy pools can be anything from greed, drama, despair or happiness. Take your pick — the possibilities are endless. You won't be able to think a thought from a particular pool unless you have beliefs with a similar frequency to that pool."

"Wait a minute," I said, waving for him to stop. "What would these energy pools look like in the real world, Mr. Airy Fairy?"

"Hmmm," Brian ponders. "Okay. Imagine a swimming pool that is filled with water but the water is blue and anything that goes into it turns blue or it splashes out. It's the same with energy pools. The energy or frequency of anything in the pool must be the same to stay in it. So how does this relate, you might ask? Well, imagine a pool of thoughts and only thoughts that are related can stay in that pool. Now imagine you are swimming or living in that pool. If this were the case, then you would only be able to think and use thoughts from the pool you are swimming or living in. For instance, let's say I am depressed. The thoughts I am limited to, are, anything about depression or becoming free of depression, anything that may cause or free me from depression, hence I am in the pool of depression and will mostly or only focus on depression related things. Thus, I am in the energetic pool of depression. Keep in mind there are many pools that you swim in on a daily basis!"

Brian points to a manual that displays the diagram for the frequencies and says, "The EFIs, otherwise known as energy pools, are explained in here. E-N," he begins to spell out the word.

I put up my hand and say, "I got it." I begin to write.

"Give me an emotion that you are having difficulty with right now."

"Shame, guilt…disappointment," I tell him.

"Well then, the second piece of homework is to write about it. And then Marvel can get into that stuff with you later."

"Mr. Marvel?"

"Yes, he is part of this process, too, Dottie. What's your deal with him anyway?"

"I'm not quite sure yet."
"He is an awesome dude and I have met a lot of dudes and dudettes in the personal growth area, believe me." Brian chuckles. "Shiatsu, rebirthing workshops, yoga, Tibetans, and chanting — you name it, I was exposed to it. There are some that can channel away and they bring in some great information, but most of them are dysfunctional in their human life, for

instance, my parents' orgy friends. And then there are some that are so damn heady, science freaks, therapeutic-like, and so literal that I just want to light one up listening to them."

"What?"

"Light up a joint," he repeats.

"You are too funny, Brian."

"For so long, I was searching for something to help me get grounded — something that made sense. Not one of these techniques gave me what I was seeking — not that they don't work for others. I just wanted 'real' clarity in this brain of mine and an experience that was worthwhile for me. Marvel excels in, and is very present, when it comes to 'out there' stuff. He is at the same time, very precise, logical, reasonable and rational when it comes to being functional as a human. You should hear him go off on the brain stuff. He almost sounds like he was Einstein in a past life. I did check his birthday, and it's in November of 1955, and Einstein died in April of 1955 — so he could technically be him. I bust Marvel about it all the time, and he always gives the same answer."

"Why do you care, Brian? Really?" I laugh.

Brian states, "And to think that I originally called him to learn about Chi Gung."

"Chi Gung?"

"It's a different form of the martial arts. I saw it on his brochure. Who knew that Mr. Marvel would turn out to be a warehouse of information that included so many techniques! This stuff is logical…it just makes sense.

"I released a lot of the baggage that I was carrying. I became an actor in my own life rather than a reactor. Today, my thoughts are so much clearer; my emotions are more balanced; my physical surroundings are in harmony. Hey, I can tolerate Leo now. That is harmony and a miracle in itself." Brian laughs at himself and continues talking.

"If you are a creator of your thoughts, you can change everything! However, in order to change them you must take ownership. In other words, admit they are yours and take responsibility for them and what has occurred because of them. Because thoughts are invisible and almost never acknowledged, most people are not aware of them nor can they even believe that they created them."

Brian checks to see if I am following him. I give him the thumbs-up.

"Each and every thought and belief is an energetic pattern. This is basically quantum physics in the human experience. Thank God for quantum physics. Now we have a science way to explain what has always been known."

"Quantum physics!? Please, explain, Brain!" I say and chuckle.

"Just look it up!"

"Ha! Well thank God for quantum physics!" I add sarcastically.

"Remember, if your thoughts continue long enough they become your beliefs and you assume they are true. Everything you experience seems real to you, but in reality, it is your beliefs that make these experiences real. They feel real to you because you believe in them. We tend to look outside ourselves to make these experiences real, but nothing outside of you can ever give you the answer or fill the void within you. The void within can only be filled with your connection to you or Source."

"It's amazing how my beliefs have affected my life!" I reply, shaking my head.

"I know, and this is only the tip of the iceberg. There's so much more!

"Once you accept beliefs as yours, you see the world slightly distorted by these beliefs. Therefore, changing your beliefs, changes your reality and what you see or experience."

"I would like to change some, uh, well a lot of this shit that I have been feeling lately," I say.

"You are not your beliefs; you are the creator of them. And what's cool is if you created these beliefs, you can undo them. I love that one! When you become a conscious observer, it gives you the ability to detach from your beliefs and decide which beliefs serve you and which ones do not. Then you can pick and choose what actions or behaviors they want to use in any experience," Brian explains.

"Wait a minute! I don't want to use *any* of my behaviors," I say and laugh. "They always get me in trouble."

"That is because you were using them without being aware," Brian counters. "Your behaviors aren't bad or wrong. It's just that up until this point they have been based on your beliefs. Once you change your beliefs you can stop having this autopilot response to your experiences and your behaviors can be tools that you can pick and choose like tools in a toolbox. It's that simple. Change your beliefs and you will change your behaviors."

"Okay. I get it," I concede. "Go on."

"Changing one's beliefs has far reaching effects. Scientifically, it has been proven that thoughts are energy. They actually carry what is called neurological weight that can be measured. This can affect the neurochemical balance in a person's brain. By changing your beliefs, you change your thoughts and your thoughts change the chemical balance in your body and your brain. Thus, you change the way you feel and also change the way you see the world."

"So this blue pill that I take could change the neurochemicals in my body?" I ask him. "And by changing my beliefs, I can change the chemical balance in my body?"

"Make a note to talk to Marvel about this, and yes, I believe you can. But do you believe it?"

I smile.

"Beliefs come from our own experience; either from this lifetime, another life experience, 'past lives,' or as an unquestioned acceptance of what other people say or do. The majority of beliefs are created at a young age, usually by six years of age. From this point on, very few new beliefs are created. The new ones that are created usually occur as a result of what we call trauma or very intense experiences."

"Tell me more."

"I know this sounds a little heady and intense but this information is so important for you to be able to make real change."

I nod.

"Anyway, as young children, we make sense of the world by creating beliefs, or what we call assumed truths about ourselves, our parents, other people, and almost everything else around us. We are like sponges, absorbing new information from all around. This helps us to understand the world and create order from all of the information being thrown at us. These beliefs create our realities. The majority of beliefs are chosen with little or no awareness. Unconscious decisions about accepting or creating beliefs occur, particularly as a child, when we watch something happen or people interact. We decide that this is the way you will act without even knowing it. Semiconscious beliefs are created when you see something done or said and you think to yourself, even though briefly. This will work for me. I will do this too."

"I can relate and understand that," I comment. "When my dad yelled at me, things would change in my body. I felt my body spinning and shaking. I would float up as if I was leaving my body while feeling really spaced out. My body felt so light, almost weightless. At the time, I was not aware I reacted in this way. I just knew that I couldn't feel my body. The next thing I knew, I behaved inappropriately by interrupting, banging into people or maybe talking about something that was totally unrelated to what was happening right in front of me. Would this be an unconscious behavior?"

"Yes. I remember you being like that as a kid," Brian recalls. "Did you leave your body, Cavarelli, when you friggin' forged my detention slip and signed my dad's name wrong?" Brian says with a grin.

"Real funny, Brain," I say with sarcasm in my voice. "You should have just signed it yourself!"

"Did you get in trouble for that?" he inquires.

"Duh…of course, I did," I say. "And I am sure you didn't, with those hippie parents of yours."

Brian reveals, "Actually, my mom told me that after they left the office, your mom and my mom were laughing their asses off at the fact that you spelled my dad's name wrong."

"No way! Seriously!?" I ask not believing that my mom would have done such a thing.

"No, I am not kidding," Brian confirms.

"Okay, give me an example of something that is semi-conscious," Brian informs.

"Semi-conscious is something that is only partial consciousness, right?" I confirm.

"Right. It is something that a person is experiencing but is only vaguely aware," Brian says.

"I would say that it would have to be when I was young. I did this thing with my teachers. It's a little embarrassing. I would get to know my teachers and connect with them. I would know their likes and dislikes and levels of frustrations. I would be aware of how much they could handle. I did it just so that they would like me. I really thought that I was just being nice, but when I got to high school, I was much more aware of why I was doing it. At first, I didn't really admit it fully, but it was running there in the back of my mind. So, if I am honest with myself now, I would have to admit that I behaved this way so that my teachers would like me and help me more; more importantly, like me and maybe even give me a better grade. If I could distract them enough, maybe, just maybe, they wouldn't recognize how stupid and bad I really was."

"Are you serious?" Brian asked.

"What part?" I ask.

"Did you really believe that you were stupid and bad?" he asks.

"I didn't believe it. I knew it," I confirm. "I knew that I was stupid from my core. That is just who I was. I was placed in the stupid class and hung with the bad kids who appeared stupid. It was a mess."

"Be sure to tell Marvel about that one," Brian suggests.

"Okay. Let me tell you a little bit about attraction now if you can even comprehend it, because you did say that you are pretty stupid."

I slap Brian on the arm.

"You are the one that believes it, not me!"

"True."

"Sometimes people," Brian continues, "believe we attract things into our life and these things come at us. If that were true, we would be victim to everything in our life because it is coming at us. Because of your beliefs, you match with a certain frequency or vibration and, because of that frequency; you are more likely to enter into environments that will support your current belief system."

I nod.

"It is not that you are a victim of circumstance and things just come toward you because you believe things. It is more that because you resonate at a certain frequency you tend to enter into environments that match with you. It gives a whole new meaning to the phrase 'birds of a feather flock together' doesn't it?" Brian quips. "Think about your family and friends, your jobs, the places you hang out and so forth. I'll bet if you look hard enough you will see how you matched up to them."

I say, "Remember my girlfriends, Katrina and Josie?"

Brian nods.

"I am supposed to hang out with them next week. I wonder if I still resonant with them."

I hope so.

"So if you are tired of having a particular experience or attracting the same people in your life, you have to change your beliefs so the thoughts will stop. There cannot be a thought without a belief system to support it. Once you create a belief and believe it to be your truth it attaches to you and becomes yours. We never question these 'truths' because we assume they are true even if they are false. Most of us are willing to look at all aspects of our lives except our beliefs. Did you ever notice that when people become defensive it is when their beliefs are challenged? Why? Because our beliefs are the foundation on which our ego is based, and if our beliefs are wrong then we are wrong or often feel wrong."

I interrupt. "Tell me more about this thing we call an ego."

"The ego is the belief a person has that tells them who they think they are or who they are supposed to be. While we are part of 'Source' or 'God,' we are here on Earth having our experiences. We have to be separate from Source in order to be here and experience. The ego is the one who carries that belief of separateness so that we can function on the planet and interact with others. The problem is the ego is like a small child that wants what it wants and will do whatever it takes to stay separate. We just have to retrain it so we can work with it rather than let it control us. The ego operates using our behavior patterns that are based on our beliefs. When beliefs are challenged, the ego is threatened and it must protect itself."

"That explains why I do such crazy things!" I say.

"Remember, we are not our beliefs," Brian cautions. "We are the creators of them. We can be conscious observers of them thereby giving us the ability to see where they do not serve us and begin to change them.

"All of your experiences and beliefs support the behavior patterns used by the ego which is an attempt by the ego to maintain its belief system and identity. The beliefs look different but they all have the same goal — maintain the current belief system. The beliefs also fool you by getting you to think the belief is 'over there' or about something or someone other than you. By falling for this misperception, you do not realize it is in you! Therefore, you do not notice it is running your life while it keeps you in the loop."

"That makes sense," I agree. "Anything that bothers you is your issue. What bothers you about others, you do now, have done, think about or believe."

"You have been reading the concepts, I see," Brian chimes in.

I smile.

"When we judge our beliefs, we are admitting they are real and that we have to 'do' something to deal with or combat them. Nothing could be farther from the truth. Judging our beliefs creates an emotional and mental attachment to them. Once we create this attachment, these beliefs have become ours!"

"So, it's an attachment to anything?" I say.

"Of course!" Brian affirms. "If you believe you need a drug to relax, you will attach to that drug. The name for that attachment is addiction."

"An emotion, like guilt with an ex-husband," I sigh and smirk.

"Yep. So, remember, beliefs eventually turn into belief systems. A belief system is often a complex design of multiple beliefs creating an entire system. This belief system could be completely self-created or adapted from a family belief system or cultural belief system. Within each person's belief system there are often unique variations to the cultural or family belief system. Belief systems are like opinions, everyone has one. However, just because you have one does not mean it is necessarily accurate or that it serves you well. This is why you should question everything and then discern and decide if it is for you. At some level, life itself is actually a belief system. Because of this you can actually create any type of life you wish. Becoming aware of your beliefs and belief systems frees you from their limitations."

"You mean I don't have to buy into anyone's stuff anymore?" I ask incredulously.

"Nope. Not unless you want to. By having this freedom, you may then re-create a new conscious perspective on how you wish to understand life. This then creates a new vibratory frequency. By changing your beliefs, you change your frequency or vibrations. It allows you to become a creator rather than a victim to your beliefs and belief systems."

"I've never really experienced being in charge of my life like that before. I am not sure I even know what to do with it." I shudder.

Brian says, "Remember, your beliefs are based upon your intent. You may intend to ignore the truth and create a fantasy reality or you can see things as they truly are. By seeing and interpreting life clearly, you can actually create the life that you want by changing what you believe. What do you believe?"

"I don't know what I believe, but I know what I want," I tell him. "I would like to be free from these guilty icky feelings."

"People will hold onto their beliefs as long as they see a payoff or benefit to keeping them. Trust me, they will fight to the death if they believe those beliefs serve them.

"Keep in mind here, Dottie, I'm telling you all these things so that you can have the freedom you have been telling me you're asking for. There is no pill for being conscious. There is only you becoming aware."

"So, let's see if I am getting this." I pause; take a deep breath. "As long as I am fearful of something ever occurring to myself or anyone in the world, I will retain that belief. When I am finished being fearful of this occurrence or finished with my pain, I will then decide that. Brian, I am wanting to be finished with this pain. How am I doing so far?"

"Great, Dottie! Keep going," says Brian supportively.

"When I recognize and see that my fear and my experience are no longer possible today with the awareness that I have, I will no longer live in the past. I am free to release the belief and see the experience as benign.

"As long as we carry what we call pain from the experience and choose to hold onto it, we will maintain that belief."

"Yes, I think you've got it," says Brian with a smile. "Trust me, when we want to hold on to a belief, we fight to the death to keep it. I had plenty of those beliefs myself. The major problem with beliefs is that you tend to believe that things will happen according to what you believe or have experienced. This puts you in the position of understanding present events based on your past. It is like having a filter over your vision as you look at your experiences. This prevents you from experiencing the 'now' because you are experiencing the now through the past. You can never be fully present or experience something truly new if you are perceiving life through your beliefs from the past. In other words, your previous beliefs limit your present experience. Make sense?"

I nod.

"Once that belief is etched in stone, our ego goes to work to support it by creating experiences that support and defend that belief. The ego must also support and defend it. If confronted by another's belief, the ego will try to discredit their challenges and prove its own beliefs," Brian says. "The deeper the belief, the harder and more threatening it is for the ego to let go of it. The removal of one belief now threatens other beliefs. Because of this, many beliefs are going to protect themselves and the defenses will become stronger and more intense.

"For example, if you believe that, 'other people judge me,' no matter what anybody says, you will find negativity in their statement to prove they are judging you. This is the ego working overtime to hold onto that belief. It has many tricks up its sleeve. This is where it gets tricky. Are you with me so far Dottie?"

I nod and flash an understanding smile.

"Because you are in the energy or frequency of being judged, you will also be critical of others and judge them. This will keep you in the energy of being judged and you become trapped in an endless cycle that you can't get out of."

"And then we wonder why life never changes. We keep ourselves trapped and don't even know we are doing it. Seems like it's almost impossible to change," I reply downheartedly.

"It's not impossible at all, but in order to change beliefs completely, you must clear their energy charge from the mind, brain, nerve pathways and emotions," Brian explains. "The energy of the belief creates its own nerve pathways, so that every time you have an experience in that energy field, it will use and

101

access those nerve pathways. Our belief systems get into every part of our being and changes must take place in a person's belief system, thought processes, the brain energetically, the brain's patterning, our mental and emotional aspects, and our heart and souls for change to be permanent."

"Wow! It's amazing how a few beliefs can affect so much," I comment.

"Yes, and it can get very complicated if you are not careful. So, I am going to give you a few tools to keep it simple. No matter how sure you are, question everything! Especially, those things you've never questioned! By questioning, you can find the source.

"Pay attention to evidence. Don't skip past something because you think you have already figured it out. A good rule of thumb is: if you think you have something figured out or believe you know it all, you probably don't.

"Look at your beliefs carefully, and fully evaluate them before you make a decision about them," Brian cautioned.

"If you are afraid to question a belief, it's a good bet there's a falsehood or lie in your belief system, or that you are hiding something. Your job is to question with curiosity, inquisitiveness and the openness of a child — pure in nature. The absolute truth will always withstand any amount of observation and questioning.

"While you are working on your beliefs, change your behaviors because if you stay in the old behaviors it supports the beliefs and makes them harder to change. Your behaviors are like food for your belief systems; so by changing your behaviors, you are basically starving it into a place where it has to change to survive. An alcoholic is a great example of this. If the alcoholic is your belief system and the alcohol is your behavior, once you quit using the alcohol, you will go through detox; therefore, changing your beliefs. While this can be very uncomfortable, once you have detoxed and changed the beliefs you no longer need the alcohol, aka behaviors, because you have shifted your belief system. The only time you will pick up a 'drink,' so to speak, is if you go back to the old belief systems.
"I lost you, didn't I? I went too far out there, yes?"

"No. I kind of get it."

"Alright, for now just remember this, Dottie. To become a creator of your experiences, you have to be conscious and aware of your thoughts and your beliefs." He then asks, "Are you full yet? You feel full. Maybe you should give yourself some time to let this all soak in. How about you go see Tim tomorrow, then come back to me in a couple of days?"

I take a breath, look at Brian and nod, "Yes, I am full." I try to let the information given soak in and keep my thoughts clear. I start to feel the energy whirling around like when I was in Glenda's presence.

I say goodbye and I drive home. I only do one thing before I go to bed. I text Tim and schedule an appointment at my house in the morning. He confirms and before I know it, I am out like a light.

CHAPTER 9

Loosening Up Your Heart

Is this a dream?

"You need to be okay with taking medication."

What? Who is that speaking? I ask.

"It won't be forever, ya know. It doesn't make you weak, Dorothy, if you take this medication. It's as simple as you having a physiological glitch that needs support. I don't want you to resist it."

This must be a dream. I don't even remember falling asleep. Or do I?

"Of course it's a dream, Dorothy. It's Glenda! Now listen. You have a lifetime of struggle here. So, you know what the struggle is. You know what it feels like. Feels familiar, doesn't it? It's a waste of time and energy to fight it. You need to feed the body properly because if you take medication without enough food or nutrition in your system, it's going to make it more difficult. So, if you need to eat at a certain time of the day so you have enough nourishment in your body, do that. You need to eat, Dottie. You can't take your medication without food because without food, it will make you hyper. For you it's a chemical thing."

It IS a dream.

"This physical thing is not your fault, you know. You blame yourself for this and you've got to stop feeling responsible for everybody and everything that doesn't go well. It's an old habit of yours."

Yes, but every time I put a pill in my mouth I feel bad.

Glenda places her gentle fingers over my mouth and says, "Dorothy, this is different. In the past taking pills and getting yourself high was to numb you. It was to check out. It isn't about that now. You need to be okay with that. Get in touch with why you did these behaviors. Maybe work on these behaviors or whatever those boys call them, family patterns, I believe they said that you must clear those. It isn't about being in the familiar uncomfortable place anymore. It's time for you to let go of all that you knew and be open to a new life; maybe start seeing things in a new way. It's about being in a space of where you can function at a level that's comfortable for you, spiritually, physically and emotionally. There is a place in this universe for allopathic medicine."

Allopathic medicine?

"Allopathic medicine ... meaning the medical world."

Oh, okay.

"Anyway, this medicine helps support the body in balancing itself but it is not the only answer. Remember: consciousness cures everything."

Glenda continues to talk. "I understand your concerns around old behaviors. Those old behaviors were a way of anaesthetizing yourself to your pain."

"Anaesthetizing?" I ask.

"It was a way to not feel, to numb yourself; to be unresponsive in feeling. So, you need to understand that allowing yourself to be balanced in the brain right now is not the same...It's allowing your brain to see what it is like to focus. You won't have to take these blue pills forever."

I open my eyes. I glance out the window. I see that it is still dark. I look over at the clock. 3am — again! I make an attempt at writing down what I experienced before I forget. I place my head back down and fall into dreamland again.

"Hi, Dottie. It's Tim."

Hello, Tim! Am I dreaming again?

"I am dressed in a tin woodman's outfit. What do YOU think?"

I see. What's up with that?

"Never mind that! I am here to teach you about the heart. Dottie, it's about dissolving the guilt from the past and truly loving yourself again. You cannot love others if you don't love yourself. Even though people try to love others without loving themselves, it is not possible."

I have plenty of guilt.

"I may have developed the courage and the brain, have the understanding and human skills that are necessary to communicate, have access to my beautiful mind and have a pretty good understanding of how things work, but I lack the connection to my own heart and soul for many reasons; mainly because I am still externally dependent on the world to reflect who I am."

What?

"*There is a fear here, Miss Dorothy,*" *Glenda interrupts.* "*That if you are to fully be who you truly are and live in your heart, you will not measure up to what everyone expects, or it may not be the way the world works or wants to see it. You are afraid to connect to your heart partially because it seems like no one in the world really appreciates a genuine heart. They seem to want you to be who they want you to be and behave the way they want you to behave rather than accept you for who you are. This leaves little room for a genuine heart in the world of men, Outside of Self.*"

How did you get so smart, Tim?

Tim's answers, "*I don't know quite when, but I sure like it!*"

I laugh.

"*So, Dottie, when we are talking about the heart, the inner heart that is related to the heart and soul not the heart of emotions like most people think. The inner heart is your direct connection to your soul, the essence of your being. Typically, humans think that the heart is about emotions and human love, but we are saying it as something greater. We often differentiate between the two hearts. The inner heart is about your connection to your soul and your spirit. The emotional heart is the heart that is about your ego personality and the world of men or what we sometimes call the outer world. The emotional heart or outer heart is limiting and always leaves you feeling empty and dependent on others.*

"*The inner heart always fills you with peace, understanding and a deep satisfaction. When you have this mental skill like I have, just check it out, look at this brain of mine.*" *Tim starts to open up his skull to show me.* "*Check it out! My brain gives me the ability to process the awareness of myself and of my environment, processing a constant stream of sensory data. Every creative thought, feeling, and plan is processed by our brain. The brain's neurons record the memory of every event in our lives that our consciousness experiences. This brain is like a computer, and our consciousness is like the computer operator. Isn't it fascinating?*"

I guess.

"*In fact, the human brain is so complicated that it remains a mystery to all those brainy scientists. My brain cells can be broken into two groups: neurons and neuroglia. They —*"

Stop that. I believe you, Tim. Close up that skull of yours, please.

"Well, okay then. I have developed these other skills that people have typically done to manage their world and their environment, to try and make their human experience more comfortable. What they don't realize is that they have sacrificed the connection to their heart and they are still externally dependent on their worth, value and feedback from the world to tell them who they are and what they should be."

Pretty cool.

"This typically leaves them resentful and empty at some point in their life and they see the world as a struggle. Eventually after many years of struggle this individual may discover life is not fulfilling and they will seek to reestablish connection to their heart. They will not know why it is not fulfilling, but they will know there is a lack of fulfillment. Typically, they will try to acquire things, accomplish things, have affairs, get kudos or titles or awards or something that says they have accomplished something. This is the unconscious desperation seeking fulfillment, but still trying to find externalized reflections to identify who they really are, which is never, never fulfilling. If they would only realize; if they stop looking to the outside world to give them their worth and value, then and only then, do they have the opportunity to become completely fulfilled and happy in their life.

"At some point, each individual discovers that no matter what they have done, no matter how much they have accomplished, there is still something missing. Hopefully, one day they will awaken and realize it is the heart. The heart is missing so they go on a journey seeking their heart. They may say things like 'I want to find myself.' They go on what we call an inner journey."

Dude, you are starting to sound like Brian.

"He's the Scarecrow like I am the Tin Woodman!"

I look at him weird. Seriously, did you just say that?

"Yeah, why?"

You guys crack me up. You are like the Tin Woodman, trying to get in touch with your heart. Just like Brian is trying to work on his brain. Too funny.

"True, true, Dottie. My approach to seeking love was distorted. I tried to get it through knowledge, but I was only seeking outside myself to reflect to me that I have connected with my heart. After a period of time I discovered that even that

didn't work. So, the search for my heart often became hopeless and difficult because it seemed that I had tried everything I knew how and had read and it still didn't lead me to my heart. So, when I switched at this point of hopelessness there were typically two paths that I could take, one being the complete surrender of trying to find fulfillment and giving up on my life and the second being the realization that everything that I ever did before didn't work so I chose the inner journey of the heart. In that desperate moment, I was seeking and fell into my own heart almost by accident and said, 'Oh, everything is within.' I now understood because I was forced into an experience and a choice. I learned that life is experiential, you know, Dottie? It is not a theory or a concept that you can read in a book. You must experience the feelings of life to heal the heart. Do you get the concept?"

Yes.

"You cannot accomplish the heart, you must live, experience and feel the heart. It is the only way for the heart to awaken. When this occurs in the individual, they realize absolute fulfillment without effort and that all external validation is useless and no longer desired."

Tim, what is that ringing?

"Sounds like a door bell," Tim says as he moves away from me.

Hey, where are you going? And what doorbell?

"It's me ringing," he clarifies.

No, it's not. How could you be ringing?

"I am. It's me!"

~

I open my eyes feeling disoriented — realizing I wasn't with Tim. It was a dream. I am quite perplexed.

I jump out of the bed and dart for the window where I could look out and see who's ringing my door bell.

It is Tim! He is here! I must have overslept. Ugh.

I open the window and call out to Tim telling him that I would be right down.

108

Within the ten minutes, I get changed, make up my face and run to the door.

I make it to the door trying to catch my breath.

"Good morning," I greet Tim. "Feels like you've been here for hours."

Tim looks confused.

"You began teaching me in my dreams last night — well actually, early this morning," I inform him.

"Really?"

"Is that how it's going to work with you guys?"

"Maybe… anything is possible!" Tim says and walks through the doorway. "Hey, whatever works. Where did I leave off… in your dreams, that is?"

"Well, let's make some coffee and I can fill you in," I answer.

Tim and I talk for hours about my dream and the basics on emotions, feelings, the heart, and the potential of real intimacy.

"Do you know why I was in charge of the heart?" Tim asks me.

"I don't know, because you are the Tin Woodman?"

"The Tin Woodman?" Tim laughs. "In the book *The Wonderful Wizard of Oz*?"

"Yes. That's what you told me last night."

"Oh, really," Tim laughs.

"Oh, don't ask."

"Well, I am in charge of the heart because I've been through many break-ups — like a ton! I have never been married. Actually, I haven't been in a relationship for more than three months in my entire life.

"What I am learning is, and what most people don't understand, is that you cannot have a full, rich, meaningful relationship with any other human being until you have or begin to have a meaningful relationship with yourself. I know, sounds weird, right?"

I shrug my shoulders.

"My conscious choice is not about mental decisions. It does, however, include them. It is about the feeling of my inner heart along with my awareness of who the other person is, their personality, the heart connection you have together and what you enjoy together. It is about a choice with a conscious heart and

109

mind. Keep in mind that the heart is synonymous with soul and mind is synonymous with your consciousness. That was a tough one to grasp for me. Do you remember me in my younger years, yes?"

"Yep, I do!" I answer him.

"Choosing with a conscious heart requires going on an inner journey of self-discovery. In this process, the objective is to learn about your patterned behaviors and belief systems that contribute to any or all challenges you have had in the past and may still have when it comes to having relationships with other human beings.

"Traditionally people have been taught that the expression and display of love is the most important way to communicate it. But, in truth, love is a feeling, not a display or a communication. You can feel if someone loves you or not, no matter what their words are. This has taken me so long to figure out, Dottie."

I smile, feeling Tim's love.

"Most times, on a deep subconscious level, relationships are sought out because you are seeking a part of yourself that you are not connected to or have never been developed fully. There is a perception that another person provides you with the opportunity to find or complete something for yourself.

"People see reflections of themselves in what others say and do. What they do for you is a great service and yet it is rarely seen that way. When others are abusive it is difficult to see that what they are doing is of any service to us but the reality is they are reflecting a part of ourselves that they don't like or want to look. Life would be much easier if we could see their actions as a gift rather than a problem."

I nod.

"Relationships are the most valuable learning opportunity we can have as human beings. If you look at it the right way they can serve you. The trick is to not blame the other person as they serve as your mirror and appreciate them for the gift of the role they play in your own self-discovery."

I ask, "Mr. Marvel taught you all this?"

"Yep," Tim answers.

"Tim, I remember when Marvel's father died in our seventh-grade year. I felt how sad he was. It brought back all my sadness of my dad dying in February that I tried so hard to forget. I felt so bad for him, but I guess it was me feeling so bad for me."

"Yep."

"You were so helpful and loving to me when my father died. You were the only person who listened to me. You seemed always connected to your heart and understood what it was like to love. You just had that in you, that gift, the words to make me understand things. You had that love in you."

"Ha, Marvel always says that to me. That I had it in me all the time. Just didn't go deep enough. I could explain it, but I didn't truly feel it and own it. I was a little afraid of it. I was raised to be afraid to open to my heart. I am learning not to be afraid of my own love for myself. I am learning to trust it now. However, yes, I knew how to help others through their pain by using my logic and reason. It's just that, feeling it myself and admitting my own pain. I didn't feel so good so I avoided it. We mentalists tend to avoid our feelings," Tim explains. "I am still working on it. I do eventually want to have a relationship. I just believe that I need to loosen up this heart a little more.

"A person who reflects yourself to you will not just be a partner, they will be a divine gift. You will find that your friendships, your family members, and your children will also show you things about yourself you may not have otherwise seen or want to see, that is, if you are paying attention.

"Remember, *people are your mirrors and teachers.* All of your relationships with others are about YOU!

"Everything you experience with others will tell you something about you, positive or negative."

I nod.

"Relationships are funny. A mistake people often make is that they want to make someone else happy. They believe they will be happy if someone else is happy. I am learning that at best all you can do is temporarily please others. It is not your job, nor do you have the ability or capability to make anyone else happy, ever!

"You are simply to love. You are to make *you* happy. In your happiness and the love shared with others, happiness exists. The process of living to make others happy is living outside of yourself. So, if you are living outside of yourself to make another happy, you will always feel abandoned, left out and like you never quite get enough of them or from them.

"This occurs partially because you are trying to use their love or responses to feel your own self-love. No matter what you do or how often you do it, it will never be satisfactory or enough because you have not taken the time to truly love yourself. It's like trying to taste a piece of cake that someone else is chewing. It's just not possible."

"True," I say. "What else?"

"So, you are ready for more?"

"Keep going!"

"Most people take care of other people believing consciously or unconsciously that it will make the other person love them back. That is what I did. If I love them in the way they wanted, then I expected to get the love that I wanted. If they didn't love me back, or in the way I wanted them to, then I was disappointed. I tended to blame them and it caused me a lot of heartache. Doing it that way was like having to buy their love through the sacrifice of myself.

"Often the thoughts that they didn't care, you could never do enough; you did everything you could do, if I only would have/could have done more. This type of love is always disappointing because you never get what you want, and you are constantly sacrificing for others. If you love in this way, you should know it will never work, or be satisfactory, because you are ultimately abandoning your own love — the love of self.

"If you take the time to get centered within yourself, and change a lot of these dysfunctional, misguided programs and love yourself first, your life will improve. Your life experience will begin to change just because you have changed. You will see that it's a very practical, logical and hands-on process. It seems to happen naturally once you have begun the change."

Tim continues, "I have a lot of work to do on unconditional love and learning to open up my heart fully to someone. Those thoughts and beliefs, that I am sure Brian told you about yesterday, really get in the way of the flow of the heart, love and consciousness. There are a lot of distortions in there."

Tim taps at his chest directly over his heart. "I am right in the middle of figuring out this relationship that I was in recently. I thought she was the one. I ruined it. I let it go. I am looking forward to truly opening my heart for the first time. Do you know what's really stopping you from your own love?" Tim asks.

"Well, there's a lot of shame involved, and yes, love and intimacy problems for me as well," I admit.

"Maybe you should give yourself some time to let this all soak in. How about you go see Leo tomorrow about some of that shame thing and then come back to me in a couple of days?"

"Okay, Tim." I reach out for a hug. "Thanks so much for sharing all this with me. I am so grateful."

"You're so very welcome." Tim embraces me after he scrunches his nose to lift his glasses.

I walk Tim to the door and as I shut it behind him, I take a deep breath and allow the feeling of the words to move through me.

This has been one hell of a week. Holy cow! Am I ready for all this? I can't imagine what's to come! I will see Leo sometime tomorrow.

What a character he is.

CHAPTER 10

"Put 'em up"— Finding Courage

The sun peeks through the clouds, breaking the darkness as it shines through my window, warming my face, letting me know that it is a new day. My mind wants to stay still and relax before the thoughts start rushing in. I feel the soft pillow on my cheek, realizing that unfortunately, I am back from dreamland. As I lay on my memory foam bed, I have a memory.

I wonder if that's why they call it "memory" foam.

Leo! My thoughts begin.

As a child, I remember Leo being very brave. Well, he *appeared* brave to me back then. Leo never seemed to be afraid to tell people what he thought — whether it was one of our football buddies from the old neighborhood, or a teacher disciplining him. That is why it was really shocking to me to hear all that talk in the café about him being a chicken.

We spent so much time together. I do remember his dad feeling angry inside. One time I was over at his house, and his dad grabbed me — just playing around — but I could feel the anger go right through me like a bolt of lightning. I didn't understand what it meant. I just remember his mom removing his hand from my arm and said, "Let go of her, Patrick." She had a concerned look in her eyes that I have never seen before. Another time, his dad yelled from the yard for Leo to come in for dinner. "Come in now, boy. Don't make me tell you twice." I felt the same lightning bolt that travelled from his dad to Leo.

When I was in my pre-teens after my dad had died, I often wondered which was better, not having a dad around or having a dad who felt like this. The point is that he always seemed to handle his dad so well. It seemed not to bother him at all.

I guess every family has their secrets. All of my siblings have different stories about how things went down in my family growing up. I guess every member of a family unit would have a different perspective and would have their own memories and own feelings and hurts about what happened. I sure have my own memories and feelings about love, pain and secrets. In fact, at a very early age, I knew what was not to be spoken, because if it was said, you would be silenced immediately.

Oh my, I am tired of these thoughts, these feelings.

I sit up and stare out the window. These past two days have been life altering and confusing, yet very eye opening. Eye opening indeed, but not enough to keep my eyes open, right now. Suddenly, a wave of tiredness suddenly washes over me. I feel myself drifting off to dreamland again.

DREAM:

"Hello, Dottie, me again! Ready to learn some more?"

Hello, Glenda. I guess so.

"Well, let's get started. Let's talk about how Marvel works with these three boys that you are now hanging out with. You might want to clear up some of this deep-seated pain you've been carrying around, Dorothy. You do know you have this, right?"

I shrug my shoulders.

"As you learn specific skills from each one of the boys, there also is the process of gaining the courage to be able to practice these skills by interacting with people."

Applying it, yes, Glenda.

"Without the courage to interact with people and use these skills, the aware person will be dysfunctional in society. Some of the most common reasons for not using these skills with others are the fear of repercussion, rejection and the fear of not being good enough, all of which apply in your case. You do realize this, right?"

I nod.

"This 'not being good enough' is a biggie for you. And this disappointment that you feel ..." Glenda widens her eyes and stretches her arms out almost dropping her wand. *"When will you look at that one, dear?*

"Many of these fears occur where courage is needed. They are due to a dependency on external circumstances, or other people to give you a sense of who you are. Basically, you depend on the world to tell you who you are and what you are worth by the way the world responds to you.

"This will trigger self-doubt and deeper belief systems about your self-worth, which will continue to occur as long as you are dependent on the external

115

world to reflect to you your worth and value. Once you have no longer any need for others to reflect to you, or tell you how good you are or how bad you are, then inner courage naturally occurs. This is because there is a type of not caring about what other people say, or do because you have discovered and connected with the deep inner parts of yourself.

"Look inside, Dorothy!" Glenda's face comes close to mine.

Startling out of my slumber, I wake up. I grab my phone and immediately call Leo.

Leo answers the phone. "Yo!"

"Hey, it's Dottie. Are you available today?" I ask.

"For you, my lady, of course," Leo says. "Come on over to the café! I have the game on!"

I arrive at the café and find a seat while Leo finishes up with a customer. Leo joins me, asking me why I look so tired.

"I've been going through a lot lately," I inform him.

"You are cute," Leo chuckling while shaking his head.

"What?" I say back.

"I am just remembering."

"Remembering what?"

"You used to spin like a tornado when we were kids. I can still see it in you — that spinning thing!" Leo laughs again and then says, "You had so many thoughts going on 'up there' in that little brain of yours."

"True, still do."

"Yeah, like what?"

"Well, first, I am just remembering how much I struggled in school. How I couldn't focus. All these memories are flooding in."

"Like what?" Leo asks.

I look up at him, my head feeling so heavy.

"Do you know that I used to see things as a kid? Like things used to move. It was very distracting and I could barely focus."

"Like what? Be clearer, give me some details, girl."

"Let's see. While I was in class, the desks would be moving around, as well as the chalk on the chalkboard. The words on a page, forget about it — they were almost impossible to keep still. I tried hard to focus and keep them still, but the 'b's' would turn into 'd's' and whole words would move around the page. I found that moving the book while I read helped a little."

"But that method wasn't conducive to the Catholic classroom," Leo explains.

"Aaah, no."

"Well, that DOES explain a lot about you, Cavarelli. You always moved so damn fast all the time. You never could stay still."

"Yep. It was better to move with everything else that was moving around me. Or if I dialoged with someone for too long, I would feel the need to move. That would then be inappropriate or rude walking away from them, especially, if I could feel something other than their words, like their unresolved emotions. It was really difficult to stay still."

"Wonder why you couldn't focus long enough to read in school. You were the ultimate emotional psychic sponge for everyone — allowing everyone to emote — taking on everyone else's feelings."

"Who? Katrina and Josie?" I ask.

"Yes. You were at their beck and call. You were responsive to their every request."

"Really?"

"Well, that's how I saw it," Leo says.

"Oh, you just never liked those two. Or I should say you couldn't stand Katrina," I tease.

"True. Katrina could have been a big fat mirror and teacher for me. I wasn't about learning anything from anybody back then, especially from THAT girl! Yes, Dottie, that would be a judgment," Leo admits while smiling.

I smile.

"Anyway, back to you. These behaviors, such as taking on other people's feelings are just family patterns that you were taught. This was, and probably still is about believing that you were responsible for the other people's feelings, or believing that you were a poor student. Patterns are unfinished experiences seeking completion."

I nod.

Leo adds, "For me, I did seek long and hard for answers until I found that crazy man."

"I am assuming that you are talking about Mr. Marvel," I say.

"Yep," Leo states. "He always says, Leo, YOU found the answers. I just guided you to it! He is the first person to show me what pure neutral love is, with no attachments. No conditions."

"Unconditional love? Does that still exist?"

"STILL exist? Why? Was there a time that you believe that it existed?"

"Yes. I believe that I knew that kind of love as a young girl before all the disappointments."

"What disappointments?"

"It's too long to go into."

"Come on. I have all day!" he says while stretching out his arms above his head and then folding his arms across his chest.

"I feel like my life is all mixed up. I finally learned to keep things still with the Adderall. This drug really helped me focus. But now, that I have everything still, things are becoming clear. Too clear. So, clear. I am not sure if I want to unravel it. I have a lot of distorted stuff in there. It's just a little scary. I am realizing that my life was not at all what I imagined or expected. It's not what I perceived my life to be. I am just really disappointed," I say as I drop my heavy head in my arms collapsing it on the table.

118

I lift my head, feeling Leo's presence move to the café door entrance. A delivery man opens the door carrying a large box. "Hey Leo, where do you want it?"

"Hold that thought, Dottie," Leo says while getting out of his seat. "Hey, Bob, come with me!"

I sit and wait for Leo. My mind wants to roam and think about anything other than this disappointment, but I force myself to remain in the feeling.

Why AM I disappointed? And about what? That is the first time that I said those words 'I am just really disappointed with life' out loud. It doesn't really seem like me to be disappointed because I am really known to be a person who is upbeat and happy. I hate seeing other people's disappointment. This is so confusing.

Leo finally returns. "First, before we dive into this whole disappointment thing, I want to back up a bit.

"Dottie, you judge yourself pretty bad. You always have. You always seemed to think you were wrong all the time, and everything was your fault. Not everyone saw this, but I did. You put up a good front. It was like everyone came first before you." Leo continues, "For God sake, remember during the soccer games, if you had too many goals — you would stop right before scoring again and wait for one of your teammates to catch up with you and then pass it off to them — so they could have as many goals as you."

"I remember."

"Remember the time that you told me your oldest sister took you and your other sister skiing for the first time, and it was so easy for you, but not for your other sister? When you noticed that your sister was having trouble, you started pretending you were having difficulty skiing. You did this just so she wouldn't look bad. God forbid if you received any praise for what you were good at."

"Yep. I remember."

"I kind of have this feeling that when you were young and things came too easy for you, you tended to stand out. You didn't like that, did you?"

"No."

"You tried to be like everyone else, right?"

119

"Yes."

"You made a judgment. You can't get anywhere in this process by judging yourself, or how you behaved back then. I know it's tough to stop judging yourself, but you must understand that it slows down your progress and makes your life hard.

"Remember Dottie, this is all about making your life easier. Start accepting your habits, the choices you made and how things played out when you were younger. You did what you did for whatever reason; to cope, survive or hide.

"So, if you find yourself judging yourself always remember this, when you judge yourself you are benefiting from it somehow. You must be getting something out of it, for example: let's say you don't want to change yet, or you are not quite ready to wake up. Keep in mind that getting something out of it isn't always positive or something you are conscious of. It could be you are just fulfilling a belief that tells you 'life is disappointing' so you then set up situations unconsciously to fail so you can be disappointed. This isn't always logical, nor does it always make sense. Trust me, patterns work beautifully in getting what you want. So, you will have to figure out what you want. Wanting to change is the first step. Do you want change?"

I nod.

"Then stop judging. You are not a victim," Leo said emphatically. "You created all this shit — the guilt, shame, disappointment. You can undo it! I've seen it happen."

"Gotcha."

"Dottie, I know a thing or two about being a victim and helpless. For years I believed that I was a victim and helpless and I put up my guard. Although, I rarely allowed anyone to see my victimhood — I pretty much just put up my guard ready to protect and defend myself and my feelings." Leo puts up his fists.

"Leo, that is just what you did in my dream the other night. You were dressed like a lion from the book *The Wonderful Wizard of Oz*, and you had your fist up. Too funny," I joke.

"So what are you trying to say, Dottie? I am a coward?" Leo holds his hand against his chest across his heart and chuckles. "I am sure that you remember me in grade school. I would fight anyone who stood in my way, or anyone that tried to expose my victim-hood. My dad showed me this pattern from his behaviors. It was embedded in me for as long as I can remember. I never knew I had that pattern 'till I met Marvel. That understanding explained so much.

"Ya gotta get this, Dottie — the belief that you have about disappointment is far deeper than you understand right now. You need to become aware of the patterns surrounding this belief. This process can lead you to that internal belief that you may not speak of or even be aware of consciously. Understand that there are behaviors and choices that support and drive your life and you are not aware of them, and that's why they seem perfectly normal and go unquestioned.

"If you ever find yourself arguing or resisting someone about a belief then you can be ninety-nine percent sure that the belief or pattern is real and it is yours.

"Those behaviors become part of your identity that must be upheld no matter what, which continues to support that belief," Leo says. "The identity piece was always so tough and even scary for me.

"Awareness is the doorway to ending unwanted patterns, feelings and ultimately beliefs. Are you following me?"

"Kind of," I answer.

"You probably should see Marvel now. He is really good at breaking it down and teaching you to release the crap that stands in your way." Leo stands up to grab some napkins for the people at the table near ours — naturally anticipating the needs of his customers.

He turns his attention towards me again. "This feeling is annoying, right? But the choice is yours, little lady. You can remain in these patterned beliefs that you have assumed are true and are operating your life unconsciously, or you can seek truth. This life can be quite confusing! Whatcha gonna do, girly?"

"Hmmmm," I say with chuckle. "What do you think?"

"Fifty-fifty percent chance I am feeling," Leo answers me and chuckles back. "Not everyone is up for it. It takes a lot of courage."

"I am going to do it!" I exclaim.

"I think that I need to toughen you up a bit, Dottie!" Leo holds up his fists. "Just kidding. You need to find the courage and toughen yourself up. I can't do it for you.

"People always talk about what they want. However, what I have found is that in order to really have what you want, it is necessary to clear your unwanted belief patterns — you know the ones — the ones that don't work anymore. You should, however, know most belief patterns operate unconsciously. You must become conscious of them. This typically means you may need assistance in doing so. So definitely call Marvel. You have to be committed to yourself. One way to do this is to be aware of your every thought and correlate your thought patterns with the way you feel. Keeping a journal of your thoughts is helpful, too. Brian and Tim kept a journal. That wasn't my thing. I was able to retain every thought right up here," Leo brags placing his finger to his temple, "and retrieve it whenever necessary."

I smile at Leo's personality.

"Most people have made an identity of who they believe they are, and the characteristics they are supposed to be, and the behaviors they are supposed to have. To dismantle this identity can be quite devastating. Like I said, there is a fifty-fifty percent chance for you," Leo states while smiling.

I roll my eyes and my lips creep into a smile.

"The purpose of shifting your beliefs is to expand and see more. So, if you could understand that as the beliefs get dismantled, you don't lose the skills you've gained. But what you do lose is the identity of who you thought you were. And it appears as if you are losing a grip on life, at least that is how it's always been for me. But the truth is that your grip is actually expanding on something greater so that you can see and be more rather than be less that you thought you were."

"How did you get so smart?" I ask.

"Actually, I was just thinking that I am starting to sound like airy fairy Brian again, aren't I?"

I smile.

"This shit can be very abstract," Leo continues emphasizing the word *shit*. "Sometimes it's tough for the ego-personality to grab and comprehend."

I nod.

"Wow, I am listening to myself," Leo responds by standing up and jumping back to everyday talk. "And realize that I gotta get out more and get away from these boys for a little — maybe go play some football. Hey, do you still play?"

"Yeah, right," I answer. "Can I get something to drink though?"

"Sure. Come on back!" Leo takes me in the back and pours me a drink to go.

I shuffle out of the café, as if I just got hit in the head with a brick, maybe several bricks. No — maybe a friggin' house of bricks. I don't know why I feel this way every time I leave one of these guys.

I struggle driving home, feeling my head a little out of whack.

Not even ten minutes after arriving home, I walk upstairs, plop on the bed and instantly fall asleep.

DREAM:

"Hey Dorothy! Wake up. It's me, Glenda!"

Dreaming again, right?

"Yep."

Is there ever a time, where I will dream like a normal person again? Dreams that don't really mean anything — dreams that are not just about teaching me something.

"No, dear. You have started this journey. You were the one who wanted to change. You were the one that was searching for Oz. You were the one that asked for this — seeking the truth that night when you left your house. Remember: you started driving and found yourself in the St. Daniel's School parking lot. Don't you remember?"

I remember. I roll my eyes.

"You were swirling like a tornado, and now here is your chance to land and possibly meet 'Glinda' from the book. Wait! You already met her, that's me. Haaaa! Are you ready to continue on your walk down this road to Oz? You have already met your scarecrow, airy fairy Brian, your Tin Woodman, Tim, and let's not forget that lion who owns the café!"

I nod.

"Dreams always mean something. Whether they are things that you cannot quite understand while you are awake and living in the third dimension or premonitions that you are too afraid to grasp or accept or about change that your normal mind cannot conceive of... yet!" Glenda smiles.

CHAPTER 11

Each Individual Has A Wizard Within

"Dorothy! Dorothy!"

Am I awake yet? I ask.

"No, not yet, Dorothy. I still need to tell you about the memories from your memory foam bed."

Sure! I giggle.

"Let's talk about your body memory."

What?

"Not that the body has a mind of its own, but that it has a remembrance of experiences. It's a 'sensate' remembrance which the remembering of sensory feelings. It is about a certain frequency that occurs. I am not talking just your physical body now. I am talking your energy bodies. When your energy bodies have had an experience, they store the memory. It's passed on to your physical body. Your body holds that memory in its cells as well.

"And when you are in it, or you are not in it, and when you are moving around the world, so to speak, and your body encounters a certain frequency or experience or is put into a position, it 'sensately' feels what going on! It associates that feeling with the other experiences that are stored. Then the body reacts. So, this is where the body would shake even though in your mind, you know it doesn't make any sense.

"I will also say that it is stored in the subconscious because again without a head your body wouldn't be reacting. So, the subconscious..."

Wait, stop, Glenda!

"Isn't that what you asked? You asked about your memory foam the other night, yes?"

I was just joking!

"Oh, okay, sweetie." Glenda smiles, giggles and then acts as if she just got away with something.

Marvel joins in. He is dressed like a wizard. He begins to talk. "You will have to apply the tools that we teach you, Dottie. It is up to you to apply this information while developing your own experience and freedom. We are not attempting to tell you we have a new discovery or found THE answer, only to share with you 'a' way to free yourself from your personal limitations. It's about setting humanity free from its bondage and limitations. Dottie, do you know that you can create an opportunity to eliminate the things that prevent you from accomplishing what you truly desire and from discovery of who you really are?"

No, I did not know that. I chuckle at Marvel's excitement.

"Brian!" Marvel says as Brian moves up next to him. "Brian, our natural feeler, can exercise his brain by helping you with your Brain, for instance, your mental focus, the aspect that he is working on himself. You know, it always helps when you teach someone else what you have just learned yourself. He actually thought that he didn't have an intellectual brain because he has been taught to speak that airy-fairy talk."

Brian nods his head, shaking some of the straw from under his scarecrow hat and says, "Do you know that you can simplify square roots of negative numbers by factoring out = i and simplifying the..." He says all this while rolling out a scroll that looks all torn up.

"And Tim, our mentalist, can exercise that heart of his by helping you with your heart, love and intimacy. He can explain to you about being a victim. I can explain to you about how you must go through the emotional gateway to get to the soul; which means that you have to go through all of your emotional wounds, feelings and misperceptions before you can connect to the true heart. Your true heart is your own inner essence that some would call the soul. You know what I am talking about, Tim. He too didn't feel that he had it in him! He loves to talk about his feelings, don't cha, Tim?"

Tim appears and chuckles, moving in closer and whispers in my ear, "Actually, he's right. It IS my favorite thing to talk about!"

"And Leo, our chicken-shit," Marvel says, as Leo appears out of nowhere. Marvel wraps his arms around Leo. "Leo, here is our mentalist but actually our feeler, too. He could mentor you on the functional stuff and more importantly, the courage it takes to live here consciously and truly happy on earth. He will definitely work with you on all of your human limitations."

"I could do that or you could watch me kick Marvel's ass," Leo comments.

"Oh, really?" Marvel says.

"All right, maybe not." Both of them laugh.

"Just go to Leo's café and watch him create a masterpiece, as he faces his fears at the same time!" Marvel says.

"Now, we add in you to the mixture, Dottie! Dottie is the neophyte, which means the beginner, the new person who struggles with her life. Her life is not working and she is not conscious of these aspects so she is the neophyte who steps onto the path of consciousness. She could encounter the new 'Brian' who is very mental and understands the mind. She has the chance to encounter 'Tim' who is the heart and she begins to understand the heart, then she encounters the 'Leo' who is a little bit of heart and a little bit of mind, but is afraid to connect to his soul. This fear is often deeper because the fear means that the illusionary reality that he believes in will disappear."

Leo smiles.

"So once Leo's heart and mind awaken, there begins to be a balance. It becomes a question of his identity. The fear that Leo encounters is the losing of his identity; which is merely only a perceived identity. There is a fear of connecting with his greater self because at that point he knows that both of those realities will dissipate. He finally steps into something new and unknown."

"True, true," Leo says putting his hand on Marvel's shoulder.

"And each one of these aspects, Heart, Mind and Soul models the challenges of an evolved human to you and you have to discover how to combine all three and make it one for yourself. So, it is the trinity becoming one within the human being.

"This is what I have taught these guys, teaching each one of them in their own path. So, the mental teaches how to awaken the heart and the heart how to awaken the mind and the one who is afraid," Marvel points to Leo. "To give in to the union of the heart and the mind. You can be taught how to give into that union, to all three pathways that you have gone through and are still working on. I understand the challenges. Been there, done that. Ultimately, we are all One Being."

Leo says, "Wait, before you wake up, Dottie. Marvel, you didn't tell her your part in this."

127

Marvel says, "All right, Leo, let's hear it. What is my part?"

"Marvel, you are the culmination of the lion, the tin man, the scarecrow and I guess now you, Dottie. Therefore, when they all combine Dottie, the neophyte, has to combine the scarecrow and the tin man in order to get to the lion. And when she has assimilated Tim, Brian and my aspects she has assimilated the trinity within. And the three-fold flame within her heart has awakened. And when that has awakened, she then becomes the union and she becomes the Marvel, or the wizard herself," Leo says.

Brian adds, "Leo, you are starting to sound like me!"

Leo answers, "You see, Dottie, I definitely gotta get out more!"

Tim adds, "Marvel is truly the mentor. Marvel is the balance of the scarecrow, the tin man and the lion. He has the wisdom because he has travelled the road and because he has travelled the road, he understands all three. He is able to mentor them toward their own inner balance."

Brian adds, "That sounds about right."

Huh?

Glenda appears.

I look at Glenda and tell her I am completely confused.

Glenda smiles and says, "That's okay! Just feel the energy of it. You don't have to understand everything with your mind, you know! So, your heart truth and your human truth have to dance together — become one dance. It's where we tell you that your spirit and your human must integrate. Your I AM Presence must be present in your human as ONE. Then your external life will automatically change. Again, you don't have to understand every word, just feel, sweetie."

Why, what do you mean?

"Dorothy, you probably just wish that you could look out into the universe, and wish upon a star and see everything over a rainbow. Well, you cannot. You have to work your way through this mess, or this beautiful, unorderly entanglement that you call life. Remember, you created it, so it's possible that you can undo it! That's the beauty of life! I am sure that you do not want to live amid the great Kansas prairies on the same old farm for the rest of her life with Uncle and Aunt. That's why you moved back to Pennsylvania, isn't that right?"

Well, not really. My ex got out of the Army and he landed a job back East.

"Neither here nor there," Glenda disregards. "You made your way back here in the hopes of changing your tornado-like life into a balanced one. Let's face it, Dorothy, you created a hell of a storm. You've been running, my dear, from your life; running from your negative inner-voice, refusing to release the beliefs of 'I am so dumb, ugly, fat, I can't do this.' You know the ones."

I smile.

"Where did these distorted beliefs about yourself come from? Why do you hold onto these thoughts, feelings and behaviors?

"These are misperceptions that you have learned from childhood. And as children, we learn our lessons very well. They are told to you so many times by others that you start to believe them. Or you have created secondary beliefs in your adulthood to hide from who you truly are."

Isn't it funny though, when we look at other people's crap, it's clear to us that these distorted beliefs are not real? Like someone thinks their dumb or fat and they are not, from our perspective, while looking at them.

"If you hadn't made the decision to go home to face your problem, you could have been still out there without shelter during a tornado or trapped in, let's say, a flimsy trailer out in Kansas. You are now choosing to go underground and learn about you, with the help of your three new friends, and Marvel, of course." Glenda continues, "Most people wait until there is a crisis to go underground and look at themselves. Take the short cut and solve the problem NOW, instead of ignoring it!"

This time I am running TO something for the right reasons, not FROM something for the wrong reasons, like my fears.

"Yes, people run for different reasons. Some run so they don't have to think. Others run so they don't have to feel. And some run so they don't have to act. Some choose to be spacey, foggy, insecure and/or scattered. So, basically, they leave their minds like the scarecrow. They are out of their minds, no pun intended, or to insult your friend. It prevents them from thinking straight. Some choose to become overly analytical, knowledge driven or remain busy with details, which prevents them from feeling like your friend, Timmy used to do. I mean the Tin Woodsman," Glenda jokes and then continues. "Some choose to isolate themselves from others, afraid to reach out; therefore, paralyzing themselves which prevents them from going after what they want."

129

Like the lion. I can't imagine being stuck inside a trailer during a tornado. I've experienced four of those nasty things, but I've never experienced trailer style. The first one hit me in Kansas. The second one hit me in New York. And the third one was right here in Pennsylvania. I think that these tornadoes are following me, Glenda, no lie.

"You might be right, my dear!" Glenda giggles and says, "The past will keep following us until it gets resolved. But you are in a safe place, just observing the tornado. Your tornado represents great change! You are entering your own house, where it's safe, underground, deep inside of you. You have decided to take responsibility for your mind, spirit and body."

I have decided to take my life back!

Both Glenda and I stand still, staring at one another.

I feel everything around me stop. The energy between us dances together, intertwining like two children creating and playing.

"Dorothy, it was a pleasure travelling with you. Let's do it again sometime." Glenda adds, "It's time to wake up!"

I know I am waking up to all these memories and feelings. Thank you for all your help!

"No, Dorothy. It's time to wake up now! Morning is waiting for you," Glenda says. "Why don't you call Mr. Marvel — today?"

I wake up! Sit up in bed and stare into space.

"What the hell?"

I take Glenda's suggestion by grabbing the phone to call someone, but it's not Mr. Marvel. I scroll down to the L's to find Leo's number.

I dial Leo. No answer. Then I dial Brian, no answer. Then Tim.

"Hey, you," Tim answers. "How ya doing?"

"Okay, my heart hurts," I respond. "Or maybe it's my head that hurts. I am not quite sure. I am having weird dreams and emotional stuff is coming up."

"Like what?" Tim says.

"Family stuff like when I was young and ex-husband stuff. I feel like I am in a tornado."

"That sounds about right. You were given a lot in a short amount of time. So, my advice to you is that Marvel is next. Go get a pen. I will give you his number."

"You mean you want me to just call him?" I ask him.

"Yes, it's time! I can feel it, and I don't always feel," Tim says. "Trust me!"

I take down Marvel's number.

~

I take the whole next day to absorb the fact that Tim wants me to call Marvel. I take the next few days to think about how I haven't called him.

I believe this is what they mean by procrastination. I rarely procrastinate — up until now. I almost always have a list or agenda of some sort to complete. I start to spin, feel overwhelmed and basically jump straight into the tornado.

After a couple of days, I can't seem to leave my house, let alone take a shower. I get up off the couch and make my way to the kitchen when I stop suddenly to notice the knocking at the kitchen door. I look closer, past the curtains on the door window, to see who it is on the other side. I walk towards the door, and find my smiling new, but old, friends.

"What?" I move towards the door giving them a look and a smile and open the door. "Are you serious, guys?"

"What?" Leo imitates me. "Yes, we are serious!"

"You are not getting off that easily," Brian says.

"You feel far away," Tim adds.

"Yeah, so we decided to come closer," Brian states.

"Come on, Dottie, let's face it," Brian says. "You led and supported our group when we had our desks up against the wall, so it's our turn to lead you."

"Brain, that was back in the second grade."

Silence.

I look at them, my insides reacting to the love that surrounds me. I attempt to block the love and the opportunity that is standing right in front of me.

Being still, I feel the love around me and try not to fill the space with unimportant chatting.

Tim asks, "Dottie, do you still have Marvel in the teacher role?"

"Do you still look at him like an authority?" Leo interrogates. "Well, get him out of there! He's not your authority. Actually, he is a chicken-shit!"

"Actually, that's what he called you in my dream last night," I laugh.

"That little shit!" Leo chuckles. "Just kidding. You should realize that he is only human and has his own set of issues. You must get that. He can help you!"

Tim adds, "If you do still have him in that role, that will be a problem."

Brian continues, "It's time to see Marvel. This authority thing will stop you from getting the help that you desire. You said that you want this, right?"

"Yes, I want it."

"Let me make it easier for you," Tim says. "Authority is simply an image you hold in your mind that tells you something else is in charge or holds power over you. You have been trained to receive this programing since birth, in the media, in your family, in your relationships, in our Catholic upbringing, because it was perceived that you need power to survive. And that power comes from taking it, or it being given to you from others. You were never taught that the power, or authority, was yours to begin with — always yours — and could never be taken away."

Brian walks past me into the living room, plops himself on my couch and turns to face us and says, "Let's take a moment to redefine the word 'power.' Power is ultimately, inner strength. That's all it is — inner strength and authority. Finding your inner strength and your own inner authority allows you to be free from all of the constraints, beliefs and illusions that you have either created or bought into."

Tim follows Brian but sits in the oversized chair across from Leo. "When you struggle with this in your human life, it is simply a metaphor for the struggle between your ego, or personality and your Spirit, your inner heart, essence or your true self. The ego, or personality, perceives, at some level, that the Spirit is a power and authority over it. It wants to be the power and authority. It wants to be the strength and the creator. So, you cut yourself off internally to your own Spirit which then allows it to perceive that it is the creator."

Leo follows suit gently sliding into the big cushions of the remaining chair. "It is an internal battle that is reflected in your human life that is not really true."

"As you expand your consciousness," Brian continues as Leo rolls his eyes at him, "you become aware that your ego or personality is a partner in your journey and actually a creation of your Spirit or an aspect. When the two come into alignment, and you are filled with the Spirit within, the ego or personality is merged and united, in what we would call a spiritual union — you find that authority issues simply dissipate. You are the strength and authority. You are the creator. There is nothing outside of you, and there is nothing in your human experience that is real. It is your creation!"

"And we know that this is difficult to believe, conceive or even understand based upon the level of conscious expansion you are at," Tim said. "But the illusion is yours, and therefore, you can restructure the illusion to have the experience you want to. Recognize that you are the strength and authority, the creator, the divine being that is having an experience in human form that you have chosen."

Brian continues, "It is yours. You are actually free from all constraints and illusions; but you have forgotten and temporarily chosen to believe you are constrained and in these circumstances, in order to complete experiences and to assist the earth in your transition on your own ascension journey to expanded awareness; it all boils down to you remembering that you are the creator and remembering this statement, "I AM the Presence. I AM that I AM. I AM the Creator, Divine Being creating.""

Leo interrupts, "Brian, you make me crazy. T-M-I." Leo puts his hand up motioning him to stop.

"I believe that I can explain this a little bit better than Mr. Brain, here. Dottie, remember this one? 'You shall have no other God's before me.' That means follow your inner wisdom and nothing else. You are the Source and you are to have no other gods before you. To do so is idolatry or worshiping of a graven image or false god. Your own connection to Source is where you will find all of your answers. You need no one, and I am talking no one to find answers or tell you who you are. Remember you are The Source as is everyone else. Each has their own path to remember their truth. Do not allow the chosen to show you your way; they are but other gods that you place in front of your own divinity. You are your own leader and you do not need a middleman to get to your own source. Idolizing false gods energetically deplete and distract you. This also means you are to be led by your spirit not your ego or the ideas and words of others. False gods are anything that leads you away from the Source within and causes you to be attached to something outside you, be it a person, place or thing. This includes leaders of any type such as ministers, presidents and scientists."

"Or teachers," Glenda floats over and appears over Leo's shoulder.

Wait, how did you get here? Glenda smiles.

Leo continues, "Idolizing or depending on these is to worship false gods. Marvel isn't the one and only wizard out there! Your wizard is within and like I said before, you are just going to have to find it!"

"Wait!" Tim looks down at his phone, scrolls down and starts to text. "I will handle this! When do your kids return home?"

"Next Tuesday night," I answer.

I think that I will keep the Glenda situation to myself. They don't seem to have noticed her. Weird.

"I am texting Marvel." Tim picks up his phone to text Marvel. I exchange a smile with him. We wait a couple minutes staring at one another.

As we wait for Marvel's response, Leo asks, "Hey, Dottie, got anything in the fridge that I can whip up for all of us to eat?"

Just before the words arrive at my lips, Tim shouts out, "Perfect. He can meet tomorrow at 10am!"

Leo strolls into the kitchen and digs into my fridge, creatively finding different ingredients to mix together that I didn't even know that I had, and prepares us a delicious meal. We all eat breakfast and say our goodbyes.

After the boys leave, I go straight to my bed and fall asleep quickly.

"Me again, Dorothy. It's Glenda!"

How ya doing?!

"Listen, sweetie. You are a divine being and a creator. And the only way you could possibly perceive, and the key word is perceive, that you do not have power and authority is for you to create the illusion, believe in it, and act upon it as if it were true. So, we would say to you now that you are the power and authority of your life as the Creator God Being that you are. No one and nothing can take away your power and authority. You are the Creator. You are the divine strength and authority in your life and experience.

"Enjoy your day with Marvel tomorrow, Dorothy!" Glenda says. "He's just a person."

I wake up to the sun shining on my face and the sound of water dripping right outside my bedroom window. I peek out the window and see water dripping from the needles of the large pine tree out front.

I am off to see the Wizard.

CHAPTER 12

Off To See The Wizard

I pull into Marvel's long stone driveway. It is still wet from the rain. There are tall grasses waving to a slight breeze on the right and woods on the left that feel enchanted by some mystical presence.

Really? Ya gotta be kidding.

As I make my way slowly up the driveway, I suddenly get this feeling that this experience will be another major turning point in my life.

As I get closer to the parking lot, a few questions enter my mind.

Am I ready and willing or even capable of doing this? Do I have the courage? Do I have the heart? Am I smart enough?

I park the car and glance at my phone again.

9:50am… I am a little early.

I reluctantly remove myself from the car and notice a skinny path that is barely visible with wet grass protruding through the stone.

Where's his office?

The path is quite bumpy and long, but once I pass the bushes, the path widens and everything opens up. With this opening, come the trees and mums that are perfectly aligned and quite smooth unlike the path. The morning glories are wet and wrap themselves around the wired fence that keeps a garden hidden from view. I look over the morning glories and count the number of plants in the small garden; celery, cucumbers and zucchini that are on their last legs, with just the leaves and stalks still standing. The last of the tomatoes and peppers are ready to be picked.

I stop and face the fence staring at Marvel's garden, a garden that I always keep saying I want but never find the time, or just never have the willingness to maintain nor the patience to wait. I remember how much I used to love the look of nature and all its beauties. The trees, veggies, flowers, freshly cut grass and even the dirt. I love all the beautiful living things in nature.

My mother never really experimented with the outdoors either. She loves looking at nature through a window or feeling a photograph. She is always the one who volunteers to stay back with the little toddlers and babies, instead of going to the beach or the park. She loves the beauty of the earth as long as she doesn't have to stay in it for too long. She doesn't want to get too close. My mother doesn't want to get too close too much; just staying on the surface suits her fine. Don't get me wrong, she loves a good conversation and all its possibilities; analyzing, debating and sharing ideas, which makes her very interesting. But when it comes to sharing what was deep inside of her; that is off limits.

I begin to remember what the boys explained to me about patterns and beliefs. Not getting too close to things such as nature was something that I was clearly taught; I guess another family pattern or core program. If I had been born into Brian's family that lived on a farm, spent family vacations sleeping in tents and hiking the Appalachian Trail, I wouldn't have had trouble digging my hands in the dirt or sitting on the grass without a towel. That would mean, up until now, all my experiences are dictated by what I was taught rather than who I really am.

Weird?

I lean in closer to notice the texture of the shiny green pepper that is dangling, just wanting to be picked.

Boy, that pepper looks good, but I don't really want to touch it. Actually, I really don't want to touch anything outside the house for that matter. And I certainly don't want to eat anything unless it comes from the grocery store, or I myself am taking it straight out from a bag in my kitchen.

I laugh at myself while backing up.

"Hello," Marvel says.

"Aaaaah!" I squeal not expecting to back up into Marvel. "You scared me. I didn't even see you."

The Wizard.

"I walked from that white building all the way over to this garden, Dottie." Marvel smiles while pointing to the building. "And you didn't see me? You didn't even feel me."

137

"What? I was hyper-focused on the pepper," I respond in defense pushing back at him.

Marvel smiles again and gives me a light touch on my forearm, and a gentle brush across the back to make his way around me. I feel his kindness, yet he stays in his own place, not invading mine.

His gentle touch allows my shoulders to relax.

After moving around me completely, he opens the fence gate to grab the pepper as well as a couple ripened tomatoes.

"I was just coming out to get that last pepper and a tomato for my omelet. What a great house to buy this time of year especially because it came with a fully grown garden. How lucky am I?" Marvels says, as he gently picks the last pepper and tomato.

I nod.

"Anyway, I will see you in a couple, in that building." Marvel points to the gray building where his office is as he disappears back in to the white building.

He's making an omelet now! It's five of ten!

My thoughts force me back to my typical mental, emotional and physical state of being, my shoulders no longer relaxed. I begin to walk towards the other building. On my way, I bend my knee upward, lifting my sandaled foot into the air to avoid touching my skin on the weeds. Light sensations on my skin always give me the willies.

I open the door and the first thing I notice is the vaulted ceiling. There is multi-colored fabric covering the ceiling and it is beautifully draped from all sides of the room. It is unlike any other ceiling that I had ever seen. Everywhere I look, there are crystals, sparkling gems and I am guessing, minerals. They are on every shelf in every nook and cranny of the building. They are in every color, shape and size.

Interesting.

I notice a comfy couch placed in the center of the room with a desk delineating the space from the rest of the large open room. The papers on the desk are in disarray.

In one corner stands a big round table and the corner adjacent to that, there are some chairs stacked up. Not much in there which leads me to believe he is still unpacking. I take a seat.

I check my phone. 10:08.

Really?

I check my texts then my email.

I jump up abruptly, finding Marvel at the door with his veggie omelet in one hand and a chocolate bar in the other.

"Hey," Marvel says.

"Hey, ya got a lot of nature out there," I answer back babbling as I always do when I get nervous.

"That's where I keep all my trees and woods," Marvel responds wittingly as he always does when responding to non-sensible replies. "I just love this place." Marvel takes a bite of his vegetable omelet. "Were you exposed to a lot of nature growing up?"

"Nope! Let's put it this way, my mom had the willow tree chopped down in the front yard because it looked messy." I laugh. "That's how much I was exposed to it."

"Seriously?" Marvel says. "A willow? That's an amazing tree!"

I shrug my shoulders.

"That tree has been used in ceremonies intended for enhancement of feeling abilities, honoring the moon as well as increasing the essence of love in our lives. It's a powerful tree." Marvel looks at me with my blank stare. "They also soak up a lot of water."

"That's ironic," I inform. "We had water in our basement for years."

"Hmmm…" he says.

"Our neighbor kept their willow tree and they never got water. Too funny…can't wait to tell my mom."

"Maybe you shouldn't. Why stir up her wrongness?" Marvel advices.

All right, he doesn't even know her and he is already talking about her wrongness. What the hell?

My eyes start to wander around the room while Marvel talks about the willow tree and all its properties. All I can hear are his words all jumbled together; too many words and coming at me way too fast.

"Many cultures have used willow bark for pain relief too. In willow bark, there is ..."

I smile at him so he thinks that I am listening.

"In the 1800s, scientists were able to…"

He is an interesting man. He hasn't aged much.

"This lead to the development of aspirin..."

Aspirin! Really?

"…It was also used for treating acne."

Acne, really?

Marvel looks at me. I feel him feel me. He is able to feel from his own space, still no invasion into my space.

"I guess it's just a reminder to keep growing and reaching higher, no matter where you are planted, right?" Marvel asks but he quickly realizes that I won't be giving him a response. "And that's why you are here, right; for some growth, yes?"

Marvel takes another bite of his omelet. "You ready?"

Are you ready, Mr. Marvel? You and your omelet.

"Okay, tell me what's going on. The boys told me that you were having some stuff come up."

It's like "the boys" are one entity or something. They are singular.

I begin to tell him about the meds I am taking. He listens with no expression.

"...and so, I have this medication thing all figured out," I explain. "They really help with communication in my life and put things in order for me, like leaving my husband."

"Really?" Marvel responds with a dry sarcasm.

"Really," I tell him.

"Wait, you left your husband?" Marvel asks. "Before figuring it out."

"No, I figured that out, too," I say.

"You did, did you?" Marvel says.

Is he not hearing me?

Marvel continues and again I am only hearing parts of what he is saying. "...for true freedom and true healing, there are no dependencies, no attachments to anything so at least understand that."

"Okay." I try to focus more on the words, rather than the feeling behind the words. The feeling behind the words, or what the boys say, the energy. His voice is soothing but the energy is quite intense. The sound of his voice is so soft and light. I could fall asleep to his voice. It's the way he so eloquently places the words and syllables together. It's smooth, unlike me.

"That's great about the meds for now. You can get as much as you can from the meds you are taking and feel what it's like to be more focused and orderly. Maybe catch up on what you missed, academically. But then there will come a time where you eventually could step into consciousness and have that true freedom without the meds. You do want freedom from all this crap, yes?"

"Yes, of course I do," I reply. "That's why I found you guys, right?"

Boy, he talks more than any of the counselors or therapists that I ever heard.

"Yep." Marvel laughs and then continues. "So it is great that you can focus, but just remember it's not permanent. Often times, certain meds can become an addiction, a forced dependency that is accepted by society. If it's prescribed, people assume it must be healthy, but the fact remains, it's still an addiction. An addiction is an addiction whether society says it is a good one or not. Addictions always limit you! Being limited is not freedom. You don't want to shop at The Limited all your life, right?"

141

Marvel waits for a reaction from me, maybe a laugh regarding his joke, a smile, anything.

I nod.

I stay staring at Marvel while he smiles at me. "OOOOkaaaay."

"I am stuck on the word addiction," I tell him. "I don't want to be addicted to anything. I did that in high school and college, self-medicated myself."

"There is no good or bad. It's just where you are, what you are wanting to experience; it becomes an addiction if you are dependent on them. Popping the pills in your mouth to get stoned or high without even being conscious of what and why you are taking them. Addictions could be anything from workaholics, helicopter moms, co-dependent spouses, alcoholics or prescribed medications; behaving in a way to avoid something else or doing something to avoid your feelings."

I nod.

"You can use the meds to catapult yourself to expand your awareness. But if you depend on them, there is a high probability you will become a victim to them and eventually there will be physical or emotional complications. So, it's about knowing that you are using them to learn how to be focused, experiencing this feeling so you feel what it's like to pay attention and be more still. Once you get this, you will be able to do it on your own. Up until now, looking at what you were avoiding seemed impossible, so you self-medicated, became addicted to whatever, maybe spinning like a tornado, yes? I'm just guessing, here." Marvel laughs.

"Maybe." I smile.

"Those feelings may have been too scary or you may have felt too guilty. But when you are ready and you clear up some of the misperceptions in that mind of yours and, clear some of the imbalances that are in your body that you put there, you can come off the meds."

I listen.

"Remember you are still a victim if you are attached to it. And any attachment does not allow you to be..." Marvel says waiting for my response to finish the sentence.

"Free," I answer.

"Okay, are you with me?" Marvel takes another bite of his omelet. "There's a lot to do here, Dottie, you do know that, right?"

I nod.

"Alright, back to your husband," Marvel says. "So, you left your husband."

"Ex-husband," I correct him.

"Well, you still feel attached to your husband, you know that, right?" Marvel says.

I make a face at him. "Ex-husband," I whisper to myself.

"You can believe me or not, but if you have any thoughts or feelings about what he is doing, feeling or saying, you are still attached."

Marvel then asks, "Why did you leave him? Why were you with him?"

"Well, he was actually a great partner! He was more of a friend, though. He was safe. It seems that he could love me the same way as what I was capable of loving at the time. If that makes any sense? He was as distorted as I was. I loved him, I thought. So that is why I was with him, and that answers the second question. I had children with him because I felt those babies wanting to come here to be with us. I literally felt them. I went with the feeling of it.

"Now, the question is why did I leave him? He didn't want to work through any feelings. I was ready to work through some of my past, what you call become free. I asked him for months. 'Come on, honey,' I said. 'Let's look at this. Honey, we are not even connected anymore.' After almost a year of this, I realized that I definitely wanted something different. So, I broke his heart and it was horrible. During the marriage, I knew that he wasn't pushing me out of my comfort zone; he let me lead. He let me call the shots. And that was okay with me, until now! Actually, it was okay up until a couple of months ago when I left him."

Marvel nods.

"I helped him find an apartment and everything. We talked everyday about our relationship for months before he physically left the house." I stop and stare at Marvel for what seems like ten minutes.

"Why did this happen, Marvel? I did really love him. Does anyone know? Are there answers out there? He didn't want to come with me." My voice got lower. "I feel so bad. I disappointed him."

"Whoa, girl, slow down," Marvel says as he puts down his plate and raises up his hand. "First of all, let's just talk about the facts. You settled so you could feel safe, yes? You settled for something that was safe, yes? Why did you do this? When did you stop following your heart, or let's say, when did you stop following you, Dottie? And why? What made you so fearful that you abandoned yourself for someone else? Herein lies many of your answers, dear."

"I thought what we were doing was 'falling in love.' I didn't know what falling in love looked like. I did love him.

"I controlled what was comfortable for me in our relationship. He allowed me space. A lot of space. We didn't put pressure on each other to grow. We had enough pressure inside of us to deal with."

"So, regarding self-growth and looking at your inner feelings, you abandoned yourself and lived a life on autopilot."

"You could say that," I answer.

"Most people blame everyone and everything else after they have abandoned their own heart. This is a common mistake. Then when they first awaken they blame and judge themselves. This too is a common mistake and misunderstanding. We will get to these later."

Marvel proceeds to fill in the missing details and questions that I have about what I have learned so far from the boys. Marvel did most of the talking while I just listened. Although several times I would say, "What?! That can't be right." And then he would say, "Whoa, girl, slow down. Let's take it one step at a time."

Marvel begins to slow it down and take it step by step. "These distorted realities that you have, and Dottie trust me you have them, will stay with you until you change the perceptions of that reality and those experiences."

At one point, Marvel says, "You're full, aren't you?"

"I think so. Wait, how do I know when I am full."

"Well, you start to see stars and you feel like you are floating off the earth."

144

"You are kidding again, right?"

"Right! When are you available again?" Marvel inquires.

"Tomorrow?"

"No, really?" Marvel responds. "I usually see people once a week, so they have time to process the information."

"Well, the kids are with their dad until next Tuesday."

"Oh, yes, the husband," Marvel says sarcastically.

"EX-husband," I push back, hiding the fact that he is amusing me with his sarcasm.

Marvel stares at me.

"Um…is tomorrow, okay?"

"You really should have a full week to soak in this information. I don't think that you understand what you are getting. It's not just the words that I am saying. How about next week at 10am ….what's today?"

"Tuesday! How about every day at 10am, until the kids return."

"How about every day at 10am, until the kids return or until you have had enough, whichever comes first."

"Deal!" I hold out my hand to shake his, like I do for some of my business clients.

Marvel smiles looking at my hand and then up to my eyes. I make contact with him and instantly relax. Upon touching Marvel's hand surprisingly, I notice an amazing excess of heat emulating from his hand. The palm of his hand is large, yet soft and gentle. I wonder about the vastness of his gentleness. It seems unexplainable.

Why is your hand so hot?

"Different, huh? And the heat of my hand is from the vibrational frequency that you physically feel that few people feel and notice."

"What? Am I that obvious, wondering about your hand?"

145

"'Cause, I can read your mind," Marvel laughs.

I roll my eyes and give him a look of disbelief.

"No, I can't. That's not my gift. I could just feel you react. And I assumed.

"Feeling is just a vibrational frequency that everyone feels but few are aware of and even fewer know how to interpret those vibrational frequencies. It's just the law of physics. Once you feel them and learn to 'accurately' interpret them, you can know what other people feel like; at least the essence of it. A lot of people try to interpret it but they usually do it through their belief systems, body language and behaviors which, for the most part, distort the interpretation. In order to interpret accurately you must be of neutral mind and open heart. When you can interpret from a neutral mind and open heart even a blind mind can see the truth."

"Oh," I say.

Warmth, open heart, expansiveness. Is this connection? It was everything I ever dreamed of, but not in the way I thought it would happen, in my mind. I search for an explanation and an emotion that would match. But there is no emotion or explanation. This is something different; more than human love. Whatever, this is it! This might just be what I am searching for!

"Okay, we will see you next week then?" Marvel says.

"No, remember, tomorrow at 10am," I correct.

"Oh, that's right," Marvel says.

"Thank you," I say. I stand up and walk towards the door. I turn around to find Marvel biting his chocolate bar with one hand and turning his computer on with the other.

"Bye," I say.

"Bye," Marvel says looking up. Marvel smiles and turns back to his computer.

I leave a little more relaxed than when I arrived.

Everything I saw on the way in looked very different than on my way out.

After judging the grounds a few hours ago, *has it been that long?* I now admire the environment. I realize that it feels different but I don't quite know why. It is comfortable, safe yet expansive and it strikes me how it is so different than the environment that I was raised in. I almost didn't want to leave.

The grass appears full and seems so happy to be alive after the rain. It also might be because the sky that is so perfectly blue, allows the sun to illuminate the rest of the earth. The grass is in such joy drinking up the water that was left from the rain. It reaches up to the sunlight and the trees and their leaves glisten in the sunlight with the droplets of dew.

The nature surrounding his buildings is far from manicured, yet now it appears wild, but in a more organized way, giving harmony to the earth — very different from the plants that are manicured in a cookie cutter neighborhood.

I drive past the woods which no longer feel mystical, but clear, present and alive.

As I make my way down the driveway, I notice it.

"Really? A rainbow. Seriously?" I say out loud.

As I pull out of the driveway and head toward the rainbow... for home, which somehow, I guess will feel different than when I left it this morning.

DREAM:

Glenda grabs my hand and leads me out of a school.

"Hurry, we are running late."

We walk and walk. Glenda keeps peeking in the stores and restaurants one at a time like she is looking for something. Glenda seems exceptionally focused tonight.

Glenda shouts, "Finally! Here it is."

I am still holding Glenda's hand as she pulls me into what seems like a bar. There are strange beings everywhere. One by one they make eye contact with Glenda through a wave or a wink.

As I walk through the bar it gets weirder and weirder. The bar goes forever and each room we enter becomes lighter and lighter. The last door leads us to an outside area where I see Marvel standing under a huge tree. He is instructing all these beings from other worlds.

Is this a dream?

"Of course, it is, Dorothy," Glenda answers.

Are you real?

"What do you think?"

I shrug my shoulders.

"Of course, I am real!"

I mean are you real down there? I did see you at the school that first day. We talked about the book The Wonderful Wizard of Oz, right?

"Yes, we talked. And?" Glenda says and points to a giant willow tree as we keep walking.

Wow, that tree looks like the tree in the movie, Avatar.

"Sort of like a willow tree with colors?" Glenda asks.

Yes!

"It is!" Glenda informs me, pulling me inside a door where I hear voices.

She leads us over to a bench where we sit down.

"Isn't he cute?" Glenda sits smiling pointing to Marvel, who is over on the other side of the room.

I guess so.

"You see, Dorothy, many humans that I work with are so very limited. They have lost their imagination and can't see or experience beyond what they have been taught. They can't hear me when I try to speak to them and they are simply unconscious. And I keep having to wake them up, to make them more aware. They keep slipping back to their habits and behavior patterns."

Glenda places her transparent hand on my shoulder.

"Ya know, just like I am doing with you.

"So, my only other alternative is to work with them in dream state. Most humans cannot hear me in the waking state, so I must bring them into dream land to teach them in hopes they will wake up and remember."

"Hey Marvel!" Glenda yells across the room. "Did you tell them about the brain yet, because Dorothy is here to listen."

Marvel looks up and spots me.

Marvel gives me a wink and says, "Oh, hey, Dottie. Glad you could join us. I was just beginning to tell the gang here about the brain."

Oh, hi.

"So, when the brain isn't developed properly there aren't enough or there aren't the proper neural pathways in the brain to be accessible for the consciousness or soul of the person to use. Remember the brain basically is a receptor for the consciousness and the soul of the person. And in a person who has difficulty speaking, communicating, understanding or writing is because there are specific neural networks that aren't in place in a high functioning order."

I glance over at Glenda who is listening to Marvel. She is smiling from ear to ear.

"Because of that there is always some disconnect between the person's heart and soul or consciousness that is beyond the physical world. This combination of the lack of neural nets and a disconnection to their soul causes the challenges in communication, writing and handling the world.

"But let me add here that if there is a perceived trauma in the person's life, it will often cause a rerouting or deleting of some neural pathways and create a disconnect between their mind and heart and soul. So, what should happen first is that the neural nets need to be developed or repaired. This means the person must go through the process of learning how to be clear. Write, speak, communicate and think clearly. Know their feelings and emotions, and then know the verbiage that goes along with those feelings so that they can make their life easier.

"As they learn it is often very challenging and difficult because the brain has to basically be restructured through the exercise of learning. So, imagine those neural nets as a wiring or antenna. Once they are established, the person's real consciousness and their heart and soul can communicate with their human

149

brain. The brain becomes a receptor for this information so they can live their human life from their heart instead of being what they have been told they are or are supposed to be by other humans....."

My eyes open.

Oh my!

I turn my head to see the time. Time to go!

I put on my clothes, grab a snack and head for Marvel's house.

CHAPTER 13

Behind The Curtain

"Hey!" I say as I walk into Marvel's open room, much more relaxed than yesterday.

"So how was dreamland last night?" Marvel asks turning around in his computer chair.

What?

"As a matter of fact, I did have some dreams last night and they were very strange."

"Yeah, like what?"

"Glenda, from Our Lady of Angels said that you were cute," I tell him.

"Glenda said I was cute, ay?"

"Yes," I respond. "So, you know her?!"

"I bet you had something to say about me being cute. Ha!"

"What makes you say that?" I ask.

"Come on, I haven't been your biggest fan lately."

"Well, I guess I liked you more when I was in the seventh grade."

Marvel laughs and adds, "And I know that I made you angry on the stage near the curtain in the gym, right?"

"I guess."

"You guess?"

"All right, I was upset!"

"Alrighty, then! You were upset! Good! Own it, no secrets to yourself and me." Marvel laughs. "You see, the thing about secrets is… someone might not say that they are mad, but most people can feel if someone is mad. And when I said those things about you needing to get 'well' yourself and start looking at what's inside of you, it was just information. You didn't have to fight it or deny it or retreat, or even believe it. You could have even questioned it."

"True."

"The question is why couldn't you have just received it. Why couldn't you have just felt it out to see if it resonated with you? Then YOU could have decided what you wanted to do with it. Instead, you wasted probably a lot of time getting mad at me, rather than seeing it as just information. You have a difficult time receiving, don't you, Dottie?" Marvel says.

"Receiving isn't just opening to listen or opening your heart. That is just the beginning. That is only the beginning of receiving. Part of receiving also is the full bathing and the absorption of the new experience or subject matter; bathing in it and absorbing in it as it permeates your field. It feels completely different than just opening your heart — feels completely different than listening to it with your mind.

"After fully receiving something, yes, you do have the option to disagree or to give it back, set it aside, whatever. Are you understanding?

"Don't make me have to drop a house on you, Dorothy, for you to get this," Marvel laughs as he lifts up his empty plate where I am certain an omelet was.

"Was that an omelet?" I ask.

"Yes, it was! It was delicious."

"No veggies today, huh?"

Marvel nods his head no and holds up his chocolate bar. He smiles and says, "So, what else about me in your dream?"

"Let's see. Well, Glenda took me by the hand to what seemed like a bar at first."

"Oh, how did you like my lecture?" Marvel says.

What?

"I will pretend you didn't just say that," I say giving Marvel a confusing look. "Anyway, she led me through a bunch of doorways to get to you. You were

152

teaching these people stuff. She asked you if you had begun teaching about the brain, yet."

"Did you learn anything?"

"Yes, I did."

"Although, what is an Arcturian and a Lyrian? Those people you were teaching looked pretty darn strange."

Why am I asking him? He wasn't there.

"An Arcturian?! If we have a couple hours, I can explain it to you!" Marvel laughs.

Seriously?

"Better yet, did you figure out who Glenda represents in your dream?" Marvel inquires.

"No, what does she represent?" I ask.

"I don't know, Dottie. What does she represent?" Marvel chuckles some more. "Anyway, Glenda and I go way back. We have been dreamland instructors of the human condition forever! That woman is pure genius, a mastermind. She is like a Sorceress." Marvel widens his eyes and smiles.

What?

I give Marvel another confusing look.

"Anyway, Dottie, back to receiving. There is an old human phrase that says, 'It is greater to give than to receive.' This is a **human** interpretation. Giving and receiving are equally as great and they are the male and female aspects of the universe in action again. And that one without the other is not whole; it is incomplete and is inaccurate. Giving is equally as important as receiving but to give without receiving is empty and to receive without giving is empty.

"You must have both pieces of this. To give and receive, knowing that giving is the external expression of receiving and that receiving is the internal expression of giving.

"If you give unto yourself and you receive it you will be whole. And that's freedom, girl!"

153

I smile.

"To give to another in the outside world and to receive from another in the outside world is to be whole. Giving and receiving are simply expressions in the external world that are two aspects of the whole. Many people can give freely, but they cannot receive. Many people can receive and not give. Both are a form of taking. Those who receive without giving are often judged by those in the outside world as takers. But those who give and do not receive are being taken from; therefore, there is 'taking' being experienced. Often that person who gives and does not receive feels or expresses that they have been taken advantage of — and, that if you can fully receive and fully give, you will never feel taken from, and there will never be 'taking.'"

My head hurts. Too many words.

"What? Too much?" Marvel asks, "You don't have to believe everything, you know. And you don't have to apply everything you hear. You must discern if it's for you. It's just information. Most people either block it out, push it away, put your wall up or fight the person internally or blend with the person, believe everything someone says, be completely in submissive position or merge completely with that person, yes?"

"Yes," I say.

"Okay, Dottie!" Marvel smiles and says, "Let's talk about the specifics with you. The boys tell me that you are struggling with some of your experiences from the past, yes?"

"Yes."

"First, we might want to look at the fact that you don't have boundaries, dear."

I say, "Okay, so I don't have boundaries?"

"That is correct."

"Okay, I am listening. See, look at me." I hold out my arms and then turn my palms facing up and sit with my legs Indian style. "This is what you call receiving, Mr. Marvel. Watch and learn!"

Marvel chuckles.
"There is a disconnect from your head to your heart." Marvel places his pointer finger on my forehead. "Why don't you tell me about your childhood? That might help."

"Well, I can remember really loving life when I attended nursery school. There was this older couple that ran it. I remember really loving them and felt their love for me. I still have my report card from there. It said something like "Dottie is a wonderful little girl who focuses and really cares about her work. She is such a pleasant little girl.""

"Wow, I wouldn't have ever written that."

"Ha!" I laugh. I notice that I am holding my breath. I take a deep breath and continue talking. "There was another time that I remember in first grade. We went over to the church at St. Daniel's School with our class. I remember the statue of the Blessed Mother Mary wiggling. Then it literally started to move and then eventually became real and came over to me. Ever since that day, she would come over and make herself known to me."

"Did you ever tell anyone about it?"

"Yeah, right, Marvel."

Marvel chuckles.

"It was tough focusing on anything else when she would come. Everything else would become transparent and I didn't care about anything else but the Blessed Mother and me. Then when it was time to go back into the classroom or to go home after Sunday Mass, I had to adjust. I really enjoyed the church experience. People's voices would vibrate the church and everything around me. I could feel it deep down inside of me.

"Everything was clear back then. But then it changed at some point. Not sure when.

"Then summer came and went, and when I returned to school for second grade, things became fuzzy. Nothing was clear. I started to spin in class and I couldn't sit still in church and it was downhill from there. In the second grade, I was spinning so much that the teacher had to place my desk against the wall. Actually, alongside those three crazy 'boys' that you work with today!"

"Ha," Marvel said. "That explains a lot."
"I just couldn't keep still. It was just so tough. My brain was like a tornado. I had trouble putting the words that I heard down on paper. I mixed up my words when I spoke and when I wrote."

Marvel interrupts, "That is the disconnect that I feel. It feels like the neural net in your brain shorted out sometime during this period."

155

"All my life I had done everything fast."

"So, you wouldn't have to feel," Marvel interrupts. "Those feelings that you are trying so hard to push down are now surging through your body, as you said earlier, like a force behind a tornado getting ready to spin. You have basically surrendered the will of your heart to this overwhelming power of the mess that is inside. These thoughts, these feelings, this fast paced life that you speak of, may be ready to show its face again."

I look at Marvel, but no sound is made, only thoughts floating around. *I have never been able to sit still long enough to feel things.*

"I do remember that you were like that in the seventh grade as well," Marvel informs. "So, it feels like you checked out of your body as a young girl, Dottie; it was during the developmental stages as a youth. While you were checked out you missed the development of your brain because it wasn't used with your consciousness. When you came back you were older, but your brain and human mind didn't develop appropriately, which caused communication and learning challenges. When that occurs, the person socially and academically falls behind while their physical body develops. By the time you reached me in the seventh grade, you were way behind, wouldn't you say?"

"Oh, definitely behind."

"So, the summer before the second grade. What happened?"

"I believe that was when my dad got sick, and now I left my husband."

"Well, that last one happened this year, missy, not before second grade," Marvel says.

"Right," I agree.

"I remember your father dying the year I was in your class," I say switching the subject.

"Yes, and I notice that you are switching the subject," Marvel corrects. Marvel stares at the picture behind the couch above my head.

I turn around and see a picture of Marvel with his arms wrapped around another man. The frame has the word "Dad" engraved on it.

"I guess that's him?" I ask.

"Yep," Marvel answers. "So back to you. In the second grade is when your dad got sick, yes?"

"Yes, but I didn't even know he was sick, until he died. I was in seventh grade when he died. I am sure that you remember." I reveal, "I didn't even know what was going on. My neighbor told me that he died. She brought me into my mom and dad's bedroom and told me."

"Really? Did the rest of the family know he was sick?" Marvel says.

"Yes, they did but nobody told ME!" I answer feeling like a kid again. "I don't know what to feel; were they just really cruel or were they trying to protect me."

"Really?" Marvel said.

"What?" I ask.

"Family patterning. Denial, silence and secrets seems to be very present in your family," Marvel says.

Denial, silence and secrets. Moving my lips but no sound is made.

I stare at the floor, knowing that Marvel is looking at me, but can't get out of the stare.

"Dottie, hello!" Marvel says as he snaps his fingers several times in my face in attempt to bring me back to earth. "Just because you didn't know about his sickness didn't mean that you didn't somehow feel what was going on in the family. Ninety percent of the human life is felt. We feel everything; sometimes we just don't pay attention to it. We are taught that the mind is in charge, not the heart."

"True, I believe that."

"Along with the family patterning of those three things, denial, silence, and secrets. Your dad's dying may have totally frazzled the neural-pathways in your brain by activated distorted emotions. All that energy would absolutely frazzle a child."

"Wait, my grandpop died when I was in second grade, too. I loved him and I spent a lot of time with him when I was three and four years old. He would drive me to the nursery school three days a week. Then we would go back to his house and I would hang out with my grandma and him."

157

"Did your neighbor tell you that he died too?" Marvel says, making light of the situation.

"No, she didn't," I say and smile. "I remember that day very clearly. I came inside from playing with my friend, Patty. My family members were acting strange. I immediately thought that I did something wrong. Then someone said, 'Grandpop died. Now why don't you go out and play, sweetie,' and I didn't say a word. I did what I was told. Patty and I walked up my street to her house; longest walk of my life."

"Wow, silence, denial and secrets," Marvel repeats.

"Oh, yeah, and do you want to hear another secret?" I add, already making the assumption that he knows that I will tell him.

"I guess I am going to hear it. What?" he says with a smirk.

"When I was six years old, my brother sexually abused me." I can feel my face fill up with guilt and wrongness.

"Really?" Marvel says.

"I didn't resist or fight. It was like I was frozen. I allowed this to occur. Can you believe that, Marvel! I denied it for years. I didn't tell anyone and I kept it a secret for years."

"Denial, silence and secret," Marvel repeats. "Summer of second grade."

"Yes," I answer. "It's everywhere, ya know. Do you know one out of every four girls are sexually abused and one out of every ten boys are sexually abused? That is just the reported abuse! I would imagine if you would include all the altar boys in the catholic parishes that didn't speak up, there would be more. Who knows what the real statistics are?"

Marvel laughs at me.

"What?"

"You jumped right back in your head, ay, mental girl? You should hang out with Tim more often."

"I did my research," I respond, ignoring Marvel's comments. "I wanted it to be exposed. In fact, I want to expose everyone who has ever abused."

158

"Dottie, be careful not to expose for the wrong reasons."

"Shouldn't we, as a society, hold individuals who abuse and possibly institutions who know about it, such as priests in Catholic Church, coaches, teachers, and therapist responsible? Damn right, we should. We need to protect our children."

"Yes, we should. Do we have the right to have a voice in this world? Yes, we do. Do we have the right to express ourselves and speak out against those individuals who have taken advantage of us? Yes! I am saying just be careful of your intentions. It sounds like you are in the energy of getting back at something or someone — like revenge. You should be mindful of how and why you do things. We can get to that a little later."

"Okay," I answer back and look at him taking a deep breath.

I continue to talk. "Okay, I'll tell you the truth. I wasn't upset with my family for not telling me sooner about my dad. After he died, I didn't get mad at anyone because I always felt like I was the reason for his sickness. I was hyper and I drove him crazy. I didn't stay with my family when my grandpop died — and I wanted to. And I didn't tell my brother, 'no.' I feel really terrible right now."

"What does it feel like?"

Terrible! What do YOU think?

"I don't know. Terrible?"

"When you think back and feel it, what does it feel like?"

I hate how I feel.

"I feel bad, but he wasn't a bad kid."

"Describe the feeling."
I shrug my shoulders.

"You do recognize that you are avoiding the question."

I stare at Marvel, my eyes telling him to stop.

"Well, we will have to get to that sometime because it's the source of many of your challenges. The longer you avoid it, the longer the real change will take. I know that you have to get to it in your own time. You might want to make it one of the first things you do so that change begins quickly or you can make it the very last thing you do, so you don't have any time left to enjoy your life. But that's up to you."

I smile. My head drops.

"I feel so guilty about my ex-husband." I lift my head up. "I spoke up and I caused someone else pain. So, what I learned early on, that you don't ask for what you want. You remain silent." I put my head back down.

"Silence avoids other people's wrath, judgment or pain. You may have caused them by speaking your heart," Marvel states. "That sounds about right."

"The 'silence of self' is major. What do you call that, Marvel? I guess our major family patterning, yes?"

Marvel nods his head and gives me a 'thumbs-up.'

"So how do I get over feeling bad about my ex-husband? I feel awful."

"Okay, so you don't want to talk about your brother I am assuming."

Nay.

"Maybe not right now," I say finally admitting to Marvel. "I just feel so bad about my ex. I get that he chose not to participate in our relationship and he didn't want to figure things out. I picked him because he was safe and he was used to that life. That was the life I lived with him; a safe life. A life I had settled for. But why didn't he come with me? Why couldn't he? I don't accept that. I don't accept that he wants to stay in denial, silence and secrets."

"Well, you better start accepting it."

"I didn't think that there was an answer to my problems because I felt like I tried all avenues. I went to therapy three times; once in high school, once in college and then once when I was pregnant. I have tried alternative stuff and religion. You name it, Marvel. I even hung out with the Quakers for a while!"

Marvel covers his mouth. *I am assuming to hide his smile and to maybe stop him from laughing* and then says, "The Quakers, huh?"

"Yes, the Quakers!"

"Don't they marry themselves, or something? There is no priest or minister present, just the congregation."

I shake my head yes.

"Okay, continue, Dottie. You went to therapy three times. Tried all this alternative stuff, and then what?"

"Well, then I took that Adderall and everything changed and everything became clear what to do — leave my husband. Then the next thing I knew, I was turning into that St. Daniels School parking lot and there you were...with answers! Well, first you insulted me, and then came the answers."

"Are you ready for some answers?" Marvel asks, smiling at my interpretation of what happened. "We can work it out together. Are you ready for it to be different?"

"What do YOU think, Marvel?" I tease, yet it was not a playful tease.

"Hey, sometimes people say they are ready, and they're not. I've been doing this a long time, Dottie."

"I'm in!"

"Okay, then, here's what we are gonna do. You are going to tell me what happened with your husband and how you perceived things went down. Then I GUESS I am going to see you EVERYDAY at 10am, at your request, because according to YOU, you can handle seeing me every day and believe that you can handle all this information without a taking a break."

"Yep!"

"Okay, go!" Marvel chuckles.

Like start now?

Marvel stares at me.

Oh, I guess so.

"Alrighty then! After my husband and I were married, we moved to Kansas for almost five years."

"Kansas, seriously?"

"I know, right?" I laugh.

"You really lived in Kansas, Dorothy, I mean Dottie," Marvel chuckles.

"Yes, I did and we lived the typical life. We both had careers. We had lots of friends. I was a grade school teacher and loved it! I learned a hell of a lot. I was only there about five years, but found myself in so many interesting, and sometimes very uncomfortable, situations. First there was this little girl in my class who died of a rare heart condition that her family didn't know she had. Then the speech therapist at school died that same year. Then there was the student who was left homeless, because her mother went to jail for drugs and prostitution. It was a really poor area. There was a lot for me to handle my first couple years of teaching. I was a good teacher, well, sort of, anyway I really loved it. I knew how to recognize the kids who were struggling. I was good at breaking down the skills and teaching in many different ways that were necessary for the different learning styles. That came natural to me, but the paperwork and the organization were overwhelming and I became very stressed out."

"Did you say a little girl died in your class? What was that like?"

"It happened during gym class, outside. It was horrible. It left such a mark on my heart."

Marvel nods.

"I was okay with the kids, and I was there for them. I just knew what to do and say when they returned to the classroom — unlike the school nurse. She and the secretary ran outside to help the gym teacher with the little girl. The secretary told me that the nurse and the gym teacher froze. The secretary held the girl, while telling the gym teacher and nurse what to do. The little girl died in her arms. You really know who people are when tragedy strikes, ya know?"

"Those are the times when the patterning reveals itself."

"Yep," I respond and then put my head down. "I will never forget that day for as long as I live. I watched twenty ten-year-olds come back from gym. The girls called my name and ran to me as they sobbed. The boys, in shock, and not knowing what to do with their emotions. We became closer than close that year. I still keep in touch with some of them."

Marvel nods and gives me an endearing smile.

I nod. I take a deep breath.

"Okay, so, after five years, we decided to move back to Pennsylvania. I began to search for answers to these feelings that were eating away at me inside. I encouraged my husband to get help searching for some answers for himself as well. He knew what it was like, this feeling. He was 'one of every ten boys' if you get my drift. He was as distorted and wounded as I was. He, however, wasn't interested in seeking help. This was not in the contract of our marriage; you know, the unspoken contract. I guess this was not what he signed up for. I didn't know that I would begin this search, or feel the passion for wanting change so badly. Most of all, I had no idea I would have to do it alone.

"I decided to do the work on my own without him. Each time I got further with my search, I would ask him, 'Do you want to come with me?' 'No, I just can't,' he would say. More inner movement for me, and again I would ask him, 'Are you coming?' 'Nope I can't,' he would say.

"Eventually, I felt the relationship slipping away. Our worlds grew further and further apart. Even more disconnected than it already was, if that was possible."

Marvel interrupts, "Two people living together in one house but in two separate realities; each in their own pain. One person who is feeling the pain from the truth surfacing, another feeling the pain of pushing down the truth while denying and suppressing that which traumatized them. Tough place to be in. It's enough to make you wanna quit, run or go numb," Marvel says.

"Sounds like you know the feeling."

"Yes, I do."

"I can't imagine how my kids were affected by this," I say, "After ten years of marriage, I decided to tell my husband that our relationship could not continue the way it had been. I told him that this was one of the most difficult things that I ever had to do. I didn't want to hurt him, but it did. I didn't want to end it, which it did. I needed to, no, I had to get help and grow past this and he didn't want to. He didn't want to come where I was going. We were both unhappy. Something had to give.

"We spent almost every night together until he moved out, talking about what went wrong. I kept telling him that it was me. He wanted to know if there was someone else. 'No, there isn't anybody else!' I would say. Trust me, relationships and sex are not the top priority on my list. The only emotional relationships in my life were work, our three kids and me, with myself. He was my friend. I loved him. I still love him. What is love anyway?"

"Well, you could love him as much as you were capable of loving him."

"What is love?" I ask. "Wait, you can tell me, can't you?"

"You are funny, Dottie. Are you ready to hear what it really is? Not what you grew up thinking it was or what you were told it was. Not what most people think it should be but what it really is. It is so much more. Love is not at all what you thought; it's so much more. So, do I know what love is? Yes, I do, Dottie. I know what it could be. Is the average human being able to love the way I know it could be? No, not yet.

"This is where the love for self comes in. That will come in time, as I share with you — self-love and real intimacy with self. Love with another person would mean unconditional love, pure acceptance of another's feelings and behaviors. The acceptance of the way another person lives, accepting people's choices and life style. For you, I am feeling that it is black or white; living in polarity, yes?" Marvel inquires.

"So, what are you saying? I should have stayed with him and accepted him?" I ask.

"There's so much more to learn here, so many variables to address that I can't tell you in one session. Be patient; you will understand in time," Marvel says.

"Are we finished?" Marvel gently asks lovingly.

"I think so."

"Okay, I will see you tomorrow, then," Marvel says. His eyes are so light, bright and beautiful.

"Yep, okay." I walk towards the door and then turn around. "Wait, Glenda. Is she real?"

"I don't know, is she?" Marvel says with a glint in his eyes.

"Grrr. Bye, you weirdo." I move my mouth back in a snarl and leave abruptly.

DREAM:

"Hello, Miss Dorothy. Glenda here! So I see Marvel is giving you a hard time about who I am."

He is a little stinker. I am your Angelic Self, silly.

164

Glenda and I begin to merge together.

Thanks for telling me who you are.

"And Marvel and I go way back."

And yes, Marvel is busting me. Hey, why am I in a crib?"

"Well, get out then," Glenda says.

But I can see someone from the crib.

Who?

This boy! He is looking at me. I am in a baby's body, looking at him from the crib.

Really? What's he doing?

He is holding school books in his hand and he is walking past the door. He gives me a look like, ha! "I am here this lifetime, too." He does not feel very nice. I can't explain it. Yuck!

~

I wake up. What the hell? Glenda? My brother?

I will ask Marvel in my session today. I get dressed, go down stairs and make some coffee. As I pour the coffee, I suddenly look up and say, "Glenda is ME! Glenda is me in my dreams. But if she's me, then how can I see her when I am awake and how can I be talking to her? I must be going crazy! I think I am losing my mind, and yet somehow, it makes sense.

CHAPTER 14

Ding Dong The Past Is Dead

"Okay, Marvel," I say trying to catch my breath.

I practically ran to his office from my car.

I place my big purse down on the couch. "Wait until I tell you about the dream I had last night. Weird…"

Marvel turns around in his computer chair and says, "So how weird was it?"

"I know who Glenda is! Hellooooo, Dottie, daaaaaa," I say out loud to myself. "Glenda is ME! I knew it all the time, ya know," I inform him.

"No, you didn't," Marvel argues as he wrinkles his eyebrows and grins at the same time.

"I did!" I say emphatically. "Oh, all right maybe not, but Glenda merging into me in my dream last night was a dead give-away."

"So, you just lied," Marvel says with a grin.

"It's called making a joke, Marvel," I say slowly and smiling.

Am I flirting with him? I stop smiling and sit down looking away from him.

Marvel responds, "So maybe she is your divine Self… possibly."

"Yeah, maybe, whatever that is," I say. I smile again.

"Do you want to know what that is?"

"Sure," I answer.

I am still smiling at him. I am flirting with my teacher. Wait, he is not my teacher. We are two grown people. But he is counseling me. So, what is this relationship we have? Just shut up, Dottie, and listen.

"Are you sure you want to know?"

"I am sure." I smile again. *Stop it, Dottie.*

I am flirting. He really isn't looking at me that way though. It's like he is oblivious to all my smiles and cute comments. Wait. Why am I flirting with him? Stop! You know what you are here for! Get focused!

"Okay, tell me!" I say. I sit up and turn business-like. *That works, being business-like, like I am with my clients.*

"Well, there is your human — everything that you experience on earth as Dottie, the human being, and all of your human wisdom from this lifetime. Then there is your soul — which is connected to you in your heart as a human being. Soul is that part of you that records every experience that you ever had in any form that you have taken. Then there is your spirit, your divine essence, which is a part of source itself. Your soul and spirit are sometimes referred to as your higher self or Divine Self respectively, but only because it is higher in vibration and frequency not because it knows more than your human; although it does, however, know more than your human self," Marvel smiles like he is having multiple conversations with God knows who else!

"That which we refer to as soul is often called higher self or something similar. Spirit is what is often referred to as God Self, because it is a piece of God. You see, Dottie, we are all ultimately divine. It is simply that we have forgotten this fact and have gotten distracted and lost in all these patterns and beliefs. When you begin to really believe that you are the beliefs and identities you have accepted as truth, you forget who you truly are. The problem is all this identity programming begins when you are born, before you are able to discern what is truth or what is other people's ideas of truth. Just remember, we are all divine and have great wisdom, no matter what we believe or have been told," Marvel concludes.

I nod, noticing his transparent face.

"Did I lose you?" Marvel asks me. "Okay, what else do you have for me today, Dottie?"

I stare at him in silence because he has that look again. His eyes turn a lighter shade of brown. His face feels lighter. His face begins to change. It changes into many faces, one after the other. A red head, an African-American, an Indian. I immediately turn away and shake it off.

"So, are you ready to go any further today?" Marvel chuckles. "Just thought I'd ask."

"You are funny, Marvel. You just get right to it, don't you?" I observe.

"Why wouldn't I?" Marvel responds. "Why waste the time? Wouldn't you rather do it now instead of waiting and wasting another thirty years? If you do it now, it's thirty more years of joy you get to experience. Makes sense, doesn't it?"

"Yes, it does."

"Did you know when I was a teenager one of my sisters gave me a movie about the discovery of being gay."

"No, I didn't know this," Marvel chuckles.

"It was called *Personal Choice*. I thought that my sister was kidding. I did not want to be near ANY human body naked, girls or boys. Maybe she wondered why I wasn't acting like a normal girl. Why I wasn't throwing myself at guys as a teen, constantly desiring the opposite sex. Some of my friends in the tenth grade were already having sex. And did you know that it just scared the hell out of me, and do you know why it scared me?" I ask Marvel. "It scared me knowing that one day I would have to see someone naked again; have to touch and see those parts and be touched by those parts. It was all disgusting."

Marvel gives me a confused look.

"Well, I wasn't doing those things as a teen, instead, I was quite busy playing sports and doing anything and everything not to feel or remember that experience. Being sexual scared the hell out of me. Did I still flirt? Yes. In a safe, cute way, that said 'I am not going any further, buddy. Just love me on the outside.' Because for me, I just didn't want anything to do with it. I wanted to live my life with my clothes on!"

Marvel smiles at my comment.

"Okay. Here goes! I had a dream about my brother last night. In my dream, we were younger, way younger. It was weird. I was an infant turned on my side lying down in a crib. The room was dark except for the light that was shining in from the hallway. It was the hallway in the house that I grew up in. When I saw him, my infant body reacted, suddenly, kind of jumped like infants do when they get startled. I was completely focused on him. He walked past the room and then turned and looked at me. Our eyes met; we locked eyes for what seemed like eternity.

"He gave me what seemed to be an insidious grin, and cocked his head as if to say, 'Yep, I am here this lifetime, too.' It was creepy."

168

"Creepy? Like how?" Marvel asks.

"I don't know, just creepy," I say.

"What does creepy mean? Like the adjective that's in the dictionary, creepy, causing an unpleasant feeling of fear or unease?"

"Seriously, you know the definition of the word creepy."

"Don't change the subject, girl," Marvel commands.

"I did not feel at ease."

"And was there fear?" he asks.

"Yes, I was kind of afraid. No…I was very afraid… like he had some power over me, a friggin' little boy. It all just seems so weird."

"Sounds like your souls recognized each other instantly — maybe a past life — but don't mind that. Did you have any other feelings?"

"It feels yucky," I answer.

"That's a child's word," Marvel observes. "Why don't you describe what happened the summer before your second-grade year, or when you remembered the incident?"

"Where do you want me to begin?"

"Where ever you want to begin."

"I was in the ninth grade when that memory surfaced. It was crazy because I never had that memory, and suddenly it was clear as day. Why then? Why at that moment? Isn't that weird, Marvel?"

"Sometimes that just happens," he informs. "Memories can be just a one-day flood — like a dam that can't be stopped sometimes. Sometimes it's our Soul calling us to action and getting on with our life's mission."

"I remember being so happy that day. I was sixteen years old and I had just gotten my license. My mom gave me a car to drive. It wasn't a new car, but it had four wheels! I was so excited. I was driving down the main strip in town on my way home from volleyball and poof, there it was, right in my lap, just like that!

"I pulled the car over and cried my eyes out. The tears just poured down my cheeks and my heart ached so bad I could barely breathe. Take it back! I thought. My whole friggin' life changed in a heartbeat, and there was nothing I could do about it. It was so weird that I blocked that whole part of my life out; one day it's not there and suddenly, it's there. I know that sounds weird, but that is exactly how it was."

I look up at Marvel to see if he is still listening. He is.

"Just like that, my world, my life and those memories changed everything. Like someone from up above came down from the heavens, or maybe hell, and handed me back that memory on a piece of paper and said, 'Here ya go, Dottie. I think that you're ready for these memories. Here's your memory from when you were six years old. Why then, did I have to be reminded at that moment, Marvel? I don't understand, Marvel."

"Yep, sometimes it happens this way," Marvel says. "Go on."

"Go on...what?"

"What were the memories?"

"What do you mean? Like the details?"

"Yes."

Seriously, Marvel? I never told anyone the details. I mean I told the other counselors how he abused me. How it was not fair and how it affected my life in so many ways. And they would say, 'It's not your fault.' All of those therapy sessions never really changed the way I felt. It definitely helped me to talk it out. But not to resolve the feelings about the details of it.

"The details are the most important part. The answers are in the details. How you felt about each detail will begin to bring you your peace, my dear. It's all in the feeling of the details... to truly feel is to truly heal."

"Okay. It was gross! He was gross."

"Define gross."

"Like how?"
"What do you mean by gross?"

"His body was gross? I don't know."

"What does gross mean to you?"

"It's just gross."

"That's a judgment."

"Well, if YOU were six and were made to put your mouth on your thirteen-year-old brother's penis as he held your head there until he finished and then have to sit there and wait for him to stop messing with your private parts, you would feel gross, too," I say starting to get a little embarrassed, but more angry, with all these details that are just flying out of my mouth.

"I understand. Why at that moment did you find it gross?"

I hear Leo in my thoughts with his fists up telling me not to fight.

"I am not sure." My head drops.

"Listen, Dottie. I am not condoning what happened. Yes, it was inappropriate and should not have happened to you or for that matter to anyone at that age. But the fact remains is that you made a judgment at that moment. The judgment is everything. It will lead you to your freedom. That act or behavior was gross, correct?"

"Yes."

How many times do I have to say it, Marvel?

"If you are like most people you believe that you are your behaviors; therefore, you believe that you were 'gross' from that act that you participated in. Also, all of the other judgments that you probably have about being gross such as possibly believing that there is something wrong with you."

Or that I am dirty and who could love such a person.

"This became a part of your identity. Then begins the rejection of self which is only followed by the assumed rejection from others because somehow they will eventually know how gross and even maybe disgusting you are. Poof! All from one simple action and a self-created belief that you had no idea what you just created. And yes, I do know that the simple action was not what should happen to a little girl, but it did."

I look up, nod and then look back down.

171

"Okay, so his body was gross. Anything else?"

"I am dirty," I answer.

"Vile, tainted, and who could love such a person?" he adds.

"Disgusting and so on." My head is still down with my arm gesturing that what he is saying is correct. All the while feeling all those horrible feelings flood through my body.

"Yes, I can feel that," he says.

I look up. Marvel's eyes are light brown — looking at me with compassion, yet not in a "I feel sorry for you" kind of way, but in a more of "Let's go girl. We have some work to do!"

I nod and put my head down again.

This is hard.

"I feel bad," I admit. I feel a cry coming up.

"Why?"

Here we go again with the whys.

I can feel my eyes beginning to well up. I try to swallow it down. "I really liked my brother and he was my only brother. Brothers were supposed to be safe, right? But he ruined everything! He ruined it for me. I will never have another chance to love someone in a normal way. He mixed up love for me, and sex for me. I will never be normal like everyone else. It made my life a constant struggle and disappointment. He screwed that up for me!"

"You are right, Dottie. He did. And this was more than two kids around the same age experimenting with each other's parts. This was a young teen that knew better and wanted to 'get off' and you happened to be there. You were convenient."

"He did. He messed me up!" I shout. "Ya know, Marvel, I didn't want to hate him. He would stick up for me in the neighborhood. He was so nice to me. I wanted him to like me. I hated him, but I felt bad for hating him."

I am so confused.

172

"It was horrible. I felt strange sensations in me, emotionally, and even weirder things in my body. And I didn't know what they meant, or even what to do with them. It was almost as if I wasn't even in my body when it was occurring."

I hold my breath.

"And see, Marvel," I point to my mouth, "I am holding my breath. I always hold my breath all the time."

Ugh. I am so messed up.

"Whoa, girl! Okay, one step at a time. There's a lot here. Are you ready to hear some stuff?"

Marvel explains, "This is a good example of you going outside of yourself and looking for satisfaction from others. Yet at the same time you know life is disappointing… hmmm, very interesting. You don't want to dislike others, you want to be liked by others and yet you dislike others who have harmed you, at least from your perception of being harmed that put you in quite a quandary. It does, however, serve a purpose to make life ultimately disappointing, doesn't it?"

I nod.

"You are mentally and emotionally reaching outside of your own self to others in order to make some sense of self, and yet at the same time, you want to be invisible. My dear, that's just simply not possible!

"You lost your innocence. You gave yourself away. You gave away yourself, without knowing it. No one can take that away except you; even if you do it without conscious thought. When things like this occur, you have to understand, at some level, or multiple levels, here's the hard part, Dottie. Are you ready?"

I nod my head.

"You were an unwitting participant. Most people don't like to think that they participated because then that carries even greater guilt and shame for participating in an incident they have judged as wrong, and then have judged themselves as being wrong for having done it."

I stare at him.

"Another reason people do not like to know this is because they cannot be a victim, and many people hang their identity on being a victim. Being a victim allows you to avoid your own responsibility for choices you feel bad about and it brings sympathy and pity which also allows you to avoid your feelings, in fact it avoids your healing. It is not to say that you don't deserve to mourn the loss of your innocence, just don't hide behind victimhood and then suffer your whole life." Marvel repeats, "Just don't hide behind victimhood and then suffer your whole life. Do you hear me?

"To admit that you unwittingly participated consciously or unconsciously, can bring about such guilt that it can actually destroy the ego personality. The individual must take responsibility for their life experience, even if they do it unconsciously."

Marvel's eyes are steady and intense.

"When you realize or admit that you have unwittingly participated consciously or unconsciously, it is not to feel guilty, bad or wrong, but to recognize that you were a participant — meaning, your body was present. Therefore, it makes you a creator, or at least a partial creator of the event. Let me repeat. Participating, simply means your body was present.

"This, in turn will empower you to realize that you create everything you experience. With this knowledge and wisdom, you can recognize that you don't need to blame anyone else for anything, and that somehow, on some level, you have unwittingly participated and created the event for the wisdom of your soul. Even though, this doesn't, or may not, make any sense to your human self. Sometimes, on the bigger picture, it makes complete sense because you are a divine being that just has forgotten who she is. You have forgotten that you are a creator of your experience, partially because when you come back to earth, you don't remember who you are for many reasons, but also because you are a young human being trying to learn the ways of this world. So, as you are so involved in learning how to be a human, you tend to forget you are a creator, as you are too busy learning."

I shake my head.

"I am saying this to you to remind you of the creator that you are which then will empower you to change your perceptions and your beliefs. This allows you to create the experiences you wish to have, rather than be a victim to the experiences you have had and have judged through misunderstandings and misinterpretations.

"Are you with me?" Marvel checks in.

174

"Yes, I am," I answer, completely present, as I closely follow the information and the feeling of this very wise man, who is now looking quite transparent.

"With what you experienced, you have to understand it's quite different than a molester who might have attacked you, or harmed you, or even raped you. The energy was different here, and the intent was different. He was a teenager looking to discover himself in his body, and probably thought it would be easy to have an experience with you. Not to mention, he was probably molested somewhere along the way by someone older, and that's probably why he was experimenting with you at such a young age."

"I think that he was molested. I heard my mom talking about it when he was an altar boy. He was ten years old. There was some priest involved. He really liked this priest, until one day he didn't want to be an altar boy anymore."

"A priest, huh?"

I nod.

"That is a whole other subject which we can talk about later. Remind me to tell you about grooming; people looking away and people never wanting to question authority, such as the Catholic Church, schools, sports, etc. Let's stick with you today, and the beliefs that you developed that really distorted your innocence, okay?"

I nod.

"Okay, so I am feeling that his intention was not to harm you but to serve himself. He was being selfish, and not considering how his six-year-old sister could be affected by this. That being the case, he was not a bad person, yet he was very inappropriate, and again had no idea of what the effects of that behavior would be."

"Really?" I respond.

"Human beings do weird things to each other, and this type of thing leaves many scars."

I stare at Marvel completely still.

"Often, when people do things like this, they have had the experience themselves. They unconsciously play the patterning of those experiences with others. Then they act like he did with you, not really knowing why he was doing it and acting as if it never happened. They don't actually do things to you, they do things for themselves. But you happen to have been affected greatly as any child would; it's all so confusing for the child. Because you really liked him and loved him, you misunderstood what love was. So, you allowed him to do what he did without knowing the full repercussions or what judgments you would form later. Otherwise, you could have screamed or bit him to make him stop. Did he threaten you?"

"No," I say.

"Then I suspect what I have said is relatively accurate."

"Really, Marvel? Is this true? He simply was just experimenting and was selfish."

And I participated. I can't even say it out loud.

"As strange as it sounds, you did unwittingly participate."

"Unwittingly?"

"Without being aware; unintentionally," he answers.

"Oh."

"I know you were little, but you could have said 'no' and fought him."

Ugh, that's tough to hear.

"That's what you call 'eating crow,' girl. Accepting and owning your behaviors."

"Even if you're six?" I say. "That's tough to hear."

"Yes, even at six. You participated, consciously or unconsciously.

"How did you benefit from this behavior?" Marvel inquires.

"Deep down, I thought that maybe he would be mad at me and I didn't want to disappoint him," I say reluctantly, "if I didn't do it. He kept pushing me and holding me, all's I can remember is, 'Come here, Dottie, come on,' and I remember saying, if I just do, it will be over with."

I take a deep breath.

"Are you okay?" Marvel says, being my only witness to the owning of a behavior that happened so long ago.

"I guess."

"Remember, what's good about this owning thing is that you now can let go of this event and see it as benign, meaning, it's not good or bad. You simply made a choice to get something, and in your case, it was to obtain or get love or what you thought was love. You no longer ever, and I mean ever, have to give yourself away for anyone or anything in any way shape or form. You gave yourself away then, but that is over now. All you have to do is love you. Do you love you?"

I shrug my shoulders.

"That's for another day, Dottie, in another session," Marvel informs and smiles.

I smile back.

"Are you okay?"

I nod.

"Ya know, Marvel, I hold back in speaking up. I hold back not to disturb everyone else's feelings."

"I've seen you do that. Well, get ready for that to change."

"How is that?"

"Why do you think that you hold back? What are you getting out of it?"

I stare into his, what are now, brilliant light eyes. "Sometimes I don't want to disturb them."

"You probably learned this family pattern of taking care of other's needs before your own, even way before your brother. "

"Seeing anyone disappointed or dissatisfied is pretty tough for me."

"Why?"

"Because I don't want to see it."

"Why?"

"People are your mirror." Brian's voice comes to me.

"Because if I see their disappointment, it will remind me of my disappointment."

"Exactly! You were listening to those boys apparently."

"Yes," I say, as I put my head down not caring about the compliment that was just given to me.

"You don't want to disturb anyone; therefore, they won't be disappointed and you won't have to see your mirror looking back at you. So, that is about you unwittingly participating. Also, manipulating to get what you want. So, you create your reality. You affect what happens to you."

I nod.

"At six, I was afraid to disappoint others. I was so disappointed because of what happened, and I was doubly disappointed that I had to remember the event when I was sixteen," I say.

"And there you go, Miss Dottie, there you have it. You formed a belief that life was a disappointment. So, from that moment on, the behaviors and choices you made assured that this belief would come true. Your behaviors subconsciously set it up for disappointment to occur.

"You sacrificed your own happiness to prevent disappointment in him, to avoid seeing self. You disappointed yourself by not following your instincts. Those behaviors became part of your identity that must be upheld no matter what, which continues to support that belief that life is disappointing. Somewhere along the line you were taught that self-sacrifice, self-disappointment and self-abuse were what you were supposed to do and accept. You may have been known for pleasing people, being easy-going and helping others, but that was all unconsciously done for other reasons. This then becomes your identity. Then after a while you may start to be burdened by this identity. Then you start to resent the identity or maybe you feel obligated by this identity that you have to live up to it or maybe you enjoyed the recognition and you don't want to stop behaving this way. You then begin to live your life split inside. You like it, and you don't like it, then you become frozen in your growth. Life may start to feel empty like your life is not your own and you are not making choices from within you, from your own heart. This emptiness all stems from this one event, this one belief that you formed about disappointment. Pretty amazing, right?"

178

I nod. *Not really.*

"Life is a disappointment. There will always be disappointments in life. Life will always hold disappointment. How do those beliefs feel? Do they feel right to you?"

As I lean over the couch, hands in my face, I begin to cry. I feel Marvel's hand near my lower back, but he doesn't touch my back. His hand makes its way towards the back of my neck. As soon as it arrives at my throat area, I feel like I am going to vomit. I continue to cry louder.

"Open up, Dottie. Let the crying carry the feelings out of your body," Marvel says.

I cry for what seems like two hours, but it's only about ten minutes.

"Dottie, what you just did is what I call conscious crying," Marvel says.

"What were you doing with your hands?" I ask.

"I was just assisting you with your process in letting it go. I can get into that later with you. I can show you how to do it yourself. It's about forgiving yourself. You did good, Dottie. You did good."

I sit on the couch for quite some time just absorbing what has happened to me. Marvel stands over by his desk quietly sorting through some of his papers. After about a half an hour, I stand up and walk toward the door like I had done for the past two days, but this time it is different. I have found it, finally. I found someone who can help me be free from this. I want it to be over. I am so thankful for Marvel and the guys. My abuser didn't seem like an abuser any longer. He was just a selfish brother that may not have realized or didn't care how much he had ruined a little girl's life. He wasn't malicious. He didn't do it to me; he did it for himself. It wasn't even about me and my worth.

He wasn't malicious. He didn't do it to me. Why do those words make everything feel so much better now?

"What is it, Dottie?" Marvel says looking at my face seeing that I don't get this fully. "He wasn't malicious."

"Let me try to break this down and explain it to you. Was this a violation of trust? Yes, it was! It's an act that uses a connection to create an event that otherwise wouldn't have happened. It's a connection that was used psychically and intuitively to get you to perform an act that you would not have

179

consciously chosen. If you didn't have those feelings for him, to be approved of and liked, you wouldn't have performed that act. His was more innocent, in some way, with only the intent to have his experience of pleasure satisfied, however inappropriate it was."

I nod.

"There is another type of non-violent act that is much more calculating. This type of individual I will call a 'groomer.' He manipulates to satisfy his needs with a naïve, emotionally vulnerable young person. This individual sets up a connection for current or future availability through psychic, emotional and mental manipulation. Your brother didn't do this. It feels like he just did it out of an impulse. There was no planning. Although, the calculating individual tends to always have some sort of 'love' making or 'caring' comments preparing you, or testing you for a response and the potential participant qualities and outcome."

I stare.

"So, are you understanding? Your brother was more innocent with only the intent to have what he wanted. Whereas the groomer's act is actually at some level a calculated rape that allows him to make it look like you participated which thereby absolving him in his mind from thinking or feeling that he committed an illegal or forced sexual act. If he grooms you, then you become a willing participant and he gets off scot-free."

I nod.

"I am just feeling that you should understand all the different kinds of acts."

Frank was a groomer. And Father Rich?

I look up at Marvel.

He now is sitting at the computer, like he does every time we finish a session. He appears calm, as always.

I manage to get myself off the couch, approach the door, turn around, and look at Marvel once again. Ding Dong the past is dead. It feels like a burden was lifted off me.

I am at the door. I stare at him a little longer than usual today.

"What?" Marvel says as he feels me looking at him.

180

Who helps him?

I finally ask out loud, "Who helps you?"

"I don't know? What do you mean who helps me?" Marvel answers me, while turning around in his computer chair with his brilliant glowing eyes and intense presence.

"Who do you talk to when you need help?" I repeat, now affected by his presence and focus that is now directed at me.

"I don't know. I guess no one. I guess me," Marvel responds.

"Oh," I say. I remain staring at him.

I start to see him, the real him. This seeing is more of a feeling and knowing; like I was looking into his soul. Sadness and a little pain starts to surface. I go deeper.

"What Dottie? What are you doing?" Marvel inquires and then smirks.

I don't understand this feeling. Although I see the love that he has for himself but it's different than most. He doesn't have the same pain I see in most people.

I am still staring. Marvel is staring back at me.

"Where are you trying to go, Dottie?"

"Nowhere." I break the stare and lower my eyes.

"Well then, stop trying to go inside of me, Dottie!" he says. "You shouldn't be trying to get into other people's space anyway, missy. Don't you have enough to do in yourself?"

"Okay," I say smiling, but completely embarrassed. I lift my head up, making eye contact with him again.

"When you stare into an individual's eyes, or stare at me the way you just did, you are energetically, or as some people say psychically, invading my inner space. This isn't good for you, and it is actually impolite, unless you are invited. Sometimes when you do that you may find things you don't like in there, or people may get upset with you and then you respond by saying 'I wasn't doing anything,' yet you were. You must be more conscious of what you are doing and its effects."

I shrug my shoulders.

"Now, shut the doors, Dottie!" Marvel teases.

What?

"Maybe you can understand this. Imagine your eyelids are like cellar doors. Shut the doors! Imagine stepping into those cyclone cellar doors, where Dorothy and her Aunt Em and Uncle Henry escape, during one of those whirlwind tornadoes. In the book *The Wonderful Wizard of Oz,* the doors to the underground, where in the middle of the family's floor inside the house, from which a ladder led down into a small hole. Did you know that?"

"No, I didn't!" I smile at the fact that he actually knows this information.

"Go there! Close those cellar doors. Go underground, so you won't be swept up by a tornado, which may stir up other people's mess. You don't want to come in here, into my stuff, my inner world. What if there is a lot of debris swirling around, or something you can't handle. Go back inside you and shut those doors. Stay inside you and mind your own business." Marvel begins to laugh at himself.

Ha! He is funny. I love him. Oh no. shit! I love him? Am I in love with him? I can't love him. That would mess everything up. I need his help.

"So are we good, today," Marvel says. "Yes?"

"Yes, okay then. Bye," I respond, look up at him and quickly turn back towards the door, trying to hide the thoughts and feelings that were just going through me. I grab the knob.

Wait. He wouldn't see those thoughts and feelings because he is not in my space, the way I was in his space just moments ago. How embarrassing! Act normal, Dottie.

"What's up, Dottie," Marvel says. "You feel weird, now. Your energy has changed."

"I'm good," I say turning around. "Thank you so much. I feel so much better about this."

"Okay, good. There are still many more good things to come, my dear," Marvel says. "So have yourself a good rest of the day."

Marvel smiles like he does after every session.

"See ya," I respond and exit through the door.

DREAM:

"Dorothy, it's Glenda! You did good today. Isn't that what Marvel said?

"Marvel sounded different than the other counselors because he is different."
Glenda giggles. "But the other reason is that suppose some of the counselors
and therapists helped you to get you to where you are now. The realization of
what happened as a child, and simply remembering the memory, talking it out.
Some of those counselors and therapists helped you to do that, right? So that
was out of the way; it prepared you to really jump into this work and expedited
the process. Dottie, you were ready to find Marvel at this time!

"You must allow your human self to express itself also. You need to realize that
only you need to accept and love yourself. It's about learning to say, he did this
to me, this happened, this was not right, and it really confused me as a little
girl. Your human self and your little girl self needs to heal. There will be
emotions, possible blame and questions for you to work through.

"Remember this will be a process. This is just the first step. Trust me. There
will be layers upon layers of thoughts, beliefs and feelings that will be
revealed. You will just have to be patient, try not to judge these feelings, and
never think you are done or deny any feeling because that would be a secret
again. When you can say this without an emotional charge, it tells you that you
are free and finally finished with this. When you are done, you will know it.

"It may take some time to fully admit that you unwittingly participated, because
that would mean that you created this yourself. You spent all of your life
blaming him for making you do this act. This was part of the healing; only if
you created this, then you can forgive yourself and undo it. Again, part of the
healing is not about the act, it is about the feelings and beliefs that are picked
up and accumulated from that act that causes you pain and eliminates any
possibility for true peace within.

"Tell the humans!" Glenda smiles.

Marvel appears!

Oh, hello, Marvel!

"Hello, Dorothy. Remember, it is all about your interpretation of what occurred. The guilt, the feeling dirty and the wrongness are all about your own perception. The healing comes when you undo these distorted thoughts, feelings and judgments. Recognizing and owning that you created these perceptions, however unconsciously, allows you to be free of them. And when you finally get it, it's empowering. No victimhood anymore! Being or perceiving oneself as a victim won't be an option. Victimhood and believing you are a victim, keeps you powerless, and worst of all, a victim. Knowing that you created those horrific thoughts, perceptions, feelings and judgments makes it possible to undo them. Does that make sense?"

Glenda floats back in. "You know, you can use this process for anyone who has such traumas — even rape. There is a movement starting about rape on college campuses. It must be known, what people do to each other in secret. Something must be done. When it becomes known to the general public, you must help those who are distorted and in pain. Learn this so you can teach others. I know that you wanted to expose these individuals who commit these kind of acts, Dottie. You wanted to expose them for the wrong reasons. Exposing others is only important if you need to protect others. Otherwise you are often seeking revenge and want to hurt those who you perceive hurt you."

I understand Glenda. A priest does this to an altar boy, and then a brother to a little sister? A trusted 'authority,' a priest, ruins multiple lives, never being reported, and never really knowing the damage that he has caused. This is just wrong!

"I see that, Dorothy!"

Yes, I was mad.

"You have a right to be mad. Own it. But now it's time for a resolution. You humans should not have to live in this pain and these distortions."

I wanted to speak up to anyone who would listen. I guess I was trying to find my voice, no matter what the cost. I wanted to expose every one of the stories that I have heard over the years. Everyone involved, and everyone that abused. I wanted not only to expose it, but wanted to physically hurt the individuals that did these things. I did want revenge.

"It distorts and ruins all the lives of the people involved. It needs to be exposed, yes, but for the right reasons. Learn it! You have been given a gift."

A gift?!

"Yes, a gift."

Listen, Glenda...

Before I speak another word, Glenda has my hand in hers and says, *"Hey you, come along with me."*

We walk over to a stage where Whitney Houston is singing to a crowd. I notice that Whitney appears to be high and not looking healthy. Glenda and I try to get closer to see Whitney from the side of the stage. I turn back around and I am startled by Oprah's presence, her face right in front of mine. With her eyes, bright and her hair perfectly in place, Oprah says to me, "Are you ready?"

I hesitate and cannot find the words to answer her. I freeze. Oprah lowers her head down clearly disappointed. Then suddenly, Oprah's face turns into the face of my high school basketball coach's brother, Frank.

I wake up startled. "What the... ?" I can still feel Frank right in front of me.

What the hell?

I am still half asleep.

Frank, what are you doing here?

Warning bells go off in my head.

It's the alarm. It sounds louder than usual. I sit up in bed.

I don't want to go there. Not him.

I get up and put my clothes on and run downstairs. I pick up my purse off the couch and then reach into the cabinet and grab my scrapbook. I open it up to the soccer championship page, pulling out the letter from Father Rich. I throw the scrapbook on the couch and head out for Marvel's place, a place that is sometimes fearful — uncomfortable at times — yet still the safest place to be in my life right now.

185

CHAPTER 15

Out Of The Castle — But Not Quite

I get out of my car and walk down the path towards the gray building. After passing the bushes, I stop to notice Marvel in his garden. He doesn't see me. I quietly slip behind the bushes as I watch him pick the rest of his ripened tomatoes.

He is a tall man; I guess around six feet; curly black hair, not much different than when he taught me in the seventh grade. I look down at my hand to count the difference in our ages.

So, he is only nine and a half years older than me. He is forty-three right now.

I look up again, still trying to feel Marvel.

He's just an ordinary man, but he had this glow to him that emulated about two feet from him. Once you get within two feet of him, you feel it. You also feel such strength inside yourself; like you could do anything.

I pick my head up to look at Marvel.

"Oh, HEY, you," says Marvel who apparently must have moved closer when I was looking down. He is within two feet of me. "See you in a couple of minutes?" He points to the gray building and off he goes into the white building.

I freeze, nodding quickly.

I move slowly, a little embarrassed, and make my way to the door of the gray building.

10:05am finally arrives and Marvel is at the door with his usual omelet and his chocolate bar.

"Alrighty, Miss Dottie," Marvel said. "What are we doing today?"

"Well," I say while attempting to check Marvel's temperature, seeing if he feels weird finding me in the bushes.

Nothing, same old Marvel.

"Not quite sure. That was a lot to take in yesterday, but thank you, Marvel, seriously."

"You are welcome," Marvel answers and then asks, "What do we have for today?"

"Well, a lot came up last night," I say with a hesitating look.

"That is typical."

"Well, this is a tough one."

"You have never revealed this one before, have you?" Marvel inquires.

"How do you know?"

"I can feel your nervous system tightening up, freaking out, something."

"I can feel it, too. This story will be tough, but I know that I have to break it apart, understand it; it's in there, hidden. Whatever he did or whatever I perceived changed things for me again.

"So, let me backtrack a bit. In fifth grade I started experimenting with boys. You know, boy-girl parties, they use to call them. I kissed many of them. This went on until about ninth grade. There was one time that a boy in seventh tried to force my head down with his hand like my brother. I freaked, and totally backed-off boys. I avoided them, and only did enough to look normal. It's funny, because you would have thought that it would have triggered the memory of my brother, but it didn't. Anyway, by eighth grade, I totally emerged myself in sports."

"Okay," Marvel says.

"Then I met this older man and I didn't want anything to do with boys anymore. Again, I did just enough so that I would look normal, doing girl things. Going to the prom and things like that. I never had any good experiences or any experiences with older men until him. And now, I am not sure that it was a good experience," I say.

"Why, no good experiences with men?" Marvel asks. "What do you mean?"

"My dad died the day before I was thirteen, my neighbor's father drank a lot and felt violent with his kids; my other neighbor's father died in a car crash,

187

and most of my teachers were nuns or females," I answer. "That was my experience with older men."

"Okay, go on. What happened?"

"Last night, I cried a lot; I couldn't stop. I really thought that I worked on almost everything in my childhood with those therapists."

"I guess there was more," Marvel states.

"Yes, but I guess I only covered certain areas and in a different way. You really gave me a new perspective on things."

Marvel nods.

"I do feel a lot better about the situation; although, now other memories are surfacing. I woke up angry, but not about my brother. It was about another situation," I say taking a deep breath.

I continue. "Right before I woke up…" and then hesitate again.

"What's his name?"

"Frank."

"What about Frank?"

"This is hard to talk about."

"Give it a try."

"This grooming thing that you talked about yesterday, ya know, with the priest. Can you tell me more about that?"

"Why don't you tell me about Frank?"

"I thought that I looked at all of this!"

"Let's talk about Frank. Start from the beginning."

"So …" I say hesitating.

I am really not sure whether I want to say it out loud. I've never told anyone about this.

My mind starts to spin. I can feel the twister starting to rumble.

Don't spin, Dottie. Breathe and focus on your heart. Now connect to it and observe the feeling. You don't have to feel it all right now. Breathe...

I want to leave. I feel myself beginning to vacate my body and feelings, but I know the twister will just follow me wherever I go. Go in the cyclone cellar doors, Dottie! Go in. Look in. It will be safe in there.

"Yes?" Marvel patiently waits. "What's happening? What are you feeling?"

"It was the first time that I was intrigued by an older man. I was fourteen years old when I first met him. He was my basketball coach's brother. He helped out at our practices."

I hesitate. "And?" Marvel asks.

"Well, he always said the right things. Although when he would talk to me at practice, I felt him looking right through me. It was almost like he was invading my space, my inner sanctum, kind of like I did to you yesterday, but more so."

"You didn't *kind of* invade my space, you did invade my space," Marvel said directly, yet kindly.

I smile and take another deep breath.

"When he was invading my space, I liked it, it somehow felt good at the moment; I didn't mind. There is something wrong with this, isn't there?"

"Keep going, Dottie. Feel into it slowly."

"Well, I am confused about all this, it's like there is a fog in my head and what really happened. After these past few days, I am now willing to see maybe a new perspective. He might have been one of those 'groomer' guys, like the priest."

"Maybe, keep talking and feeling."

"Well, I really liked him."

"Why did you like him?"

189

"I just did. He was real. He felt wise. He talked Spiritual. I felt like I knew him well. I felt really comfortable and almost like he understood me."

"Understood what, Dottie?"

"He understood me, like no one else did. Boy that sounds weird when I say it out loud as an adult.

"For years, I thought he was the one who helped me work through the beginning stages of this whole sexual abuse thing. He did help me; but I am not too sure that it was really helpful. And then he said those things about his niece. 'My niece was sitting right here on my lap and I got an erection.' What the hell, Marvel? That's fucked up, right? I sat frozen when he said it and then I allowed him to continue. Can you believe that? I ignored what he said. And I can't really remember what I learned. He did make my brother out to be an evil person; a major abuser. But now today, after you explained this whole patterning and belief systems thing, and unwittingly participation thing and most importantly, my brother's possible intentions. I am so confused."

"Keep going."

He continued to say weird things. For instance, one time he said, 'My niece was on my lap and I got very hard.' That was just as bad, wasn't it?"

"Yes," Marvel says. "Did you say you were at his house at fourteen years old?"

"Yes. I was at his house."

Marvel says, "Was your mom aware of these sessions?"

"No, my mom was not aware," I answer. "And I just thought of something else. After him, there was no one else that I really thought about. I mean like in a boyfriend way! I think that I had dated one guy for a little, but a part of me, especially in my mind, was with Frank. I don't even know what that even means, except that I felt committed. When I was nineteen, my freshman year of college, I had a relationship with a guy who was twenty-nine, the same age as Frank. Again, I felt I was already taken."

I am so confused.

My mind dove straight towards the twister. It didn't even wind up; it went right to light speed.

"Whoa, girl, back up!" Marvel says. "Did you have a sexual relationship with this guy at fourteen?!"

The twister suddenly stops and drops me right onto the ground, *not literally.* Whoa, what the fuck just happened.

Out of the Castle? Not quite yet.

I look up at Marvel. His intense voice keeps my attention on him as opposed to the after effects of the twister. His intensity grounds me a bit.

"No, I didn't," I respond quickly, "but I did later when I was twenty."

"Oh, no," Marvel says. "Let's back up a bit. So, you met him when you were fourteen?"

"Yes, fourteen," I say.

"And then he came and helped out during your basketball practices. He also did sessions with you at his place without your mom knowing, and then you didn't really have any serious relationships with anyone until this other older guy, yes?"

"Yes, this guy, Dan," I answer.

"And then you had sex with Frank at the age of twenty, your sophomore year of college?" Marvel inquires.

"Yes, but I didn't actually have intercourse with him. We did other things, but I wanted to be with him. He didn't force me. I consented. God, I hated saying that just now."

I reluctantly say, "Well, I think that I wanted to be with him."

"Well you either wanted to or not," Marvel says.

"Marvel, I went over to his house on my spring break with the intention of telling him that I loved him because I thought that was love, but as soon as I kissed him, it felt like I was kissing my brother, or something. It was gross, ick. My gut totally contradicted what I was thinking."

"Oh, so then you weren't with him?" Marvel asks.

"Well, as soon as I kissed him, it felt weird. And then I felt bad because I kissed him, and so I felt obligated to do something. I didn't have sex with him. We just did other things," I say.

Like that was different, Dottie.

"Oh my, lies, ties and obligation," Marvel says shockingly. "So, you gave yourself away again, Dottie."

"I did," I agree. "I hate when you say it like that. Ugh! Why do I feel like shit right now?"

Marvel answers, "You feel like shit because there was a moment when it didn't feel right, and you had a choice to say what you wanted and yet you allowed someone else's desires and needs to take precedence over your own. You knew in your heart it was not in your best interest, nor was it pure of heart."

"True," I say reluctantly.

"So, what made you decide to go to his place at fourteen? How did that happen?"

"Well, like I said before, he was around during my ninth-grade season and everyone knew him. So, by tenth grade, our team was having some trouble getting along, so our coach suggested that our whole team do a group session with him."

"Why wasn't the session done at the school?" Marvel says.

"Because he wasn't with the school; he was a counselor for another school."

"Really?" Marvel says looking confused.

"When we were there, I remember how he worked with everyone on the team. It was kind of cool. He would bow and hold his hands in prayer when saying hello and goodbye, Namaste, like they do today in yoga. He seemed to really have it together and helped the group. So, after this group session with the team, I asked him if I could come over another time. I told him that I was sexually abused and that I had already discussed this with his sister, our coach. I said that she said that she counsels teens privately, and that he might be able to help me."

"He said that he could help you, didn't he?" Marvel says.

I nod.

"Of course he did."

"What are you telling me, Marvel."

"Just continue, Dottie."

"I still had thoughts about him, comparing him to every guy I met and believing that he was the one that helped me to work stuff out."

"Then what happened?"

"When I was twenty, I went to see him. He suggested we go out and sit on a blanket on the grass in his yard. As soon as I told him that I lost my virginity to that twenty-nine-year old guy Dan, he got weird inside. As you would say, and now I get it, his whole energy changed. I told him all about my first experience and how it was so great. Dan was twenty-nine and he was so sensitive and understanding about what I had been through. He waited for me to tell him when I was ready to be intimate. Dan and I weren't together until six months into the relationship. He was so very kind. He took me to a hotel for the first time. He made it really special for me. He kept checking if I was okay — the whole step of the way."

Marvel listens.

"I thought that Frank would have been happy for me now that I was normal."

"Normal?"

"Yes, normal, Marvel!

"But when I told Frank, again, he felt so strange. In fact, I had never felt Frank like this before. I don't remember what he said. I just remember how he felt. Shortly after telling him about my first experience, he asked me to come inside to hang in the bedroom. At that point, I thought that would be the moment that I would tell him that I believed that I was in love with him and ask him what he thought about it. I felt that I was experienced enough and mature enough to share my body with the one that I loved. The guy I loved for all these years — since I was fourteen years old."

"Okay," Marvel says.

I dreadfully continue. "He then says to me, 'Don't get too serious about this.' Those words broke my heart. That was the first knife in my heart. Then he said, 'My fiancé would probably join us if she was around.' That was the second knife to my heart. But like I told you before, Marvel, that wasn't how it was supposed to turn out; again, yuck, it was like kissing my brother."

"Based on the little bit that you just told me, I would say he was grooming you, waiting for the day that you would come back," Marvel informs. "It just feels like to me that he was psychically pulling on you and drew you in."

"Seriously?" I ask. "If this was true, why did the coach bring him around a bunch of teens?"

"Maybe she didn't know," Marvel says. "Or maybe she was too blind because he was her brother — too many possibilities."

I put my head down in disgrace as Marvel stays still and waits.

"A couple weeks later, Frank drove his motorcycle up to my college — I didn't even invite him. He wanted to hang, he says. He sat in my living room and flirted with my friend who had just revealed to me that she was sexually abused."

"Did he stay over?" Marvel asks.

"I still didn't have intercourse with him."

Did I really say those words out loud?

"Don't tell me…you felt obligated."

"Yes, the bastard stayed over. I just did stuff with him, but I hated it and I hated myself for it. It was exactly what happened with my brother."

"In what way?"

"The third time with my brother I was fully aware of what was happening and I was clear about not wanting to participate, but I did anyway. Ugh."

"Do you remember the details of the first and second time with your brother?"

"Not really, but I know that there was a first and second time. The first time, it was in the tub. The second time we were in my mom and dad's bedroom. I don't really remember how I got there and how it ended. I just remember

194

looking up at their crucifix above their bed and performing the same act on my brother."

I nod my head and then cover my eyes with both hands.

Bastard...I am so stupid.

"Do you believe that I allowed this to happen again with Frank? Stupid!

"Do you know that years later, one of my friends told me that Frank was in some trouble with messing around with a couple of the girls at the school where he taught. The friend told me adamantly to 'stay away from that man,' he's trouble. I should have listened."

"Of course he was," Marvel asks, "Did you really think that you were the only one?"

My head stays down until the heat from the anger in me enters my face. "I also heard that he married that fiancé — who he once counseled and she already had four young girls."

I want to scream.

"Do you wanna hear the worst part, Marvel?"

"No," Marvel says. "Maybe not. Okay, yes, tell me."

"I invited him and his sister to my wedding," I reluctantly say. My head and shoulders drop; my hands cover my face which was filling more and more with anger.

"Dottie, accept it, you did it. You made choices. Try not to judge it," Marvel says. "I know it feels terrible, but this is the beginning of your healing."

"I friggin' hate him. He could have abused those girls as well," I say. "When I think about that, it makes me want to spin! It makes me want to go after him and expose him!"

"Ugh, that's the problem with you girls," Marvel says. "These guys seem very open and appear well-balanced, spiritually, and you girls don't know that they are grooming you. I've seen these folks."

I look up to listen.

"Your openness was taken advantaged of and he constantly made sexual undertones that ran alongside the assistance, which with his behaviors and your own dysfunctional allowances eventually caused more damage. Oh, Dottie. You had to re-experience the situation of when you were six years old all over again. It's the owning of your behaviors and a little bit of your eating crow that will get you through this. I know that is difficult, but this will change your life if you are able to really listen to me and apply what I am telling you.

"Remember, this a violation of trust. It's an act committed by a 'groomer.' He manipulated you to satisfy his needs with a naïve, emotionally vulnerable young girl. This guy, Frank, set up a connection for current or future availability through psychic, emotional and mental manipulation. This calculating individual tested you for a response and as a potential participant, to get what he wanted."

I stare at Marvel. His words and logical understandings still don't take the pain away. The judgment is strong.

"As I told you yesterday, this act is actually at some level a calculated rape that allows him to make it look like you participated, thereby absolving him in his mind from thinking or feeling that he committed an illegal or forced sexual act. If he grooms you then, you become a willing participant and he gets off scot free."

I nod.

"Think about it. Your brother was a mirror for him. He saw the reflection of what he himself was doing. He became charged, you said, right?"

"Yes. He talked about him like he was evil. He really felt charged — almost as if it bothered him inside."

"Anything that bothers you is your issue. Do you remember that concept?"

I take a deep breath. "Yes." My head and shoulders slump down.

"Girls are easier to groom in our society. After boys reach a certain age, they are harder to groom. Therefore, a ten-year-old altar boy is a perfect target for those priests."

I nod.

"We might be done for today."

"How about priests? I think Father Rich was a groomer."

"Oh, no, who is Father Rich?"

"Do you remember when my dad crossed over in the seventh grade?"

"Crossed over?" Marvel chuckles at my wording. "Crossed over what? A bridge, a highway?"

I give Marvel a look showing him that I don't want to joke right now.

"I know what you mean. Just teasing, Cavarelli! Go on."

"But you remember, right?"

"Of course, I remember."

"Well, during that period, I felt so alone. I didn't know who to talk to. So, in the seventh grade, I confided in Father Rich, who was the pastor at Camp Newmann. Again, I remember really liking him and wanting to talk to him about my sadness. He seemed loving. He made me feel better, but at the same time, and what I never wanted to admit, I found him to be so sweet, a little flirty, but loving and all over me at times, like yesterday, what I definitely did to you."

Marvel smiles. "I like it, direct and honest about what you did."

"So, what happened?" Marvel sighs.

"I remember when he placed his hand on my knee, to console me. I blew it off all these years by saying, 'He probably just shouldn't be a priest. He probably needed to be married so he could have sex.' He was a very nice man. I just loved this man. He was spiritual. He married Don and me. He wasn't a good man, was he, Marvel?"

"Tell me more."

"Well, after knowing Father Rich in grade school, he was transferred to my high school and was named the school ministry director. So, in other words, he followed my class. He was very well-liked. I remember him being at all our games — and I was in three sports. Then, in my tenth-grade year, he was transferred to an all-boys high school. The reason why I am telling you this is because I found an article about him in one of my old scrapbooks. It stated that he would miss the good spirit at my high school and 'being spoiled by all the girls.'

"After being transferred to the all-boys school, he would periodically come back to attend our games. I didn't think anything of it, because I loved the man. I remember he was there when we won our soccer championship. What the hell?

"Marvel, did you hear about the allegations against the Catholic Church?"

"Yes. And?"

"I just spoke to my friend, Josie, yesterday, and she mentioned that Father Rich was one of those priests." I continue as my heart beat speeds up, "Our Father Rich was up on charges for sexual abuse! I don't want to believe it."

"Really?"

"She told me that during confessions, he would touch her thigh, too. She also said that when she was in the tenth grade, she and her friend were invited to sleep over at this house. Father Rich picked the girls up in his van. They slept in the bedroom next to Father Rich's. He came into the bedroom where they were sleeping and said, 'Now girls, don't feel uncomfortable. Sometimes what we do here is just wear our underwear and t-shirts. You can come on over to my room and we can hug and stuff.'"

"Really?"

"Oh, my God, Marvel!! I want to scream."

I stop talking, as I breathe with short, quick breaths. "I can't catch my breath," I inform Marvel.

"Breathe, Dottie."

I take a deep breath then continue. "Those girls didn't go to his bedroom that night, but how about all the other girls that were invited over there! Girls like me who couldn't say no and felt obligated! I am so angry!"

"I see that."

"He was sent away several times to one of those recovery places and then put back in circulation! He had finished up at one of those recovery places in 1977.

"He met me in 1978, when I was in the eighth grade. So, he was back in the system again. What the hell?"

"Yep. Sounds like that was their system; a system designed for the priests of the Catholic Church. I have this feeling that Father Rich was taught this system. You do know this didn't just start with Father Rich. This has been going on for years!"

"Why?"

"Why, what?"

"Why did he pick me? How did he know?" I put my head down, while reaching in my purse to hand Marvel a letter written to me from Father Rich. "I found this in my scrapbook the other day."

Marvel reads the letter out loud to me.

Dear Dorothy,
Congratulations on your achieving the Soccer Championship! I can always remember that the little "skinny" girl I knew as an eighth grader is now part of history. Wow! I am really excited about you and the team's successes. Now don't forget our pact about you coming down for a visit and giving us a lot of time for talking and laughing. You are only about twelve minutes away from me; so, if you don't show up I'll...

Marvel stops and looks up at me. "What does that mean?"

"I have no idea," I answer.

Marvel continues reading:

Dorothy, you are a great person.

"Oh, here it comes; the compliments. All the things that a girl like you, searches for — a girl who feels less than and not good enough, wants to hear."

I think the world of you and I am happy with all your accomplishments, so don't get down on yourself or put yourself down. I believe in you.
God Bless and Love,
Father Rich

"He's gross. What the hell, Marvel?" I add, "Jesus, why do they find me, or why do I find them?"

"You didn't visit him, right?"

"No, I didn't. I was too fucking busy with giving myself away to groomer Frank. Ugh." I reluctantly say, feeling the guilt and shame of the situation.

"Dottie, again, you must forgive yourself on all levels, even though consciously or unconsciously, for what you unwittingly participated in."

I look up at Marvel and nod. I then go inside the cellar doors to forgive myself.

"Remember, Dottie, forgiveness is the act of letting go of something. In this case, it is letting go of your judgments of yourself and your actions," Marvel says.

Marvel then guides me through his process for forgiving yourself.

Marvel waits until I am finished before he says, "Again, you and those girls were deceived by Father Rich, who used his spiritual title to deceive the young. Yes, he may have listened to you, and at that moment seem to be genuine. But at the same time, he was deceiving others and even himself. There are so many possibilities here. He could have been grooming you, meaning he was setting you up so that he may take advantage of you at a future time. He started with connecting to you through your heart with the hopes of creating a vulnerability which would then allow him the opportunity to take advantage of you. Or, he could have been honest at that very moment and still living his other life of deception. It's hard to say. This, unfortunately, is what some unhealthy people do to other fellow human beings."

I nod.

"You expected these people to be who they said they were, and when you found out that they were not, the feelings of being deceived, betrayed and disappointment came up for you. Basically, at that moment, you perceive it as your life was a lie and so were the people you trusted. What you didn't realize is that it came about because you were a naïve, innocent child. Very few people are truly honest with themselves, or the world.

"Often people are not truly honest because they don't realize that they are living a life of self-deception. And then there are some that consciously deceive others, either because they have hidden motives, or they secretly know that they are worthless and unlovable — just like you did what you did because of your perceived worthlessness, Dottie."

I nod.

"Remember it always goes back to you. How have you deceived the people around you? How have you deceived yourself?"

I listen.

"Ultimately it is always about how you deceived yourself. What I mean is that when you stop listening to your heart and you begin to look to other people to fulfill you or make you feel any certain way you have abandoned yourself. Then when you go about your life pretending you are Dottie, or whoever, you are deceiving yourself by denying that the truth lies within your own heart. What people don't realize is that the love everyone is seeking is within them. They are the source of their own love, And, they become so focused on other people to provide them with confirmation of love that they forget who they truly are. Because of this they always find disappointment in their life and in their relationships. It is not possible to find the love you seek in someone else or outside of you."

I nod.

"Relationships that are truly fulfilling occur when two individuals find the love within themselves and consciously choose to share it with each other. In this type of relationship there is never disappointment. That isn't to say that they don't have differing opinions. When two people come together in this way there is only love because each of them are love itself and they are choosing to share their own love and not look to the other person to complete or fulfill them. These stories about finding your other half for your true love are always focused on another person. These stories are so misleading and in a way, keep people controlled and malleable. The only true love is inside you and when you discover that you will never feel deceived or disappointed again!

"Now let me sum this up. There are two levels of deception and disappointment here. The first one comes from the human aspect of you that is seeking your fulfillment from other people. The second one comes from inside of you where you are not connected to your own essence, your own heart, your own love. You must work through the human aspect with all of its disappointments and sorrows and then do the second one by becoming connected to your own heart and your own love. Then and only then does the final healing come. You, and anyone who this has happened to, must remember three things. First, it wasn't your fault – the adults were supposed to be responsible. Second, you were a child – so don't blame yourself. Third, it can all be changed – not the events, but how you feel inside."

I take a deep breath.

Too many people accept what has happened as a permanent wound and at best cope. I know for a fact Dottie; you can change the way you feel and think about anything…and I mean anything. But only if you choose and find some way or someone that really knows how. They then can assist you in doing it for yourself. Never come at this from the point of view that someone else has the answers and can save you, No. You must view it as, 'I have the answer and someone or something will help me to remember.' Remember, Dottie, there is no place like home and home is inside of you!"

I nod.

"Now, are you full?"

"Maybe," I say and take another deep breath.

"Ya know," I say.

Marvel interrupts and says, "Guess not."

"For years I thought that my brother had to believe and understand me in order for me to heal, but that wasn't the case at all in my experience. I really thought that confronting him would be the answer and I would be normal after that. I believed what the experts said, that it would begin to make me feel better."

Marvel nods.

"So, two years after I got married, I confronted my brother by writing him a letter explaining how his behaviors and actions really messed me up in more ways than he could imagine. But this proved to be an additional trauma rather than a completion."

"Really why?" says Marvel, smiling. "I guess that you are ready to keep going."

"Yes. Weeks after I wrote the letter, my brother was at my mom's house. When I saw him, he acted like nothing happened. He attempted to converse with me, like he had not received my letter."

"Secrets, silence and denial. Avoidance was in full gear."

"Right!"

"I simply said to him, 'I am not talking to you until you address the letter.' At that point he threw up his arms and said, 'You're fucking crazy.'

"I had expected something like that, but it was still tough to hear. I was prepared for adversity and tried to stay calm and feel it out. He then stormed out of my mom's house. What I didn't know was that the worst was yet to come. For some reason, I felt that I could say this to him in front of whoever was there because they wouldn't know what I was talking about. I only said, 'I am not talking to you until you address the letter.' Well, that was not the case, in this situation.

"My sister, who was with him at the time, says, 'How dare you bring that up in front of me.' I thought, bring what up? How did she know what was in this letter? Her emotional attack cut right through me like a knife, bringing to the surface all the wrongness, fear, shame and guilt that I was already struggling with. At the time, I just wanted to die. I was just in shock. I froze. This was the hardest thing that I ever had to do and it took every bit of courage to work up the nerve to confront him and tell him how I felt.

"The idea of my sister commenting about something she knew nothing about infuriated me. She didn't know what he and I had to work out. She caused me more pain. I felt like I was back to the beginning. It was like she was saying do not under no circumstances bring up this secret. I should have told her to get the hell out of my space."

My anger is stirring. "What gave her the right to say this?!"

Wow, I am really angry right now.

"Okay, get angry. You don't have to do anything with it. Just accept that you have it. You can transform it. Now why are you so angry? You don't sound angry. You feel angry, but you just don't sound it."

"I am angry, damn it! How does that sound? How dare she discount and minimize my feelings and throw that anger at me involving something so important to me, and my growth. I hated her. I was so angry, and betrayed. I felt blindsided. Why would she get involved in my business? How dare her feel that she had the right to fucking suppress my growth? This had nothing to do with her, just something he and I would have to work out. She sat in judgment of me without knowing what either of us had to work through. Didn't she have anything better to do? This happened like eight years ago and I still feel pissed. Why can't I get over this, Marvel?"

"Maybe you don't understand it yet. What happened next?"
"After getting screamed at, I went over to my aunt's house, which was next door – thank God she wasn't home," I say.

"Why?"

"Because we Cavarelli's don't show our emotional breakdowns, and all my emotions spilled out when I arrived at my aunt's.

"I sat on my aunt's couch while my body violently shook. I literally shook for what seemed like an eternity. The shaking was uncontrollable. I thought this was not how it was supposed to play out. It was supposed to be a release; it was supposed to be a healing. I cried for what seemed like an hour.

"About an hour later, I walked outside to see if my sister's car was gone, which it was. To my surprise, my brother was in his car next to mine, waiting for me. He called from the window saying, 'Hey, I'm ready to talk.' I was shocked!"

Marvel's eyes widen, "Really?"

"We went for a ride and he told me that it wasn't him. So, I said to him, 'Maybe it was my dad.' He immediately said, 'No, it wasn't Dad.' In fact, he kept saying that it wasn't our dad; almost like he didn't want to taint the name of a person who was dead. I could feel the inside of him, saying, 'Dottie, I cannot admit this right now.' I almost felt bad for him. It was weird. I could feel his guilt and shame.

"Well, that was enough for me. I was okay because I saw the insides of him struggling with something that he wasn't able to handle right now."

"Well, you said it to him. You should be proud of yourself that you said it — for you!" Marvel encourages me. "It is a shame, that he couldn't say that it was him, for his sake. He might have been able to heal and possibly see the truth about himself."

"Instead he chose to live the life on drugs for a pretty long time. I hear now that he is clean though."

"Well, that is good," Marvel says.

"I was just glad that it was over," I admit.

"Days later, this hidden secret did come up between my mom and me. After I told her, she immediately told me that it happened to her as well. I was shocked. She did tell me her story. It was very different than mine. Nevertheless, when she heard what had happened again to her own daughter, she was devastated. I will never forget what she said, 'But I was so careful of making sure that it didn't happen to my children.' She felt so bad. There was nothing I could say to make her feel better. I saw and felt the guilt piling up all around her. On that very same weekend, my mom told me that my brother told her that sometimes we do stupid things that hurt other people and will never be forgiven."

"Interesting," Marvel responds.

"I know, right?" I tell him.

"He needed to forgive himself."

"I know."

"But that is not your problem; this is about you and your happiness and more importantly, your forgiveness. Right, Dottie?"

"Right!" I agree. "Well, after I confronted him, the weeks went on, I dropped more into my wrongness than ever. I could have spent the time working through the abuse stuff, but my sister interrupted that. I blamed her. I hated her for what she did. As you guys would say, and I understand now, I hated her behaviors. You are not your behaviors."

"Yep."

"I flew back to Kansas and I had to live with this hate. It was the worst feeling that I have ever felt because I loved my sister. She was ten years older than me. She used to change my diapers. She brought me everywhere. I felt her love. She was the purest love that I had experienced. She loved me and did not seem to want anything from me then. I felt loved by her. She modeled her love through what she showed me and how it felt. Today, I don't see that love in her. It's gone. It feels like she now wants something or me to be some way for her. I remember when her eyes sparkled and she felt light. What happened to her? What changed her? Where did the love go?"

"There are too many potentials and reasons."

"I tried to forget about it and became busy and numb. I went back to living a shut-down, and what you called yesterday the 'typical polarized' life."

"Until you took those meds what, a year and a half ago? And then woke up and divorced your husband," Marvel adds.
"Yes," I smile knowing that was meant to be sarcastic.

Marvel smiles.

205

"And then I found you behind the curtain at the gym."

"Yes, you did."

I smile at Marvel.

"Okay, is there anything else?"

"Yes. I can see the abused-like feeling around certain people. I shake when I feel a sexual abuser or when someone has been sexually abused. Will this ever go away?"

"Well..." Marvel says.

I interrupt. "They have it in their eyes and around them. I can feel it. That is how I can tell. What is that? It's not fun, and will this ever go away? Sorry, I interrupted you."

Marvel jumps in. "It may never go away. First, it is your judgment of what you see that is distressing you. Next and most importantly, is the answer to what it is. Because you were abused, your psychic senses may have been activated. You are attuned to the energy of that experience and to most energies or feelings that are related to that type of trauma."

I nod.

"Let me give you a simple explanation of energy. Energy is a frequency — sort of like a radio station frequency. Whatever station you dial on the radio it picks up the frequency, or energy, of the signal that the radio station is sending. This then allows you to hear it, and even feel the vibrations. This is what energy is in the everyday world. This is explained in the science of physics.

"Now back to you. Once you had that experience of being abused you became attuned to the energy of the experience and energy of people who have had a similar experience. Understand that as human beings we experience energy through feeling and we may often say we feel or see something that isn't there, that's because we are feeling the frequency and it is not visible. So now that you have had that experience you see or feel that frequency wherever it is or whenever you are attuned to it. Like I said it is not fun because you judge it and it brings up the memory or feelings of your own trauma when you see or feel it. "I feel these things all the time. The difference between you and me is that I don't judge them. I simply look at them and decide whether I want to feel them or not. As long as I make no judgments on them, they do not distress me, and they are like watching a movie that I am not emotionally involved in. The only

206

reason they do not affect me today is because I have worked on my personal issues One day, hopefully, if you resolve your own issues, you will be free to see these things without judgment. When you reach that point, you will find that your new 'sight' is a gift and can help you and others if you choose to apply it in that way. This ability to see or feel these things is a gift from your soul that allows you, and actually pushes you, to become free of your painful memories."

I nod.

"Anything else?"

"You said something yesterday about giving yourself away."

"Yes."

"I think that I did that a lot over the years. There were times when I started to stand out in girls' basketball. I didn't want anyone to feel less than the way I felt in the classroom — incompetent or not good enough. I would slow down and try to help them — purposely not playing to my potential."

"Well, that was stupid," he comments and then chuckles.

"Yeah, I see that now."

"I didn't want them to feel bad. Would this be that thing you said about disappointing others yesterday — about other people's disappointment, bringing up for me my own disappointment?"

"Yes!"

"I was always more concerned about other people's feelings than my own. I always seemed to put other people first. I always wondered why I did that."

"Yes…you did everything in your power not to see your own disappointment."

"Ever since I can remember, it seems to be the only way to survive."

"Yes. That's what happens when you are in a belief system. You are doing things and behaving ways that you are unaware of and assume are normal, never realizing that this is simply a belief system with patterned behaviors. In your case, the belief that life is disappointing is a core belief system; therefore, you would never be able to be completely happy with life nor would you be able to accept compliments, notoriety or acknowledgment without resisting

207

them. Because in the pattern when you resist these things you support the belief that life is disappointing and in that typically you never get what you really want and have to settle for something less."

"I was actually thinking that my plan worked; staying even or on the same level with my peers so no one would feel bad. I fit in and no one could see me."

"Fitting in? Why would you want to do that?"

I smile at Marvel, knowing that this is something he could never do. It was just not in his make-up.

"Okay, there is one more thing before I go. Very unrelated."

"Oh, how unusual for you — bringing up an unrelated topic."

"Shut up," I say, smiling.

"My daughter, Megan, is hearing voices. She told me a couple weeks ago. She has seen colors before, but voices? A normal parent would probably take her to a psychologist. But I know that they would just put her on medication, right?"

"You mean a psychiatrist. A psychiatrist would provide the drugs," Marvel corrects me.

"Well, a psychiatrist. Whatever," I answer.

"What is she hearing?" Marvel says.

"She says she hears someone clearly saying her name over and over. And it won't stop."

"Well, sometimes that happens to the young because they are still very sensitive and can feel and remember the unseen; most adults don't believe in." Marvel adds, "Sometimes our spirit-guides don't understand that they can scare us when they talk to us because we don't remember who we are.

"Alright, girl. You have been through a lot today," Marvel states. "Go relax and I will see you tomorrow."

"Thank you," I say with such gratitude. "Seriously, that was just, wow. I don't know what that was, but it was great."

"Life changing?"

"Yes, life changing," I say. "Thank you so very much."

"You are so very welcome, my dear. Now go get some rest!"

Marvel stands up walks over to the computer and waits for me to gather myself.

"You know, I always feel like I should be speaking to groups, but I am so scared to speak in public, which makes sense now. My body shakes sometimes when I get up and speak in front of people. Maybe you can go with me when I am ready."

"Right, back in your mind, again huh?" Marvel laughs. "Sure, Dottie, but there is a lot to do first. It might be months."

"I know. I am willing to put in the time. You're gonna help me, right? You know how to do this, right?"

"Yes, I know how to do this," Marvel responds with a little chuckle. "But you will have to apply the things I teach you every week. There will be layers upon layers."

"I am ready for this, Marvel. If you can show me, I will trust you and be patient. Thank you so much for yesterday too. I really appreciate it. Words cannot express how much... I don't know... I just know that was big."

"You're welcome," Marvel says.

I look at Marvel as he stands there patiently.

"What Dottie?" he asks.

Don't say it.

"By the way..." I say.

I am saying it.

"I really..." I say, hesitating, "I really think that I like you."

"What? Well, I know that you like me."

"No, I mean that I like you in a different way, more than just a counselor or whatever you are. Marvel..."

209

Don't say it.

"I believe that I am in love with you."

"No, Dottie. You are not in love with me. You have these feelings all mixed up, because I am helping you. It's called transference. This is not what we are doing here. It's not what I do."

Marvel taps me lightly on my shoulder and leans back to grab his chocolate bar.

"Transference? What's that?" I inquire.

How embarrassing.

"Transference is when someone transfers their feelings that they have towards someone else onto another person — instead of the original person. In your case, right now, it's called love transference. This is very common in this business. It goes like this. You start to have strong feelings about the person that is helping you." Marvel continues, "He reminds you of someone from your past — maybe your father or brother — and then you transfer the feelings that you had towards a dad. You want him to meet the needs you had towards Dad. So, it's really simple. I am not your dad, or whoever you are needing or chasing." Marvel smiles and bites his chocolate. "Get it?"

"Really?" I say still, feeling a little weird. "So I can trust you? I can still figure all this out with you because I want this pain to end, Marvel!" I take a deep breath.

"I know. And yes, you can trust me."

"I can still talk about my feelings and thoughts without getting…ya know," I say.

So, embarrassing.

"Yes, you can, without getting…you know," Marvel repeats and smiles. "Remember: denial, silence and secrets are some of your patterns. You don't have to deny anything; you don't have to be silent anymore. Think of this as a space to safely work through these feelings."

Marvel says clearly, and without hesitation, "Do you hear me, Dottie? You can trust me that I will not in any way take advantage of you. I believe that you had enough of that in this lifetime, don't ya think?"

"True. So, this is a natural thing, right?" I question. "So this happens all the time… people falling in love with their counselors."

"Not all the time, but it is quite common. You have a lot to learn about self-love."

I am still a little embarrassed. Ugh.

"Yep," he says, with such ease and assurance, yet very lovingly, like a parent treats a child, gently and nurturing.

I actually start to feel a little more relaxed about it. I remove it from my thoughts for the moment; then sit there with Marvel quietly.

"Thank you," I say quietly.

"You are welcome," Marvel answers mirroring back the quiet disposition I am currently in.

"I guess I have some work to do. Nothing is going to stop me now." I look at Marvel wanting some reassurance again.

I am not in love with him, thank God!

Marvel, still standing at the computer, gently glides into his chair as he always does when the session is coming to the end.

"One more thing. Could I bring Megan with me tomorrow?"

"Who's Megan?" Marvel turns in his chair.

"Remember, Megan my daughter? Sees colors, hears voices."

"Oh yeah, yeah, sure."

"See you tomorrow?"

"Yep!" Marvel turns around to face his computer.

"Hey, Marvel," I say.

"Yessss, my dear," Marvel turns around again in his chair.

"It won't be weird for us now, right?"

211

"Why would it be weird?" Marvel asks.

"Well, because I said that," I respond.

"Said what?"

"Ya know, that transference thing."

"You know," Marvel said sarcastically. "No, it won't."

"Thank God, because I think that you are the only one that can help me through this crap. Thanks for being in my life right now."

"Yep." Marvel smiles. "See you and your daughter tomorrow."

Marvel turns back towards his computer and I exit through the door.

DREAM:

"Hello, Dottie! Glenda here!

"Just so you know, that struggling through life only occurs because of your mind. Your mind gets in the way, Dottie!"

I know.

"It interferes with the way things are, and the natural flow of life. Your mind makes judgments and opinions and forms attitudes and behaviors based upon judgments and personal needs or preferences."

I know.

"As a human, you have grown up with many misconceptions about what should be, could be, or might be. Because of this, it has created many struggles in your life that are not necessary. They have become so common that you believe it is normal and that's the way it should be. So many people have done the same things and have the same opinions that this has become an accepted way of life. I would like to suggest that this is not at all necessary and it is only due to your old programming and false beliefs about the way life should be.

"Listen to your heart! It's time to spend more time in your heart and less in your mind."

I know.

I smile at Glenda.

CHAPTER 16

The Munchkins

Christopher, Megan, Kacey, and I sit on the couch in Marvel's office waiting for him to arrive. As I sit there, I take note of Megan's and Kacey's clothes. Both are dressed like me, yet have a slightly different look and style.

Marvel enters the office with the usual — his omelet in one hand and chocolate bar in the other. I introduce the kids, and then send Chris and Kacey outside.

"Okay, Miss Megan," Marvel gently touches Megan's hand as we all sit in Marvel's office and I cautiously watch impatiently. "So tell me about these voices of yours."

Megan looks at me for some reassurance. "You can tell him, Megan."

"They keep saying, 'Megan, Megan, Megan.' And sometimes I can't hear my teacher because they are so loud. I get out of my desk and go to the back of the room sometimes — pretending to get my pencil or snack. I am hoping that the voices go away by the time I come back to my desk. And they get so mad at me because I don't get my work done. They say that I am wasting time by getting out of my seat. They say that I am slow at everything. Slow when I get my pencils in my book bag, or slow when I go back to get my lunch," Megan says.

"Who gets mad at you and says you are slow?" Marvel asks.

"My teachers," Megan answers.

"So the voices are only saying Megan, Megan, Megan?"

Megan nods.

"Okay, and the teachers are the ones telling you that you are wasting time and being slow."

"Yes."

Marvel looks up at me and smiles.

She wasn't clear. She sounds like me.

I get up and glance through the window to make sure Christopher is watching Kacey. I brought them along so they could all be together while I did my session. As I watch them, I can hear Megan talking to Marvel about her friends at school. They talk about everything but the voices. I gaze over at them, giving Megan some space with him. I start to space out — then force myself back to their conversation.

Marvel says, "Okay, Megan. I don't think they are going to bother you anymore. It was great to meet you."

Megan giggles, places her hand on Marvel's shoulder and says, "Thank you, Michael, you rock!"

"Wait, wait, missy, what just happened? Are you okay, Megan? Everything is good?"

"Yeah, Mom, they are not gonna bother me anymore. Michael told me that they didn't realize that they were scaring me. They aren't gonna do it anymore. They didn't know that they were scaring a little girl! Right, Michael?" Megan looks back at Marvel and smiles.

"Oh, really. Just like that?" I say, looking at Marvel.

Marvel is smiling at Megan, and then turns his focus to me. "Yep, just like that. They just didn't know, did they, Megan?"

"Yup," Megan agrees. "Bye, Mom."

"Where ya going?" I ask.

"I told her to go get my eleven-year-old upstairs so he can take all the kids on the trampoline," Marvel answers. "It will give us a chance to talk, Dottie."

"Is that okay, Mom?" Megan informs.

"Sure," I respond.

"Thanks, Michael!" Megan says as she passes me and opens the door and exits.

Marvel turns to Megan again and says, "Now go have fun on that trampoline. Remind my son, Jay, not to jump too high. He tends to get a little crazy. We don't want your little sister to become a skyrocket and get lost in our woods."

"A skyrocket?" Megan asks.

"A skyrocket is a firework that goes into the air and explodes into many sparks of colors," Marvel informs.

"Like the colors that I always see around people?" Megan asks.

Marvel chuckles, "Yeah, kind of."

Megan exits out the door to go find Jay.

"She's got you on a first name basis now, ay."

"I guess so," Marvel smiles.

"Oh boy, Marvel. What the hell happened?" I inquire.

"Just what she said. They didn't realize that they were scaring her. They aren't going to bother her anymore," Marvel answers. "I talked to them."

"Oh really? You talked to them?! And?" I ask.

Silence.

"Is that all you going to give me?"

"What do you want me to tell you?" Marvel laughs. "Do you really want to know the details?"

I sigh and say, "Aaaa…yeah."

Marvel gives me one of his typical looks.

"You really are not gonna tell me how you were able to talk to them, and what you said?"

"Wouldn't you rather work on you today; something more productive?"

I nod, rolling my eyes. "Okay."

"Okay, so we are all right?" Marvel says, "So what will it be for today, Dottie?"

I hesitate and stare at Marvel for a bit, and then begin talking. "You know, I told those teachers to back off of Megan and not to stifle her. I told them she was having a difficult time."

"Good for you!"

Silence again.

"Hey, Marvel. Did I tell you about the time in high school, I took a classmate to get an abortion? We cut school and went during the school day. The pain that she had to endure was just another highlight of my high school years. She asked me and I couldn't say no. I felt the pain that she was going through, not to mention the fear."

"Why did you tell me that story?"

"Why did she ask me?" I inquire. "I barely knew her. We talked in class a couple of times. One day she broke down crying; telling me she was pregnant, and asking me if I could take her.

"I just know that watching her return to school that day was so painful. It was just another secret. I don't blame her. What were her choices, to be shamed and humiliated to have a child when she was a child herself? To be ridiculed by the adults and deal with the wrongness that is implied by the Catholic Church? I believe she did the right thing for her. As I recall, I don't believe she told a soul. Can you imagine how that feels — to be in that position? To be the young girl making that choice? I helped her that day with as much truth and integrity as I could muster."

Marvel is still.

"I never found out why she asked me and it was just silenced. I could feel her pain; emotionally and physically."

"So you feel people," Marvel asks.

"Yes," I say. "Pretty much; it kind of sucks to feel pain. I would like to feel love. Love inside, love for me again, as you would say."

"Dottie, sometimes, the pain and suffering that you feel only magnifies and your own inner pain — all that pain you had buried all those years ago. Make sense?"

"Yep."

"You will still feel pain until you are detached from it," Marvel said. "What else? Anything else?"

217

"Yes, I have another question. Can you help explain this?" Dottie says.

"I can try," Marvel says. "Give it a whirl, Miss Tornado Girl!"

"I will ignore that comment," I smile.

"When I was living in Kansas, I had a friend named Susan. She had a young daughter that developed a brain tumor. Something very strange happened to me while I was in the hospital. We were waiting to hear the test results for her daughter. While in the waiting room, there was a girl about eleven years old playing cards. She clearly was a cancer patient — a bald head and beautiful smile. She looked up periodically at me. I saw the light. Ya, know, like the light around Mary."

"Mary?" he asks.

"The Blessed Mother Mary," I answer.

"Oh, yes," Marvel remembers.

"I continued talking to my friend in the waiting room. I looked back and forth at the cancer patient. I felt the need to go over to this little girl. It was like my insides were being pulled over to her, as my body stayed still. 'Go over, Dottie.' 'No,' I answered back. Seriously, it was the strangest feeling ever. I didn't listen to myself and I stayed talking to Susan. Susan even said, 'What's wrong with you? Why are you acting weird?' I told her nothing and I ignored this feeling.

"Then the next day, I went back to the hospital to visit Susan's daughter. I was told to go to a certain room. I walked down the hall and entered the assigned room. To my surprise, the glowing eleven year old that was in the waiting room the day before, was in the room lying on bed staring back at me. She said hi and I said hi back. We stared at each other until a nurse came in. The nurse asked me if I was looking for the girl that was here yesterday. I told her yes, and she informed me that Susan's daughter had been reassigned to a different room. I said goodbye to this girl in the bed, but I didn't want to leave her. Weird."

"I guess you were supposed to connect with her," Marvel says.

"Why?" I ask.

"Does it matter?" Marvel responds. "That brain just doesn't want to let go, does it?"

"Well, I am not finished."

"Of course, you're not," Marvel chuckles.

"Well, then I went to Susan's daughter's new room. Susan and her mother were there. They said that they had to go talk to the doctor and they would be right back. They asked if I could stay there with her daughter. She was sleeping. I stayed. I looked at her and felt for her. She was so young. This little girl had already been through so much. I placed my hand on her head where the tumor was."

Marvel's eyes start to radiate, light up. Light brown eyes.

"Well, it wasn't long before I had to run to the bathroom to throw up. On the way to the bathroom, I had a severe pain in my head. What was that?" I inquire. "This really affected me, Marvel."

"The only thing that I can make of that is that you resonated with the little girl's brain tumor and also, why she developed it." Marvel says and continues. "That tumor felt like abandonment from her adopted parents."

"How did you know she was adopted?" I say.

"Wild guess, I don't know," Marvel says. "Anyway, you may have resonated with the abandonment."

"I made up other stories."

"Of, course you did," Marvel responds following a chuckle.

"I thought that I transferred the tumor to me. It kind of scared the crap out of me," I say. "I had the pain on the side of the head where her tumor was. I got extremely dizzy and then threw up in the bathroom, which were in fact, her symptoms."

"You aren't that powerful, Dottie," Marvel says. "You wouldn't have gotten her brain tumor."

"I am just saying," I laugh out loud. "I just didn't know what to think."

"That's the problem with people who know how to transform energy; they create stories about what they feel or see," Marvel says.

"I was what?"

"Your intention was to help, maybe heal, maybe pray for Susan's daughter. Was it not?"

"Yes."

"Well, there ya have it."

"There I have what?"

Marvel holds up his palm in front of his mouth where I know that he is smiling.

I see you smiling, Marvel.

"Sometimes, when people are hurt, I can see things inside of them. I can sense something around it.

"Well, you could develop that more, but that's for another day. Let's not get off topic. Let's talk about you and your own pain, Dottie."

"Okay," I say, "About this abandonment thing. I wasn't adopted or abandoned."

"You weren't adopted but were you abandoned?" Marvel says.

"No," I answer. "Who abandoned me?"

"Who do you think abandoned you as a child, not intentional, well, maybe intentionally via spirit, but not consciously? Who left you?"

My dad. He left.

"Think, seventh grade, Dottie. What happened in the seventh grade?" Marvel reveals.

Dad left me. The words wouldn't come out.

"Your dad left you…didn't he?"

Silence.

"Dottie, did he not in fact leave this earth, yes? You have to remember to always look at your life from your perspective. How you perceived things. How you were affected. Again, people don't do things to you, they do things for themselves. But when things are done to you, you still may be affected by them. People are not their behaviors. If you understand this from all levels, then you will not judge people's actions towards you."

"Yes, he did," I confirm. "I was so mad at him when he was here. I used to say that I hated him. And then he left. I felt so bad and so guilty for hating him. I drove him away. I was always a pain in his ass."

"There's some beliefs," Marvel says. "How's that feel in your body?"

"Shitty!"

"I was really mad at him for leaving and I was mad at him because he was mean!"

"Do you hear yourself? They are a child's words that you had placed in there. This is good, Dottie. Listen, it's okay that you felt that way. You don't have to deny these feelings. It was what it was. Now you must realize that it wasn't your fault that he died. Again, you were not that powerful," Marvel smiles.

I put my head down.

"He left for his own reasons. And he is saying that he didn't realize how sensitive his family here on earth was until he left. He is learning about that now before he comes back down again. He is so very sorry that you had to go through all this pain. Most of all, he is sorry that he made you feel unsure of yourself."

I listen to the words coming out of Marvel's mouth with my head down as the tears fell. I thought maybe that I felt my dad right next to me, but I wasn't sure. "Thank you, Marvel," I utter. "Was that YOU talking or my dad talking."

"A little bit of both."

I look up at Marvel. Then I look back down.

We finish the appointment; leave the building and continue to talk. We are interrupted by Kacey, who is crying next to the trampoline. The others didn't even notice the crying, because their focus was on the turkeys and their youngsters waddling down by the pond. I notice Jay walking next to the turkeys, directing Megan and Chris to walk quietly not to disrupt the animals' flow.

Marvel quickly walks over to where Kacey is. I follow behind.
"What seems to be the problem, Kacey?" Marvel asks.

"I can't move this grrr… trampoline over… ugh… here," Kacey grunted. "Ugh…grrr…I want it in the sun."

"Kacey, you're six. You can't move that trampoline!" I answer.

"Why not?!" Kacey continues to grunt.

I look at Marvel and whisper under my breath, "She tries to move her bedroom furniture sometimes. She actually moved some of it which I don't even know how she did it. She's constantly trying to do stuff like this."

Marvel holds up his pointer finger to me and places it to his lips.

He places his hands on Kacey's shoulder and says, "Kacey, you can't do the same things that you did before you got to earth."

"Really?" Kacey stops pushing the trampoline and looks up at him.

"Yes, really," Marvel said.

They look at each other for a second and then Kacey says, "Okay."

Kacey then runs over to join her brother and sister to watch the turkeys down by the pond.

"What just happened there?" I say.

"We all could probably move things much easier before we got here, I would imagine." Marvel continues, "I don't think that she has been on this earth many times. Again, do you really want an explanation? Maybe something we can discuss and learn later."

Marvel smiles, his brown eyes sparkling in the sunlight.

I call for the kids down by the pond. As they approach the two of us, Marvel holds out his arm for Jay, "Hey, buddy, did you have fun?"

"Yeah, that was fun," Jay said. "Did you notice, there is one less poult?"

"I didn't," Marvel answers.

"Poult?" Chris asks.

"A baby turkey," Jay answers.

222

"These turkeys are awesome," Marvel says making a connection with my son, Chris.

"I know, right? Your place rocks!" Chris says.

"Call me Michael," Marvel says.

I give Marvel another look.

"What?" Marvel looks at me. "Chris and I go way back…multiple lifetimes, he and I."

"You crack me up," I say, smiling.

"Later, Michael," Chris says.

"Thanks," Megan joins in.

"Don't move that trampoline without me," Kacey shouts and high fives Marvel.

"Let's go, guys," I tell them.

CHAPTER 17

Sleeping With The Poppies

It's 8pm. The kids are back with their dad, and I wait to be picked up by my friends.

It's time to take a break.

Katrina beeps the horn several times. She was at the curb in front of my house. She keeps beeping until I show my face at the door. I wave to them and laugh at their persistence. I then turn around and lock the door.

"Let's go, Cavarelli! We're thirsty!" Katrina yells from the driver's seat as she waves her university beer cup in the air.

"Yeah, yeah, I hear ya," I answer.

"So, did the rest of the neighborhood, Katrina." Josie unbuckles her seatbelt so that she can lean around Katrina as she yells to me from the passenger's seat.

Katrina leans her head away from Josie, placing her hand to her ear attempting to block Josie's voice. "Josie, not so loud," she shouts.

I slide into the backseat, right into the girls' energetic bubble, *as the gang would say.*

As Katrina puts the car in drive, I feel myself easily blending with them; completing the unit of three that we do so well together. Bossy Katrina, timid Josie and easy-going Dottie. This unit was developed a very long time ago.

"So, what have you been up to, girl?" Josie says turning around in her seat. "You look different since the last time we saw you."

"What was that... like... seven years ago?" Katrina asks as she steps on the gas.

"I think it was about eight years ago," Josie corrects her.

"Still have to correct me, ay?" Katrina says laughing while whipping around the corner.

"I'm just saying...we took that trip out to Kansas in the winter of 2001 and we...."

"Oh, put a sock in it, already, Josie," Katrina sneers, "We don't need details, do we Dottie?"

"I'm just saying," Josie laughs and says. "Dottie, she's still the same old Katrina, nice and bossy."

"I see that," I agree.

"Anyway, what have you been up to — besides divorcing your hubby? Which by the way," Katrina says leaning back to touch me as Josie grabs the steering wheel, "I can't believe that you are no longer with him. He was so cool. What the hell happened?"

"Ya got three hours, Katrina?" I tell her, "It's a long story."

"Oh yeah, we got all night, girl," Katrina answers attempting to do a high five with me.

"Okay, so where do you wanna go?" Josie asks.

"Some place close," I say.

"How about The Pub? They have a pool table," Katrina suggests.

Josie adds, "I haven't been to the old neighborhood in forever."

I have... I was just there... and it changed my whole life.

I look at the girls to see if they notice the expression on my face; the happiness that I feel about understanding my life and getting closer to that love.

"Yay, that works. So we can walk to the Emerald Diner afterwards," Katrina says loudly and smiles.

Has she always spoken this loud?

"Okay, sounds good," I reply noticing that my voice volume is not matching hers. I stare out the window ready to move to my thoughts again.

"Why ya so quiet, Dottie?" Katrina asks.

"I don't know," I answer. "Just going through a lot lately."

"Are you okay?" Josie says with concern.

"Like what?" Katrina shouts again.

I shrug my shoulders.

"You are even talking so damn quiet. What's up, Dottie?" Katrina says.

"It's all good, guys." I reassure her increasing my voice volume slightly.

"Josie, I did want to ask you something, though. Did you ever go with Father Rich after that one time?"

"Why?"

"Just wondering."

"Oh, are you talking about that pervert, Father Rich? What an asshole." Katrina says. "That fuck-head messed with my little ten-year-old brother when I was in high school, while the rest of my family was busy mourning my sister's death! He lives over at a treatment center in Delaware. I'd like to go hunt him down and give him a piece of my mind."

My heart beat speeds up. Wow, I feel the charge inside of me. Is that Katrina's charge or mine? I can't tell.

"I always knew something was weird about that guy. Everyone thought he was so cute. NOT!" Katrina adds.

Josie finally speaks, "No, Dottie. I never went back there, but I believe my friend did."

Silence.

Katrina drives through the back streets until she gets to the old neighborhood. As we drive through town, I notice that everything appears different. Lately, I have been in my own little world. *Well, the Marvel, Leo, Tim, and Brian world.*

More silence.

But now my world has changed. The level of impact that this new information has on me seems unexplainable. I feel clearer than ever before.
These two girls were so much a part of my past. It *seems like yesterday that I was in the 'Katrina and Josie' world.*

I ask myself, why am I still friends with them? Was the trauma from high school the only thing that bound us together? What if that didn't happen? Would we have remained friends? I wasn't even part of this original cool group. I was the jock that they took in for their amusement. "The jock that parties. Ha! You crack me up Cavarelli!" was what Heidi would always say.

She is no longer on this earth, although I feel her sometimes, or I feel a hologram of her memories, *as Brian would say*. She was an amazing singer and guitar player. Every weekend, the cool group would head out to Taylor Park to drink, smoke and play music. It was only a few times that I was invited, before it happened. But those few times changed my life. Listening to the sounds of Neil Young, brought music back to my life, it invigorated me and made me feel alive again.

Being stoned and falling in love with that music — that music that I heard so many times from my older sister's room — the music about love and peace. I remember the music allowed the cells in my body to dance with joy, who knows, it may have been the beers and pot?

Katrina and Josie don't sing or play music anymore. I look up at Katrina and then Josie, the two that were spared. Katrina was in the car originally, but was dropped off, to run away with her boyfriend, before the tragic accident occurred.

Josie was sick that day, so she decided not to go. I wasn't asked to go that day. It must have been fate. Being in a head-on collision killing everyone in the car was my saving grace for being new to the group, and for being not invited. That day for the first time in my life I was glad to be forgotten.

Katrina just wasn't the same after that. Her sister and her best friend, Heidi, died on the same day. When I heard about the crash, I called Katrina's house immediately. I will never forget her dad's words. "Who is this? I need to know who was in the car. My two daughters... oh my god... where are they? The car went up in flames. I can't wait any longer. We are waiting. We have to identify them by their teeth. Do you know who was in the car? Tell me who was in the car?" I couldn't give him any answers. I didn't know. I felt his pain, more like terror. His questions struck a dagger of agony through my heart. I felt helpless.

The three of us have shared so much in such a short time. I had always felt that we were permanently connected after that day. Although, I feel so different these days. Those two girls now feel so far away from me. They are in the same car at this very moment. I love them. They will always be a part of me.

I stay staring at Katrina and Josie. I wondered why them. Why were they spared? What purpose did the universe have for them that they are still here?

I gaze out the window, wanting to push down these feelings of loss and forget. But I can't. The feelings of indebtedness and obligation to Katrina and Josie were strong.

After the accident, I could never listen to Neil Young without seeing Heidi and the gang playing at the park. It was both happy and sad at the same time, just like much of my life. Wow, a theme that runs through my life. Everything is both happy and sad. So much pain and so much love.

We pass Leo's café. I move my head closer to the window to see if any of them are in there. If they are, it is too packed to notice. I smile at the fact that the café is succeeding and Leo is now living his dream. Good for him!

Suddenly, I realize that I don't have a seatbelt on when I lightly bang my head on the window as a result of Katrina's driving skills. Josie notices and says, "Whoa, Katrina, slow down on the turns. Dottie just hit her head on the window."

Josie doesn't miss anything; her surroundings, so controlled.

"Oops, sorry about that, girl," Katrina said. "Well, maybe that will knock some sense into you. Ha!"

"Sorry" instead of "my apologies" or "I apologize" does sound so different now. Just one of the perspectives that the boys had introduced; the energy behind the words of sorry, feeling more *obligatory* vs. my apologies. Wow, what a difference. I want to tell her, but would she understand? Would she even care? My guess is no, she wouldn't.

It's none of your business anyway, Dottie, the boys would say. Just focus on you. It's all about you and your experience.

Katrina pulls into The Pub parking lot and turns off the ignition. "All right, who's ready? I am," she says as she opens the door.

We get out of the car and Katrina and Josie walk towards the building. I stop to notice the building that I have seen a million times before.

Josie turns around in her seat. "What's up, Dottie?"

"Nothing. I'm just noticing this building seems older than I remember, that's all," I say, staring out the window. "I wonder how old it is?"

"Why do you care?" Katrina asks with an attitude.

"Just wondering," I say.

It looks and feels so dark and dingy, almost heavy, even though it looks like it had a fresh coat of paint on it. Funny how the paint doesn't disguise how it feels. I guess it must be the same with clothes and people. I look down at my clothes, and then at the girls' clothes.

I have a whole new perspective on life and how things look and feel. It is like someone just turned the light on in a room and now, even if the light goes off and no matter how dark it gets, I will still know the light that shines in the room.

"I believe that they just painted this place," Josie says with a smile.

Katrina ignores both of us and heads for the building with Josie right behind her, keeping one eye on me and one on Katrina. I slowly catch up to them.

Katrina swings the door open enough for Josie and me to get in, although I move slowly to notice the details of the place while the two girls make their way to the bar area. Katrina orders three beers and two shots, one for her and one for me, knowing that Josie will refuse a shot and drink light and volunteer to drive. I am looking up, checking out the ceiling and beams that are quite clean. Yet the place still feels dirty, but didn't look dirty.

Suddenly, I feel Katrina's hand on my elbow pulling it towards the bar. "Get over here, girl! What is your deal? Have a drink with me."

"I'm coming, girl," I answer switching my focus to the girls.
I give into being unaware and allow my consciousness to fade away.

I feel myself going. Going, going, now gone... gone to sleep with the girls.

We drink our beers and shots at the bar; play pool; talk about old times and, of course, make fun of each other. I fall right into their world and really start to enjoy the break from being conscious and aware of everything around me. By the time we are ready to head for the diner, Katrina has had three additional shots. I had my one beer and refused the second shot, and Josie has had only her three quarters of a beer. Josie grabs the keys from Katrina and volunteers to drive home after we finish at the diner.

We make our way across the street to the diner at about 11:30. Katrina stops the cars, waving her arms around pretending to direct traffic for her friends to get to the other side. Josie and I laugh while we cross the street and turn around waiting for Katrina.

"All right, Katrina, that's enough, get out of the street," Josie yells and then finally lets out a sigh of relieve when Katrina is safely across the street.

"Still taking care of the girls, ay, Josie?" I ask, then putting my hand over my mouth, thinking — that would stop the words from being heard.

No filters when there is alcohol in the system.

Josie looks at me, and smiles, after my comment, and Katrina is oblivious to any words that are being said. I comment that I am really tired and probably can't stay too long. Katrina laughs at me and calls me a wimpy old lady.

Katrina finds a seat in the back of the diner and Josie follows her. I head for the bathroom, walk pass the table towards the back and then turn around to say, "Guys, I gotta go to..." But suddenly, someone else's body abruptly stops me from moving. I look up and there he is again.

Really?

"What a surprise," I say with sarcasm. "Bumping into you again, what's up with that?"

"I don't know, what's up with that," Marvel jokes. "Maybe you should look where you are walking."

"Maybe you should warn me where you're walking," I say laughing.

"Being aware has its benefits, of which I can see you are not practicing at this moment."

"Ha...real funny," I say. "What are you doing here?"

"Getting take-out," he answers. "And you?"

"Hanging out with friends. Oh, but guess what, Marvel?" I say, touching his arm. "You are not going to believe what my daughter did when she got home."

"What's that?" Marvel laughs at the subject change.

230

"When we got home, she looks in the bathroom mirror, no lie, and tells me to come look. 'Look at what?' I say. 'That,' she says pointing to the mirror. I then say, 'What?' She repeats, 'That.' I then say, 'Yeah, that's you, honey!' She then says, 'I know, that's me, Mom. But look!' It was like she saw herself for the first time."

"She probably did," Marvel says.

"Saw herself for the first time?!"

"Yes. Dottie, there was a lot of crap around that girl, not to mention that her consciousness was not even in her body." Marvel adds, "Anyway, so that's pretty cool. Sounds like she just landed."

"Landed?" I ask.

"Another time…Dottie, the bathrooms are calling us." Marvel points to the bathroom as he motions for me to lead the way.

I lead the way towards the bathroom, continuing to talk. "Her eyes look clearer, ya know," I say as I turn my head slightly back to keep talking.

"So unlike your eyes right now."

I freeze for a sec and then continue to talk, noticing that Marvel's directness doesn't feel as intense with the alcohol running through my system.

"But seriously, I never noticed that my daughter's eyes weren't clear."

I stop at the bathroom, facing Marvel square on, standing between the two doors, reading male and female. "Weird, right?" I put my head down. "Gosh, I love her."

Marvel smiles at my comment and then gives me a smirk.

"What?" I ask.

"Well, I told you to take a break. I didn't mean take a break from consciousness."

"You're funny. Just so you know, I usually don't go out like this. I used to. But this is a reunion of some sort."

Marvel chuckles and discreetly glances down at my clothes.

"What?" I ask.

"Nothing."

"No, really, what?" I ask, following his eyes down to my clothes. "My clothes?"

"Yes. Did you look at yourself in the mirror before you left your house," Marvel says, raising his eyebrows.

"I was out with friends, Marvel. Gotta blend in a little, ya know?" I chuckle. "What? Am I showing too much?"

"Dottie, you show too much at our sessions so I am used to it by now."

"No, I don't!"

"Yes, you do," Marvel jokes. "Are we going to do this again? Back and forth. Husband, ex-husband, husband, ex-husband."

I roll my eyes and smile. "Ex-husband. Just kidding."

I look down at my clothes again and take a deep breath. *What do I wear at our sessions? I don't even remember.*

"There I go again. I insulted you, didn't I?" Marvel inquires. "You did want to learn, right?"

"No, you didn't insult me, and yes, I want to learn."

"Then I upset you, yes?" Marvel asks. "I can feel you, Dottie. Maybe I should shut up when I see you outside of a session. I always seem to upset you."

"No, it's just tough sometimes to swallow. Eating crow and all. That's one of your concepts, isn't it?" I say sarcastically.

It is so nice that I can joke with him and things don't have to be weird.

"Do you know that crows are very smart, powerful birds? They are instilled with the wisdom to know oneself beyond the limitations of one-dimensional thinking."

Oh gosh, you are weird. "Oh, Marvel, you are such a nerd, but a cute nerd," I add.

232

"Okay, I accept that," Marvel says proudly.

"So!?" I ask.

"So what?"

I smile.

"Okay, if you want to know the truth, just look in the mirror before you come to a session. Look at the gym shorts or black stretch pants that you wear. It might not show up here," Marvel says motioning to his chest area. "But a guy's eyes," Marvel says pointing to the men's room, "will go right there." He makes a motion toward his private areas. "Just because you are not showing cleavage, doesn't mean you are not advertising other parts. You might just want to rethink what you are putting out there. I'm just saying, as you would say."

"Okay, I will look at it. Question everything, right?" I say with a smile. "I need to question this to see if it feels right to me."

"Wow, you have been listening but this one you don't need to question." Marvel teases. "Just look in the mirror. It will tell you what you need to know."

"Ha! You crack me up, Marvel. Later. I have to pee." I plow through the door.

I finish in the bathroom and head to the table where there is a waitress waiting to get my order.

I skip over to the table, pick up a menu and look at it. As I glance at the menu, out of the corner of my eye, I notice Marvel walking by. I discreetly look up, give him a smile and wave. He waves back. I watch him as he pays for his food, still pretending to look at the menu. He exits the building, walks down the path to his car alone.

"Dottie, have you decided?" Katrina says.

"Decided on what?" I ask.

"Food!" Josie inquires. "And who was that guy you were talking to at the bathrooms."

"What guy?" Katrina asks as she scans the diner.

"Oh nobody," I answer. "I will have the egg salad sandwich on rye, please."

The next morning, I awake.

No dreams last night.

I reach for my phone. I notice that I have received a text.

> Brian: my apologies, girl, to text you so early.
> Michael forgot to tell u that u won't be
> having a session with him today. Saturdays
> we all.meet at Leo's café. 10am. C U there?

> Me: C U there!

I check the time, and it is already 9:30. I get ready and make my way downstairs by 9:45. I walk by the living room mirror noticing my clothes. I back up to the mirror to look at my clothes. I hear Marvel's words from last night. I guess a longer shirt covering my front area might work better. But this IS the style. This IS what everyone is wearing.

I look again trying to pull the shirt over my butt and front but, when I let go, it creeps upward again. I take a deep breath and then run back up the stairs to change.

I arrive at Leo's café by 10:10 in a longer shirt and a sweater on top. As I get out of the car, I join a family at the entrance of the café. The two little girls, one about four and one a couple years older, beat me to the door. The girls open the door and hold it open for me, and then wait for their mom and dad. As I pass them, I notice their short shirts that do not cover their flowered stretch pants. I smile at them and then discreetly glance back at their mom's clothing. Yep, black stretches, shirt just barely covering her butt.

Ha! And we wonder why men stare at our body parts. Okay, Marvel, ya got a point.

I go inside and find Marvel and the boys already engaged in conversation. I grab another chair and quietly place myself in between Tim and Marvel.

"Hey, Dottie," Tim says. Leo gives me a nod.

"Tough night, girl?" Brian says.

"No, I am good," I answer. Leo laughs and looks at me like he knew I was out last night; implying I got wasted as he makes the motion of drinking.

Marvel smiles at me as he continues to talk to the group. Sometimes, there is this feeling in Marvel's eyes that is indescribable. It is strange, yet interesting. It's this focus and love and twinkle that I have never seen in anyone before. It is calm and steady, yet expansive. You don't want to interrupt it ever, because it flows so nicely and pours out of his mouth so clearly. I listen to him this time, hearing the energy behind the words, feeling the expansiveness radiating from his body. I turn and look at him seeing the energy around him. I then reach my hand up and touch his arm. Marvel continues to talk as he glances at my touch. He finishes his sentence and then looks at me along with three other pair of eyes.

"Oh, sorry," I quickly pull my hand away, a little embarrassed. "I could see the heat coming from your body and I just well, wanted to see, um, if it was warm."

Silence.

"Well, is it?" Leo asks.

"Yes, as a matter of fact, it is," I tell him, thankful that Leo breaks the silence.

"Okay, are we going to talk about my body temperature all day, or are we gonna get this finished," Marvel says with a laugh.

Marvel glances at me.

I sit back in my chair and decide to allow the feelings and information to come to me this time. I listen as the boys interject back and forth with Marvel.

We eat breakfast that Leo prepares and we talk some more before the lunch crowd invades our space.

"Do you feel that, guys?" Marvel says referring to the people entering or passing by our space.

"Yep! Oh. How about that one?" Tim adds.

Heading for the door is the 'stretch pants' family of four that I encountered earlier outside.

"Look, Marvel! Look what they are wearing," I say.

"Yep!" Marvel answers. The boys look at me like I have three heads.

"Most girls are taught at a very young age to dress for the outside world; choosing what to wear and putting on make-up. The only reason why anyone puts on make-up is to present themselves to someone else. Otherwise, you would stand in front of the mirror all day. And since most people don't, you should know that you put on the make-up in order to get a response from the outside world about yourself. So, in a way, it's kind of how you see your own self-reflection without standing in front of a mirror; you are dressing for those other people so those other people can look at you. They can respond to you and tell you how nice you look, or give you a glance or a look just to stimulate a feeling in you so you can feel good about yourself."

Boy that was a long sentence!

"So, it's the illusion that one can feel good about oneself — by dressing up or putting on make-up. In our society, women are taught at a very young age to present themselves and their bodies so that men will reflect to them their worth and value. But on a bigger scale, it's about marketing — it's about selling clothes. It's also about selling make-up and about making money. So, they trick these young women into believing that their worth and value is in their clothes and make-up."

"I am not giving up make-up, Marvel!" I smile. "But I understand the worth and value stuff. Yesterday's session was quite the eye-opener!"

"And the women can throw away their self-esteem to a falsely reflective value that they assume is their own," Tim also adds.

I look at the boys, a little hesitant to share more.

I jump in the conversation. "Most women who wear those tight stretch pants are revealing their entire body for all to view. I guess that by wearing that stuff, it's really only for other people because you can't really even see your own body. So why would I or someone want everyone to see their naked body?"

"Yes, why?" Leo asks.

"And it looks like you just have a different colored skin on," I continue.

Marvel interrupts, "Yes, dressing and wearing make-up is really for other people to see. The common theme is to say, 'It makes me feel good or I like just dressing up.' You never really see yourself once your clothes are on. And have you ever noticed that you don't even feel that make-up or your clothes after you have worn them. So, you're not really seeing yourself or really enjoying yourself in your clothes. So it really is about the outside world and how they reflect to you something that seems to be missing within yourself, about your own sense of value, beauty or worth."

I add, "We wonder why men stare at our body parts." I look up and see the four of them, four men, staring at me.

"You don't have to worry about us, Dottie. We don't see you like that," Brian confirms.

"Thanks, Brian." I get up, mess up Brian's hair and excuse myself.

"I am going to the bathroom to take my make-up off. Ha! NOT!"

I return only to find only Marvel at the table. The other three are over by the café television.

"I see that you tried some different clothes today," Marvel comments.

"You noticed that, ay…as you would say?" I ask.

"How can you not notice?" Marvel teases.

"Oh, shush," I fire back.

"A completely different energy."

"Really?"

"Yes. You look very nice, by the way."

"Why thank you, Marvel."

"Ask the guys," Marvel says pointing to the three guys who sit back down, which changes the energy at the table.

"Let's not and say we did," I say as my eyes widen, shooting a look at Marvel to shush.

"So who did you go out with last night, Cavarelli?" Leo says.

"Why do you want to know?" I say as I slap Brian's high five.

"Because if you were out with that girl, Katrina, I would want to know," Leo answers.

"Seriously, Leo?" I inquire, "Wasn't that over in high school?"

"Most definitely, but I saw her last night crossing the street... well, actually she wasn't crossing the street, she was directing traffic at like 11:30 near the Emerald Diner while I was driving down Main," Leo states. "I thought about stepping on the accelerator."

"Leo!" I gasp.

"Oh, come on Dottie. I wouldn't do that," Leo teases. "Or maybe I would, depending on my mood. She does know how to get under someone's skin. She is a bad influence, on anybody. Why are you still hanging out with her?"

"No one can really influence or force you to do anything," I say, "Unless you allow it. Isn't that right, guys?"

Marvel smiles at the dialogue that is taking place.

"Unless you really want to... somewhere inside," Tim says.

"Do you guys remember Katrina?" Leo asks.

"You got a point, Leo," Tim agrees. Brian nods.

"You sound like you are still charged about it," I say repeating some of the groups' lingo.

"I guess I still am," Leo admits. "Guess I gotta work on that one."

"So... if you saw Katrina, you probably saw me last night," I tell him.

"No, I didn't," Leo informs.

"Still going to The Pub then the Emerald Diner?" Brian jokes.

"Is that a judgment?" I say, as I look at Brian in defense.

"No. Are you judging it, Dottie?" Leo inquires.

"No, I don't think so," I say, "But I did make a choice to go into another world with them — unlike where we are now. Consciousness, as you guys would say. But I haven't seen these girls for a year. What else would I do with them anyway? That's what we do together."

238

I start to ramble on and on. I tell the boys how Katrina is still crazy as ever, just like in high school, and Josie is still trying to take care of her. I tell them how I blended with them and didn't stay in my own space last night. I talked about the memories I had about why we became friends, and the bond that we shared.

We chat for like two hours. Every time our issues would surface, we would address them. We work together as a group. As I spend more and more time with these boys, I begin to see the differences and the similarities within myself.

I start to realize that I am a combination of all three of these guys — the discerning mind, the loving heart, and the bravery that sometimes is required in life. I have learned so much over this past week. Marvel says that he hears that I will *pick up* this information pretty quickly. I don't know who he hears it from, but his eyes are all lit up when he says it. I can only assume it is one of those spirits that's hanging around him. He says that if I would just wake up, and turn the channel, I could be tuned into to myself all the time. Whatever that means.

I look forward to each day in learning more about this process and more importantly, discovering the issues within me that one day will allow me to be free from this prison of guilt, shame and fear.

I turn to Marvel and ask for another appointment.

"I will not be available tomorrow unfortunately, Dottie," Marvel says.

"Air balloon ride time," Tim remarks.

"That's right, Dottie. The boys and I are going on a trip," Marvel confirms.

"It was Marvel's idea, of course," Brian says. "Something about Mr. Chicken Shit over here getting over his fear of heights."

"Wanna go?" Leo says. "In place of me!"

"Sure!" I answer. "I would love to, if the rest of you don't mind."

"It only fits four people," Brian says. "And you are going, Leo! If anyone, it will be me sitting out. I am not afraid of anything. Well, except for fire."

"Guess we will have to have a bonfire next, Brain!" Leo says.

"Yes, I still want to come, but not in place of you, Brian. Actually, I would just like to tag along. Watch you go up."

"We can get two balloons!" Marvel suggests.

"Okay, thanks," I graciously say.

"Afterwards, they are driving me to the airport," Marvel informs.

"You can ride down with us. Maybe we can all go out to eat or something," Brian suggests.

"Really? Sure! Sounds great," I say, turning to Marvel. "Where ya going, Marvel?"

Marvel says, "London, Europe. Just visiting a few people."

"How long?" I inquire.

"Just for a few weeks," Marvel says. "Be back by November first."

"Oh," I say.

"The boys will be here for you. Right, boys?" Marvel says.

"Yep," Brian says. Leo and Tim nod.

"Okay, thanks. And yes, I definitely want to go tomorrow."

Afterwards, they fill me in on all of the arrangements for tomorrow's trip; we say our goodbyes. I leave feeling good, as usual.

CHAPTER 18

Missing The Balloon Ride

It's morning. I sit up in bed, not fully in my body yet. I rub my eyes, and then stretch my arms in the air as I let out a long yawn. I lie back down in bed pulling the covers up to my chin and reflect on last night.

No dreams again.

I wrote a lot before going to bed. Memories were pouring out of me. I reflect on last night's thoughts and memories.

How could I possibly change this feeling of always wanting someone's approval? It's true what Marvel says. That feeling is with me all the time. Why did I have this feeling? Was this too, a result of the abuse? Or maybe, why did this abuse even happen to me?

There are so many questions. I remember wanting to please my teachers, my mother and my sisters — although I am learning that there is always something to gain from the approval.

With teachers, it was getting a better grade. With Mom, it was making sure that she still loved me, and felt I was special. I knew that she thought that I was special. I held onto that identity of feeling special — I couldn't just know that I was special, regardless of what she thought. I had to have someone confirm that for me back then.

Funny.

Regarding my sisters, I wanted them to love me, too — through all the sibling competition that we were taught. I also wanted to be like them and keep up with them.

I am seeing that I acted out by pleasing all of them, and not following my own heart and desire. I was left with this shame inside that would never disappear, until I followed my own heart.

This morning, as I reflect, I am grateful for these understandings and releases that have changed my life. I do understand now that the beliefs that I developed from the abuse are the things that keep me in my pain, not so much on the actual act of the abuse but how I perceived the act; for example, dirty and wrong. This is actually quite odd to me.

The concept, "People don't do things to you, they do things for themselves," was pretty powerful for me when I first heard it. I now know that it isn't even about me; in fact, that statement changed everything for me. One sentence changed my whole perspective. How could that be? "He didn't do what he did to hurt you, Dottie." I whisper Marvel's words out loud. I tear up again just saying the words. He was just being selfish and wasn't thinking of you at all; never thinking of the consequences that it would have on a little girl.

I had caused this guilt and shame at six years old. Me! I had caused it! I can't believe that I can say this now! Since I caused it, I can undo it. The fact remains is that I can get rid of any feelings and perceived beliefs that I create. Before I started this new journey, these feelings were a part of me; I was dug in. I truly believed that I could never be rid of this — perceived pain.

I actually have the choice to be healed. It's going to take some work, but I am up for the challenge.

Although as I reflect on it, I can't imagine those memories and guilty feelings not interfering with an intimate relationship; I do hope that it's possible.

Deep down, I don't really believe that it can happen.

The guilt and shame and dirty feelings have always been present with every intimate experience that I have ever had up until now. Could it be different? Maybe I should try it with someone. I should find someone, to see if it works. My relaxed eyes slowly glance over at the clock.

"OH shit! It's Sunday!" I shout. "Hot air balloon day!" I jump up tossing the covers halfway across the room. I look for my socks, pants, shirt and then shoes. I stop and look over at the clock again.

Like looking at the time could change the fact that it reads 11:22.

I am late…way late. We were all supposed to meet at Leo's at 10:30.

Damn.

I scramble to my phone to see if they had texted me.

Damn.

I discover multiple texts:

> where are u grl

242

we can wait another 10 marvel not here yet

what's the deal sleepyhead we are leaving

another late night Cavarelli

going going gone

u snooze you lose

alright cavarelli you will miss breakfast
meet us there girl r time for the balloon
is twelve thirty

I get ready in ten minutes. I put a brush through my hair, brush the front of my teeth and make it to the car by 11:32. I stop at the first gas station, fill the tank, get a drink and pop an Adderall.

I maneuver in and out of traffic until I arrive at the entrance to the park. I find a spot that is quite a distance from where the people and the balloons are. I run with a backpack over my shoulders and find Marvel and the boys at approximately 12:30.

I have made it. I don't know how I made it, but I am here on time.

Brian and Tim's hot air balloon has already taken off, but they yell from their balloon and motion me to hop into Leo and Marvel's balloon.

"Where have you been, girl?" Leo teases, "Late night?"

I smile at Leo while sliding into the other balloon contraption. I shut the door behind me and get ready to answer Leo, when my phone rings.

I answer my phone. It is Don telling me that he thinks Christopher broke his foot. I abruptly open the basket and jump out. I stand there talking to my ex as I watch Marvel and Leo fly away. A part of me is bummed that I will not have the opportunity to fly high in the sky, detaching from earth for just a little while — and the other part of me goes right into the patterns of being a mother. I can hear the words coming in, "I should have been there. I hope it didn't hurt."

With my phone in between my shoulder and ear, I say, "Oh... okay... I will be right there... yes... okay." I hang up the phone.

"Gotta go guys. Christopher… my son… he might have broken his foot." I smile and wave to the boys as they enter into the air without me.

"Have fun, you guys!" I watch them go up. "You go, Leo, don't be afraid."

"Bye, Dottie. Go do what you have to do." Marvel speaks louder as I run towards my car. "See ya when I get back."

"Oh, yeah, have a good trip, Michael," I yell running to the car.

I just called the man, Michael?

I return to my car and pull away, looking back in the rearview mirror, only seeing mixed stones flying above the dust cloud. I make a right out of the parking lot.

I see the light ahead getting ready to turn yellow. I speed up hoping to arrive at the light before it turns red. I sigh at the car in front of me; a car that is going way under the speed limit. Her bumper sticker reads: Go ahead, speed ahead of me. I'll meet you up at the red light.

"Get out of the left lane please!" I shout out loud.

I move over to the right lane, catching up to the slow car. I glance at the annoying lady driving, and then speed ahead of her towards the light that is now turning red. I slam on my brakes.

Ugh, damn!

The old woman pulls up beside me to my left.

Really?

I feel the essence of the woman pulling at me to look at her. I give in and look. To my surprise, it is Glenda.

Seriously?

"Hey, Dorothy," Glenda says smiling at what she calls me. "Slow down, missy."

"Hey, you," I say. "I am in a hurry. How are you?"

"Wonderful. You know me," Glenda exclaims. "Why in such a rush?"

244

"Christopher, my son, may have broken his foot," I explain.

"He'll be okay," Glenda reassures. "Don't let your fears drive you into a tree."

"Okay, Glenda. Thanks!" I answer. "Hey, I have had a few dreams about you."

"So, I've been in your dreams lately? Cool. What did I say?" Glenda says as she looks up at the light turning green. "Listen, Dottie, I am always around. I will be watching you."

"Bye, Glenda," I say. I step on the gas and pull away. Something was strange about Glenda today. Her eyes, no maybe her hair … it may have been the light around her head that sparkled in the sun. I continue to accelerate. I look in my rearview mirror, then in my side mirrors and I realize Glenda's car isn't behind me. In fact, she isn't anywhere. Where'd she go?

Glenda was nowhere in sight.

What? Weird.

I turn my focus towards the road and slam on my gas pedal.

I meet Don and Christopher at the hospital, and spend all day with the both of them. The girls have already been dropped off at my mom's house. I sit with Don and Christopher. I watch Chris and remember his high tolerance for pain. As a matter of fact, Chris has a high tolerance for many things, which always helps with the company he keeps. He doesn't talk much, except when he has something to say. He listens a lot. He is definitely more of a feeler than he is a mentalist. He usually means what he says, and at times, he withdraws if the feeling is too tense. He decides on his own experience and you can't tell him otherwise. I respect that in him. There is another side of him that is playful, and almost a little crazy, which probably is the cause of him being in the hospital.

"Mom, it's definitely broken."

"You don't know that, honey."

"I can feel it. I felt it crack," Chris explains.

"You felt it crack or heard it crack," his dad asks.

"Felt it," Chris answers looking at me knowing that I will understand.

His dad and I stare at him.

"Look, guys, it's right in there," Chris says.

"I am looking at your foot and it looks normal to me. It doesn't seem to be swollen," his dad observes.

"It's broken," Chris said. "I don't want it to be broken, but it's broken. I was messing with Megan and she landed right on me."

I look at him, the same look I give him when he gets crazy, and is too rough with the girls.

"Mom, she tackled me first!"

I smile and he smiles back.

The x-ray reveals that it is broken. The three of us finish up at the hospital around four, and arrive at my mom's house around five.

I enter my mom's house. Of course, the girls are downstairs playing in a room that she set up for all the grandchildren. That is just the kind of person she is. She would give you the shirt off her back, even if it was her last shirt. No, literally, she has given me the shirt off her back. "But Mom you just bought that." She'd say, "Oh, I can buy another one." We can buy another one is very big for her.

I enter the house with the intention of applying some of the skills that I have learned. I am sure to witness and observe many of the patterns and behaviors that ignite my mom when my ex is around. Mom likes him but then she doesn't. I guess she can't make up her mind. She has always been this way about men in general, but she is especially tuned into her daughter's mates. I always tell Don not to take it personally. "It's not about you. That's just how she is," I would say.

Today I will try to do more observing than judging my mom, but of course this is always a struggle for me.

'Be an observer, not a judge.' 'You cannot judge what you do not know.' 'Own your behaviors.' 'Accept people for who they are.' 'The only people you can judge is yourself.'

There's so much to learn.

'People are your teachers and mirrors.' 'Anything that bothers you is your issue.'

Yes, mom bothers me, but is this really an issue. Am I like her? Do I behave like mom?

I am greeted by my mom who is smiling. Always glad to see anyone that walked through that door!
"Hi, Mom!" I say.

"Hello, hello everyone!" Mom shouts.

"Hi, Mom! I am going to..." Mom gets busy with Chris's foot and so I stop talking mid-sentence. My family has a habit of this. You get interrupted before you finish your sentence or a word or even have a thought for that matter. Lots of spinning!

"...to the bathroom," I whisper.

Marvel and the boys would have a field day in this family. They would have a blast!

I go to the bathroom and sit on the toilet. I start to look around at the pretty bathroom. It has mauve and light blue colors with doilies everywhere. The memories start to float in.

I thought my memory foam was the only thing that stimulated the memories.

I laugh.

From the age of three until I was five years old, I hung out at my grandpop Clarence and grandmom Lulu's house. I was the youngest of five children and my mom was ready to go back to work. I guess she was just ready to be with adults. I didn't blame her.

I start to wonder if I had been affected by my grandparents' patterns as well, because I hung out with them at such an early age. I guess that they had the same patterns as my mom; she simply inherited those identical patterns from them.

Daaaaaa...Dottie.

Anyway, my grandpop was so very cute. I loved sitting on his big green leather chair. "Don't worry about that grandmom of yours, she's this... she's that." I could feel his love for her. In their own old-fashioned way. I did get to experience the way relationships worked back then, I guess. It was a very different feeling than my mom and dad.

247

I remember feeling the love that Grandpop had for me. I remember his gray car — sitting in the front seat with my little red sneakers. I remember Grandpop glancing at me with love. My feet didn't reach the floor, and I didn't wear a seatbelt. I remember it so vividly. Like it was yesterday.
Weird, how you keep certain memories.

He used to say to my mom, "I don't need a rear-view mirror. I don't need to know what is behind me, just in front of me. The people behind me need to make sure that they don't hit me."

My grandmom was totally different from him. She always talked to me about what she always wanted to accomplish in her life. I was like a witness to her disappointments — and her successes. I guess I was the perfect person to talk to. A three year old who wouldn't judge her or may not remember what was said to tell others.

One day I overheard Grandmom Lulu say that her father, my great grandpop Carmen, messed around with her siblings. I didn't really know what 'messed around' was, until I became an adult and put it all together.

When I told my mom about my brother, she shared with me that her Pop-Pop Carmen used to go into her room and mess around with her. It was that day that I realized that it was my Grandmom Lulu's father.

My mom felt shaky before beginning the story about the abuse, but I guess when she found out about my brother, the guilt must have spun her around and out it came. Word vomit. She said that she never told anyone before.

From time to time, I would ask her how she felt about it, and it would always be the same answer. "He was a dirty old man that didn't know any better. What's the use in talking about it?" From the outside, it seemed like it didn't even bother her, but unfortunately, I knew better. I could feel her insides. Every time that I would bring it up and ask her how it felt, I would hear the same response. "It doesn't matter why or when it happened. I was only there for two weeks anyway."

That didn't answer my question, Mom!

"It was a long time ago, Dottie. It's best sometimes to put the past behind you."

The past always has a way of creeping in.

I wouldn't pressure her for an answer. They were her feelings and her memories.

I became friends with my mom's cousin, Caroline, and of course, she revealed her sexual abuse from the same Pop-Pop. In fact, she showed me the house where it all happened. I can't help but imagine all of those grandchildren. When will it stop? I feel the twister stirring.

Tap, tap, tap!

"Honey, you okay in there?" Mom quietly says.

She would never get too close to explore those feelings. Those feelings affected her in so many ways.

"Yeah, I'll be out in a sec, Mom," I say, my mom's voice triggering me to her disapproval of Don.

Is that how I treat Don?

Mom is nice to Don, plays around with him and says all the right things to him. How did she really feel about him?

Mom's words about men start to pour out all over the bathroom.

"Dottie, you can't rely on men. Yes, they are wonderful, but don't expect them to come through for you when it really counts. If you want something done, do it yourself."

The words continue to pour.

"Never rely on men for your money. Make your own money. You are good at that, go for it. Start your own business."

My mom invisibly projects out to me.

Tap, tap, tap.

"Almost done, Mom," I shout from the bathroom, rolling my eyes.

I come out of the bathroom. I feel her trying to feel me. She knows that something is up. She checks again.

"Hey, Mom, do you remember my friend, Brian's mom, Mrs. Spear?" I divert her.

"Oh, yes," she recalls. "The hippie!"

"Brian told me that you and his mom were laughing hysterically about me signing his dad's name wrong on the detention slip. You waited until you got outside, away from the school, before you burst out laughing. Is that what happened?"

"Totally true!" she confirms. "Come on, Dorothy. That was so funny! You signed his name, Brain!"

I smile.

"Why do you ask, sweetie?"

"Just wondering."

My mom had a great sense of humor and surprisingly wasn't prejudice; considering all of her other judgments about life and self. I just loved that about her.

She still went to church every Sunday. She would always say, "I just like going to Mass, Dottie. I get something out of it. Every time I go!" She still attended even though the church had disappointed her by not checking on her after my dad had died.

Father Rich checked on me.

Even when the priest yelled at her for using birth control after her fifth child.

She supported gay rights. She would always say, "I could never have an abortion, Dottie, but a woman should have the right to have one if she wants to." She would always say to me, "My faith is with God, not the institution."

"Mom, I love you, ya know."

"I love you too, sweetie."

The other kids join us from downstairs. I watch my mom charm the grandchildren. She is like a snake charmer, without that stick that is waved in front of a snake. I watch my children smile at her, soaking up all the love that radiates out of her. They light up when they see her!

Afterwards, the five of us go back to Don's place. We have dinner and then hang in the rec room. It feels like old times, yet not.

Nothing about my ex and me is the same.

It is like someone has shined a light on my life. Even if I turn the light off, there will be me sitting in the dark like old times, yet I already know what is waiting for me.

I have seen it!

I stay with them until the kids go to sleep. As I approach the door to leave, Don stops me. He stands there wanting to say something.

Nothing is coming out.

"What?" I ask him.

"Dottie, I couldn't come," he answers.

"Come where?" I ask again.

"With you, I know that you wanted me to, I just couldn't. And I knew that it was over, our marriage, I mean. I thought about leaving you, a year before you told me." Don continues, "So I am sorry for giving you such a hard time about you wanting to end it."

"Seriously?" I ask him. "You thought about leaving me?" I have to say this out loud because I still can't believe my ears.

"Yes, I am sorry. I just couldn't come with you. It was too hard. Actually, it is too hard now. It's too much." I stand there looking at him, not really knowing what to say.

"You don't have to feel guilty anymore." Don continues, "Are you happy?"

"Yes, I am."

I say still repeating the words in my head, "I thought about leaving you."

I am frozen.

I then smile and take a deep breath and breathe out all the guilt that has been inside of me for a year.

"And you?" I ask. "Are you happy?"

"Yeah, I'm pretty happy. I'm good," he says giving a half of a smile. "I love you, ya know."

"I love you, too, Don."

I leave the house with many thoughts. I get in my car and hear the words again.

I thought about leaving you.

All that guilt I felt for leaving him and ruining his life. And he knew that it wasn't working. He wouldn't admit that to me. Why?

Marvel would say, "Maybe it was too hard. Maybe that was as far as he could go or wanted to go."

Everyone is ready in his or her own time. Hurt is not getting what you want.

Thank you, Don.

By the time I make it back to my place it is nine. I am exhausted. I find Marvel's concepts folder on the dining room table and bring it up to the bedroom. I plop on my bed and am ready to learn more. I open up the folder.

- Speak so others can understand
- Keep no secrets, they separate and destroy
- Resolving issues in the present resolves issues from the past
- See what it is you really see, not what you want to see
- Don't make your home your emotional litter box
- There are no relationship issues, only individual ones
- Clear the issues that make you unhappy
- You must eat crow to grow

As I read these concepts one by one, they seem pretty simple. Something tells me that there is more to them, just like the four individuals that have been teaching me. I can't quite put my finger on it.

You must feel to heal. Unconditional acceptance is the first step toward unconditional love.

My eyes grow tired as I keep reading. I am out cold before turning the next page.

DREAM:

"Hello, Dorothy. It's Glenda. I didn't think that you would ever stop reading!"

What?

"The concepts!" Glenda answers. "Anywho, as you would say. I haven't seen you in a while. Where have you been?"

What do you mean...where have I been? Where have you been? I go to sleep every night, aren't you supposed to be the one popping into my dreams?

"Yes, I suppose that's true. I guess my magic wand was being repaired so I couldn't travel. And my bubble was thinning. Ha!!"

You are funny tonight!

"How do you know it's nighttime? And that it is not morning time!"

I wake up with a smile on my face.

Crazy Glenda!

It's three in the morning.

I make my way down to my office, catching up on my office work. I can't call any companies, but there is plenty of paperwork that has to get done.

My life has changed with my new-found friends and their beautiful words; although recruiting seems to be the same. It just comes easy to me. I can do this job without any effort. My company is flexible as long as I produce. I feel grateful to have this flexible job.

I can breathe better. I start to make smarter choices for myself, not for other people. There are more important things in life than organizing and categorizing. There is this desire, more like hope, that this life can be more than just the controlling of life to avoid the guilt and shame and feelings of wrongness.

I see the importance of truly owning my feelings which is still somewhat difficult. I still tend to want to keep some of those feelings hidden. I know that there is so much more to learn.

For the rest of the month of October, my life follows a schedule of recruiting in the morning hours, then meeting the guys at the café almost every day around one, then after school, I am with the kids. I am with them until they go to bed; except the days that their dad has them. On those days, I am with kids until their dad gets back from work. The schedule flows quite nicely.

When Halloween arrives, I help Kacey decide what she is going to wear. Kacey always has some trouble deciding what to wear. Back and forth she will take you. On top of that, she always has issues with the costume fabric and how it feels on her skin.

Don't even think about touching her hair.

She finally decides on the Maleficent character costume which will require some hair brushing. No one in the family looks forward to this process. I must always prepare for the changing of the costume at any given moment. I always have at least two other back-ups — just in case. She is a combination of spunky, finicky and sweet, wrapped up in one.

This year, Halloween will be different for me. Instead of being frustrated, I will try to look at myself and what the experience mirrors back about me. With Kacey, there is always plenty to mirror back. She is a gigantic mirror for me!

Megan's behavior, on the other hand, is subtle. It's easy for me to be able to see the mirror. She keeps to herself and says the right things so she will not be seen. People, who are more mental have a hard time feeling, will not notice. Megan tends to stay hidden when she wants to be hidden. Although she does get noticed when she allows the world to see her completed creations. I never should worry about finding a costume for Megan. She always manages to single-handedly put together something amazing. One year, she created a *Lord of the Rings* character that was just sensational. She just says things like, "Mom, where's the yarn? Or Mom, do you remember that cloth that we used that one time?"

Christopher is a totally different story when it comes to Halloween. He is kind of a "get it together the last-minute type." We always think, no way, he will never get it done in time, and poof, he always will find something to wear.

I realize I have the strong qualities of both girls. They both want what they want — one in silence and one more vocal. They are both sensitive and can feel so much, but Megan holds it in and Kacey purges it. I can see the consequences of each behavior. Megan's feelings will completely be swallowed back in her body which causes her to feel bloated sometimes, also withdraw, retreat to her own world, and possibly miss out on an experience. However, Kacey is another story. Kacey's behavior brings the backlash of others, and then feels the repercussions and consequences that follows, like being removed from a group; therefore, missing out on a possible experience. Megan will find others to retreat to, like friends, sports or other families. Kacey is more of a one-on-one girl. She isolates herself from humans and channels her love into her animals — her rabbit and her dad's dog.

Marvel tells me that if I change and work my way to a more neutral balanced space, I could model this balance to the girls. I suppose that the girls will then have a chance to be something other than *borrowed patterns* from me. They are not their behaviors. They have the chance to become fully free-thinking human beings, which could result in having experiences that they decide — not simply ones that come from our family patterning.

A smile appears on my face when I feel how much I love them, and how much I appreciate their differences, and more importantly the reflections they mirror back to me. I now realize that their behaviors and beliefs about life are simply the patterns that I have taught them.

I have a quick thought to tell the girls right now as I watch them getting ready — wanting to save them from their future pain that may lie ahead. But that is not the exercise. I am to observe.

Halloween night is quite different than every other year as a family. I have begun to perceive each individual differently, even their dad. Normally, I don't want him near me because I have to feel the guilt and disappointment of the divorce. But now, I look forward to seeing him so I can apply what I have learned.

This year my costume is "Happy!" No literally, one of the seven dwarfs. "Happy," a true reflection of how I have been feeling this past year. Don jokes with me about happiness only coming after he leaves my life. We laugh about it. I am also happy that I can joke with him. I can actually enjoy him more — almost as if I see him as a friend again.

Speak so others can understand I remember reading last night.

I smile again, although the smiley face make-up line that's drawn on my face makes me look like I am extremely happy.

The night ends with Kacey running into the house, saying that she must take the costume off now. It feels so tight and icky, and her make-up feels like it is running into her eyes. Which it wasn't. And of course, her hair hurt from being pulled up in a bun for the horn head to fit. Again, Kacey mirrors back to me my own childhood, and how I was so bothered by the different materials on my skin.

Kacey embraces the Maleficent role so completely, being both beautiful and terribly frustrated at the same time. Kacey knows this and plays the part well. But it isn't easy on her dad and me. No detail is missed, right down to the pointy teeth in the back of her mouth. We worked together to bring Maleficent to life. Kacey wants it all.

Who can blame her? It is Halloween.

Kacey insists on having the chiseled, high cheekbones, a nose piece, pointy ears and sharp teeth, just like the movie. However, she did turn down every other costume that we had suggested — claiming that they were too icky and annoying. She settled with the make-up, horns and a black dress.

Now she is in the house taking it all off as quickly as possible. Halloween has been a success, but more importantly, I learn a great deal. It is after eleven, when the kids finally decide to go to bed. Kacey sleeps at my house, Megan at her dads, and Chris stays over at his friend's house. We did make a pact, that on holidays, the kids can sleep at either of the houses, except if one of us has something to do.

DREAM:

Hello, Marvel.

"Hello, Dottie."

Can I ask you something?

"Of course."

Well, I was thinking about what you said the day before yesterday about the denial, silence and secrets and then yesterday about the sensitivities.

"That wasn't yesterday, that was when I did a session with you the week before last, when I was in town. I am away now."

I know, Marvel. That's why this is a dream!

"That's true."
"Hi, guys," Glenda chimes in.

Well, hello, Glenda! I say.

"It's time to move, Dorothy. Do you mind if I take her for a moment, Marvel?"

"Not at all," Marvel answers.

Where are we going?

"You need to lead this parade."

What parade?

"Come on." Glenda gently reaches out for my hand. *"Follow me, dear."*

She brings me to a parade and lifts me up and places me on a beautiful white float, surrounded by many angels. They all smile at me gently placing their hands on my shoulders and face. They are glad to see me. They wave to the crowd as we float by. I start to wave. Soon I see the end of the parade approaching. Before the angels and I remove ourselves from the float, one of my sisters appears with some of her friends from the courthouse. "It's time, Dottie. Follow me," she says.

Where?

"You'll see."

She brings me to a room full of keys: old ones, new ones, all different shapes and sizes.

What are these to?

"Some of the prisons."

Really?

"Yes. You can enlighten these people in prison. Help them. There are so many men and women in there that have been abused."

My eyes open. Huh. These dreams...Holy shit!

CHAPTER 19

Knock Your Heels Together Three Times... To Carry You Home.

The next morning, I drop Kacey off at school and then go back to my home office to make a few phone calls. I finish up around twelve-thirty.

I head for Leo's café where I find Leo, Brian, Tim, and Marvel at their usual table. It is definitely a different dynamic with Marvel physically there.

"You see, guys," Marvel continues, "when you find yourself getting involved in other people's stuff, you have to know that you are going into someone else's illusion, outside of your illusion, into someone else's illusion. Somewhere you are abandoning your illusion to go live someone else's dream. You have heard that expression, right boys? Living someone else's dream and that's what this is.

"So, when they say you can be anything or anyone, that's true. But you can't do it as a human being, because a human being is limited by design. Its design is limited. Its design is the illusion. So, you cannot create an illusion from the illusion, but you can create an illusion from the illusion, but you won't really be the creator. So, you must understand this is done in the consciousness not in the human. With the consciousness, you can be aware of what's done in the human, and have the illusion that you are consciously creating using the human experience. But you can't be the human being creating illusions, because that would just be another illusion.

"I know that was a little heady," Marvel states.

Yeah, just a little bit, Marvel. Ha!

"But if you get the essence of it, you will be able to awaken from the dream and know that you are the creator of the dream. You will then be able to create any dream that you want to create, consciously or become the conscious dreamer, the awakened dreamer, the dream walker, the inter-dimensional traveller.

"The problem that most people will have is letting go of the illusion, and what they thought they knew was real. And everything they thought that they were experiencing was real. And to realize that nothing that you are experiencing is real, except in your reality. It's kind of hard for the ego and personality to adjust to. And to just understand that the ego and personality are simply for our navigation. It's the navigation system and starship you will use in the world of illusion; when you leave the world of illusion, that is when it will no longer be necessary.

"So, if you can follow this conceptually, it can assist you in your awakening. You will find that knowing that spiritual gifts are not really gifts, they are just who you are. So, you don't really have any gifts at all. It's kind of like waking up Christmas morning on planet earth and realizing that none of those gifts were left by Santa. That you bought those gifts and you woke up in the morning to see those gifts. And then you act surprised when you saw them," Marvel said as he swings his arms in the air. 'Oh, look! Santa left gifts?' While you pretend that you didn't go out and buy them and place them under the tree."

Oh, my, Marvel.

"So there is the story of illusion if you can follow it. It's a simplified view of the illusion of this reality," Marvel says as he backs up into me.

"Oh, hey, Dottie. I didn't see you there," Marvel says.

"Of course you didn't." I smile.

"How have ya been?" Marvel asks.

"Good. Learned a lot these past couple weeks when you were away," I answer. "And life is strange these days — you are in my head a lot. I would certainly like to make an appointment with you. Maybe Tuesday?"

"Like tomorrow?"

"Yeah, sure, will that work?"

"Sure."

After Marvel finishes his talk on illusion, I share with the group what I have learned about my ex's patterns and how I wanted so badly to tell him what I have been doing.

"Guys, it's killing me that I can't say anything," I tell them.

"Why do you want to tell him?" Brian asks.

"Because. So he can be aware of this."

259

"Did he ask for your help?" Tim asks.

"Not really."

"Did he or didn't he?" Leo asks.

"I guess he didn't."

"Did he or didn't he?" Leo repeats.

"He didn't."

"This is what we were talking about, Marvel," Brian informs. "She has a tough time being direct. You guys remember me when I wasn't direct, and really airy fairy, back in the days when I thought I didn't have a brain."

"Then you found out that you had it in you all the time, didn't you Brian," Marvel exclaims.

"Yep!" Brian answers.

"Well, not all the time," Leo jokes. "He seems to lose it every once in a while." Leo puts his arm around Brian. They both smile.

"Wait. You guys were talking about me?" I inquire.

"Of course, we were talking about you," Tim says. "You are on this team, remember?"

"You are like our experiment," Brian says.

Tim adds, "You are the newbie on the team."

"I feel like a rat in this experience. And I am the new rat. You are not gonna start poking at me, are you?"

"No. We may tackle you, though," Leo teases, "like we used to do in football."

"Imagine that?" I laugh, and notice Marvel looking at me. "What, Marvel? I played football like a guy before the seventh grade when I was less girly."

"So what you are saying is that you were girly in the seventh grade." Marvel smiles.

"Believe me; she didn't play like a guy. You were definitely a girl, or girly as you would say. You were a girl who could run and catch any ball."

"Yeah, I was," I say. "It was not so good when I stopped playing football with the guys."

"Why?" asks Brian.

"Because I started kissing boys instead, and it still haunts me to this day. A lot of stuff is coming up, and I really need that appointment."

The boys chuckle.

"Okay," Marvel says.

"Are appointments included?" I inquire.

"Sort of," Brian says. "We actually haven't discussed it, but we are realizing that more appointments with Marvel are needed. Or, you are just moving way too fast for us."

"Well, you guys should have known that I am a quick study."

"I guess you are," Marvel says smirking.

"How much do you normally charge for an appointment?"

"Yes, Marvel," Leo says wrapping his arms around Marvel's neck. "How much?"

"Wait 'til you hear this, Dottie," Brian says.

Marvel answers, "Sixty dollars."

"Sixty dollars!" Leo repeats. "Can you imagine that, for all that information, for the changing of someone's life, sixty dollars?"

"So, I can pay you, will that work?"

"That will work," Marvel smiles.

Thanksgiving comes and goes, and so does Christmas. I am quite busy during this time, with work, my ADD coaching projects, kids, group sessions at the café with the guys, and doing sessions with Marvel. I work with Marvel once a week every Tuesday. After a couple weeks, I tell Marvel that sixty dollars per week IS ridiculous for what I am getting because sometimes I work with him almost two hours at a time.

I work with Marvel for months. Then those months turn into a year.

This year, I have learned so much, so many new perspectives on life, thanks to Marvel and the guys.

As I continue to see Marvel once a week, I start to feel freer. In fact, I never say that I am done with any issue because there are so many levels to these patterns. I usually say, "I released another big piece, guys!" I am grateful.

I start to notice changes in my physical body, mental capacity, as well as my emotional state. I release some of the baggage, including weaning myself off the medication. I never intended to remove myself from these meds. The medication was making me speed, instead of making me balanced. I seem not to need them anymore.

I start becoming an actor in my own life, rather than a reactor. My thoughts remain clear until the next big opening. I start eating better and exercising regularly. I become more focused, and I find it easier to adequately shift from one task to another — instead of hyper-focusing. I turn my absence of impulsivity to a fun, loving, safe spontaneity. I keep my hyperactivity where it is appropriate, in business and pick-up basketball and soccer games. I save the "Serious Dottie," for conversations with my children and conversations with deeper relationships, like Marvel and the boys, of course.

My reading ability changes from a "slow process of comprehending" words to this unbelievable flood of easy-flowing comprehension at a fast rate. I start learning to be aware and honest of why I am angry. I start to have partial understandings about the sex issue, but I am not dating anyone seriously yet, so I am a little limited in that category. I want to start soon though.

I feel like I was in a dark tornado before I met Marvel and the guys. Now I am beginning to see myself in the eye of the tornado. I try to see everything from the eye. Marvel will joke and say, "From the third eye, Dottie," not the eye of the tornado.

At this point, everything is about *The Wonderful Wizard of Oz*. I am Dorothy and I am waking up!

I start working part-time at Marvel's school, which allows me to cut down my workload at the recruiting agency. I increase the number of ADHD clients in my coaching business. I know more now so I can better advise them. Marvel and I often laugh at his original comment to me behind curtain, "How can you help people with ADD if you are not well yourself."

By December, my ADD coaching business starts to take off.

I also stretch myself this year. I am doing an introductory talk at a women's correctional facility. There are fifty-two women present. I am shocked to find myself standing in front of that many women. I didn't realize that there would be that many. I am nervous, but I manage my way through it. I ask the women if they want me to come back to teach them some more. I explain to them that I have had my own inner prison bars around me all my life. I could share with them what I had learned. I ask them if they would be interested in learning how to remove some of their own inner bars?

My anxiety shoots through the roof when I get a call from the prison, telling me that fifty women sign up!

What was I thinking!

I know that the only person that can help me with these talks is the Wizard — Mr. Michael Marvel!

It is New Year's Eve and the kids go with their dad to a party. I stay home alone. That's how I want it. Katrina and Josie had asked me to go out, but I turned them down because this year will be different. Things are good for me. This New Year, I don't know why, but it feels symbolic for me; like it is a new beginning, a beginning of a new life. I am strong, alone and okay with it.

On New Year's Eve, I decide to send an email to Marvel asking him if he could come with me to give a talk at this women's correctional facility in Philadelphia.

"What tonight?" he emails back. I feel his familiar sarcasm through my computer.

"No, not tonight; it's in February."

"And you are emailing me now."

"Yeah, why not?"
"Why aren't you out and about tonight on New Year's Eve?"

"Nope. It's just me tonight! And I am liking it."

"Well, okay. Enjoy your night, and yes, I will go with you."

"Awesome!" I write back.

I wonder what Marvel is planning for tonight? He didn't say. Of course, he didn't say. He is not one to share stuff like that unless he is asked.

But he has agreed to go with me to the prison. Thank God!

I wake up and feel amazing! It's a new year and I am ready to tackle anything. I feel better than I ever have. The fear, guilt and shame has subsided. What I have learned from the guys is to never think that an issue is completely over. Sometimes it's tough when you feel like you are on top of the world, like right now!

~

It is February, so I contact Marvel to tell him that it is time to plan the prison program. I am excited, and I feel that I am prepared to take on all these women's challenges with Marvel's help, of course.

I pick up Marvel early in the morning.

Thank God he hasn't brought his omelet and chocolate bar.

I tell him that I am leaving for Italy with all my sisters the next day. So many exciting things! Talking with Marvel in the prison and then Italy! What a life!

Marvel and I get through security easily at the prison. Marvel makes a comment under his breath to me, teasing me that he is glad that I didn't pack any today.

We make a connection, like we always do, smiling at one another.

They direct us to the room where we will speak. The room is sterile. It is big in size and the walls are a hideous color. In fact, I have never seen such a color; it is a mixture of brown and green. No windows, pictures or paintings on the walls. The only things that are on the walls are the three or four security guards leaning up against them.

I stand there in front of these women with their eyes bright, ready to receive some answers from me. I can't help but see their pain so clearly. I could resonate with their pain, as I stand there looking at them.

Thank God that I invited Marvel. This is way over my head. There is no way that I could have pulled this off. What if he would have said no. Well, he is here, now. There are too many women, too much pain, and I am still working through my own pain.

I walk around the desks where all the ladies are sitting, while Marvel still stands behind the desks in the front of the room. I talk a little about what they can expect from the workshop. I turn around to the front and look at Marvel. He is standing there looking at me— feeling like he was when I asked him that question about who helps him. He certainly is feeling different, not at all like he is when he is helping me during a session.

What are you doing, Marvel? I take a step closer towards him. Marvel? Marvel? Was he nervous? What's wrong with him?

There is a moment of silence. I wait what seems like an hour. He then takes one step and then another past the desk.

Thank God.

And it happens! It is like he enters a threshold of some sort, like he does when he is on a roll during a session— in that corner space at Leo's café.

He speaks and then speaks some more and doesn't stop. I eventually sit down and just listen to him as he talks to the group. *Thank God he showed up.*

He helps this one woman who cries in front of everyone, and by the looks of the other inmates, she is a woman who rarely behaves this way.

Her name is Sunshine. She's a woman that hasn't spoken to her mother in twenty-three years. She is actually listening to Michael and considering the possibility to reach out to her mother. She is reaching out to her mother without giving up her power and seeing the situation as more neutral. I watch it happen. I watch her life change in front of my eyes. The others stay focused on Sunshine, then Michael — Sunshine, then Michael. They watch in disbelief. There is their fellow inmate, soaking it all in — maybe wondering, 'if Sunshine can do this, so can I.' I watch the women from my chair, something that I have seen many times before. Sunshine starts to really break down. I turn to look at the security guards who stand right behind me.

"No way! Sunshine!" one guard says.

"Impossible!" another joins in.

After the workshop, the women talk to Michael. They are all around him; some crying and some smiling. I knew that this was where he was supposed to be. In front of people sharing, his wisdom, his purity, his love.

I watch him. "How sweet," I say under my breath.

I love this man. I love him.

We drive home. Neither of us speaks until Marvel breaks the silence.

"So, how did we do?" he asks, looking at me from the driver's seat. "Why ya so quiet, Dottie?'

I smile.

"You usually have everything completely analyzed by now," Marvel teases.

I can't say much other than, "You did good, Marvel. That Sunshine got a lot. It probably changed her life forever."

I know that if I really start talking, I will say those words again.

I love you! Why don't you see it, Marvel?

I jump out of the car the minute Marvel's foot touches the brake in front of my house.

"See ya when I get back," I say.

"Okay, then. Enjoy your sisters," Marvel says as he looks at me through the window.

"Knowing you, you will have lots to talk about when you return. I am sure that there will be lots for you to discover."

I look back at him. "Yes, I am sure!" Although something was discovered today… something that has become very clear, but I won't say it. I am not going to say it again.

"See ya. Have a great two weeks!" I tell him as I turn towards the house.

You are the one.

CHAPTER 20

There's No Place Like Home

The back wheels of our plane are just about to touchdown on Philadelphia soil.

Actually, not on soil, more like asphalt.

I am on my way back home from Italy. What a trip! The plane comes to a complete stop. If I could open the window that my face is leaning on, and get out, I would have, but I am not the only one on this plane. The people around me seem quite content where they are, sleeping. I feel that eight hours is enough time to spend on a plane.

All my sisters are still sleeping, except for the one who is reading and typing her novel. She seems so hyper-focused. I always admired her for her focus. I sit and watch her edit, her eyes filled with life, happiness and contentment. She has this glow that I have never seen in her before.

One time when I was younger, I saw colors of red on her forehead that looked like little lightning bolts. I saw it on her forehead. I didn't know what that color meant. I just knew she was very angry with me about something.

But today, on this plane, as I look at her, her whole body seems to turn white, and as I stare at her some more, her body becomes transparent. Much like Marvel when he talks to the guys and me. I guess my sister is in love right now with what she is doing. I wonder if she loves herself and feels the love that I see right now; the love that Marvel talks about — the love that he has for himself. If I ask my sister, she probably will laugh at me.

The flight attendant's voice that goes off on the loud speaker brings me back to my body.

I turn away from my sister and notice that the plane's motor is off; therefore, a sign that we are closer to getting off the plane. I watch the rest of these humans just starting to re-enter their bodies.

It's two o'clock in the morning when my brother-in-law, Dean, drops me off and I say a quick goodbye to the gang. My memory foam is calling me. I look forward to sleeping in my own bed. The quicker I sleep, the quicker the sun will be out. As soon as the sun is out, I can have that conversation with Marvel.

There was a lot that I had discovered in Italy, and many other things that became clear to me. I turn the key in the front door, noticing the loud chirping bird sounds right next to the door. I put my bags down to find my keys. I glance over at the sound. Two cardinals are looking at me — one male and one female. Too tired to care, I place the key in the door, turn and open it. I drop my bags in the living room and head for my bed.

DREAM:

"Hello Missy! You have been away."

I know Glenda. Since you are in my dreams, you could have come to Italy too, ya weirdo.

"Yes, I suppose. Anyway, so you saw two cardinals, ay? Do you know what they mean?"

No.

"It reminds us to step into our natural confidence as if we were born to lead with grace and nobility. Those who see cardinals are energetic, love life, and happily help others when they can."

Thanks, Glenda. You saved me some time. Now I don't have to look up what the cardinals symbolize.

Glenda says, not recognizing my sarcasm, "Cardinals show that you are self-confident just for being you. Nice not to have to justify yourself, your vision or even your life, right, Dorothy?"

I wake up to bird sounds. I lean up and look out the window. No birds. I rub my eyes and then lean over to the end table for my phone. I text Marvel.

> Me: is everyone still meeting today at leos

> Marvel: yep

I arrive at Leo's to find Marvel and Leo already engaged in conversation. Getting the tail end of it, Marvel says, "Realizing that this was just a small example of how we humans treat each other, without thought or awareness, never realizing the effects our behaviors have on others."

"So true," Leo agrees. "Now, later in life I realize this may too have included my dad. He was not bad, only his behaviors that he chose sucked. They caused some problems for me and the rest of my family. I guess I just needed a reminder. I actually don't feel scared anymore."

Marvel stares into Leo's eyes. "You got the courage to overcome this, Leo, you really do. Good for you, man!"

I sit and listen as the silence seems still, yet the energy that Leo was releasing was moving. The absorption of the words and understandings were also moving, seeping slowly into Leo's consciousness. I wait for it to stop, sitting still, *the only place that I do not mind being still for.* Tim and Brian quietly join in.

"Hey, Tim, Brian," Marvel says, and then notices me, "and Dottie, hey you! How was your trip?"

"Oh, it was so great!"

Marvel and the boys smile at me.

"I learned so much being with my sisters for that long."

"Tell me more," Marvel says. "Have a seat."

"First of all, Italy was absolutely amazing. It's probably going to take me several months for everything to sink in. I just learned so much, about me, about my family, about so much. My sisters are just incredible. I realize how much I look for their approval. I am starting to realize how much I take on other people's feelings. I discovered some more family patterns that I never knew existed. I finally didn't judge them, well, at this very moment."

Marvel and the guys smile.

"Still lots to learn though."

"As always," Tim says.

"Of course," Marvel says.

"Thank you guys so much for everything that you have given me. Seriously, thank you!"

"That's wonderful. Sounds like you are on your way." Marvel smiles.

270

"Yes," I say. "I did visit Europe when I was eighteen with a soccer club, although I just didn't remember it being so beautiful. I loved the small town character from Florence down to Rome. There was this feeling in Rome, at the Vatican City. I actually was out of my mind, well not out of my mind crazy, but out of my mind and in my heart. The painted walls were breathtaking. That place is without a doubt, one of the greatest art places of all times. It was magnificent. I swear God is literally there." The boys chuckle.

"They didn't let me in to the Vatican at first."

"What do you mean? They didn't let you in?" Brian says.

"I wasn't wearing enough clothing," I say. Marvel smiles.

"No, not what you think, ya weirdo," I say looking at Marvel, giving him a shove. "I have to tell you that I didn't wear my stretch pants the entire trip. What happened was that I needed a scarf to cover my shoulders. They won't let you in sleeveless."

I continue to talk as they all stare at me, giving me all their attention.

I stop talking for a sec and say, "Gosh, I really missed you guys."

"So when I stepped into the Sistine Chapel, the place completely enveloped me. It literally did, guys. I felt a presence like I have never felt before. Everything in that place is breathtaking, and the history, oh my, from the outside walk into the amazing Sistine Chapel's painted ceilings by Michelangelo, Jesus!"

"Yes, Jesus probably hangs out there," Marvel says.

"Well, I don't know about Jesus, but I know his mother was there."

"Oh, that's right, the Blessed Mother Mary and you are buds," Marvel remembers.

I smile and continue. "From the outside, the Chapel gives an entirely different look then what's inside. It has these strong looking walls out front and then this indescribable lightness inside. Michelangelo's work inside, oh my! Do you know that dude managed to complete this artistic work all by himself! It makes you just want to pick up a brush."

271

"You crack me up, Dottie," Leo jokes. "Next thing you know, she will sign up for an art class."

"Actually, I was already looking at taking some drawing class. I want to try pastels."

"Oh, Jesus," Brian says.

"Him again?" Marvel says.

"Anyway, it was wonderful!" I exclaim. "We should all go sometime." I glance at all the guys, one by one and then stop at Marvel. We lock eyes for a moment.

And you my dear, we need to talk.

We talked as a group for a little and then Marvel did some teaching about the difference between feelings and emotions — how they are two separate yet similar subjects.

"When we speak of feeling, we are referring to your complete sensate experience and emotions, for example, happiness, sadness, anger or fear. The sensate body is an electro-magnetic field that surrounds the physical body. This field senses all the energy or frequencies in your environment. This information is then transmitted and interpreted to your mind and physical body. Your mind and physical body interpret and respond to this information based on your beliefs, knowings, soul memory and genetic makeup. This information is technically light and sound vibration. This light and sound vibration also stimulates your DNA and RNA which then activates memories and codes within your DNA and RNA."

"Are you sure that you weren't Einstein, Marvel?" I say.

"He's sure," Tim and Brian answer. Leo high fives me.

"Try looking up Herman Minkowski from Germany. He was Einstein's professor and then colleague."

"What?" the guys shout out.

"Just saying, as Dottie would say," Marvel jokes.

272

"Do you mean to tell me that you might have been this Herman Minkowski guy in another life.?" Leo asks. Tim and Brian grab their phones looking up Herman on the internet.

Silence.

Then Tim reads, "Herman Minkowski was a Jewish German mathematician, professor at blah, blah, blah. He created and developed the geometry of numbers and used geometrical methods to solve problems in number theory, mathematical physics and the theory of relativity. He is best known for his work in relativity, in which he showed in 1907 that his former student, Albert Einstein's special theory of relativity —1905, could be understood geometrically as a theory of four-dimensional space-time, since known as the "Minkowski Spacetime."

The guys break out in laughter as Marvel smiles.

We finish up our meeting and I ask Marvel to stay after to talk. The boys eventually clear out and Marvel takes a seat next to mine.

"Sure, what's up, Cavarelli?"

"Well, I thought about this a lot."

"Oh no," Marvel teases. "You have that look in your eyes again."

"No seriously, listen," I tell him. "There is something that I need to tell you."

"That's funny. I heard something about you driving over here today; didn't really know what it meant."

"What did it say?"

"Well, you tell me first."

"I like you and it's not just like... I like you like I love you. There is something here, Marvel. Let's face it. Our sessions are not like the sessions we used to do. We are now working together; talking about doing another workshop. Maybe we should give this a try. I don't even know what that means. When I was in Italy, something became clear to me."

"Oh, what is that?"

"You… you became clear."

Marvel smiles, but this time there is a sparkle in his eyes that I have never seen before, or I am in my own illusion. I laugh to myself, as I look at him waiting for the same response that he gave me last year.

"After you texted me back I heard, 'She will help you to begin to open up your heart again.' Didn't know if that message was for me, or what?"

"Of course it was for you! So, what do you think?"

"Well, what I feel is… maybe. I don't know."

I smile.

"We can give it a try, or I don't know, or something."

He stumbles over his words, finding it difficult to phrase his words and

thoughts. *How sweet.*

"Would you like to go with me to a workshop in upstate Pennsylvania? I suppose we could talk about it a little then. How does that sound?"

"Sure. That sounds good," I answer.

"But let's take it slow, okay?" Marvel asks.

"Sure." I smile. My heart pops. It feels this joy.

Then I feel the anxiety start to set in.

DREAM:

The bear sits and eats his honey. He is so happy sitting there with the earth underneath him. He feels the earth; it's cool, not too cold or hot. He eats his honey so pleasing to the mouth. He looks up to see where his Love is.

"Where is she today, he says? Probably flying around; she can never stay still."

"But that is what he loves about her. She, the bird, is so happy when she flies. When she returns, they reconnect and love one another. Yes, he knows they are so different, and he accepts this. She also accepts him. They are committed to being together — despite their differences. They just love hanging together in this third dimension.

"Two egos, two personalities, two souls, so different, yet loving each other's essence. They would be together forever and even after this life, when they are able to travel together to other dimensions. But the truth is, they get to love each other now. They get to brainstorm and create together; nurturing each other and touching each other."

The bear looks up and sees her coming toward his cave. He smiles and she flies right in on his shoulder sliding down across from him.

The bear turns into Marvel and the bird, becomes me.

We roll around naked, feeling our hearts and bodies bound together. We both look up at the sunlight that bursts in through the opening of our home. We smile while soaking in the sunlight!

A chariot appears which is pulled by white horses. Glenda is inside.

"Hello, Glenda." Marvel and I acknowledge her.

"Hello," she answers. "How do you like the chariot, Dorothy. It's like in the book The Wonderful Wizard of Oz."

"You are crazy, you know that right?"

"Yes, I know. But do you know a bear and bird are able to love together. You two are so very different. Bear, you like to spend most of your time in this beautiful cave." Glenda looks around.

"And Bird, you love to spread your wings and fly. Keep flying because that is who you are. Take the time to just reassure your bear every once in a while, that you will be back. You'll always come back.

"And Bear, you enjoy your earth and magnificent cave. Please be patient. Don't get so cranky with Bird when she pokes at you. Bird, don't poke so much — open up more, let him in."

My eyes open. My heart starts pounding remembering the dream.
Can I completely let him in?

275

CHAPTER 21

The Journey Back Home

The kids just left for their dad's. I wait for Marvel to arrive. Anxious, yet excited.

He picks me up and the three-hour car ride feels like a twenty-four-hour ride, half of it was spent in silence. Strange, yet peaceful. We talk about every subject, but us.

I am a little nervous, so I talk excessively.

"In high school, I excelled in sports. As soon as I stepped on the court or field, I felt great pleasure," I say.

"So basically, what you are telling me is that you are still attached to your identity as an athlete and as a girl who helps her peers with personal issues?" Marvel asks. "Do I have this right?"

"Yes, it still is my identity. I am definitely tied to that. It's what kept me going all these years, Marvel. Actually, still today, knowing that I have that skill, makes me feel good. Another form of attachment. Huh?"

Marvel gives me a thumbs-up as he steers the car.

"I was perceived as, yes, one of the 'jocks' of my high school. So, when I received the most outstanding athlete award in my senior year, it wasn't a surprise to most people; although it was a surprise to me. I went out with my party friends that morning before school because it was our field day. It was basically, fun and games all day. Unfortunately, when receiving the award from our principal, who was a priest, I was wasted. My party friends thought it was hysterical. Most of my jock friends had no clue that my vision was blurry, walking up to the stage to receive the award. My teachers were so very excited for me and my mom was in the back of the gym even prouder."

"Seriously? Did you get caught?" Marvel asks.

"Nope," I say, "I was amazing at hiding it."

"Well, let's face it," Marvel says, "you were good at hiding secrets and playing everyone's game. Although, if you got caught, think of the disappointment that you would have experienced. You would have been setting yourself up again for shame, embarrassment and humiliation."

"That is true! Jesus, that would have been embarrassing."

Marvel nods.

"There are so many questions about my life now that I want to look at. This past year and a half with you and the info given has changed my perceptions about the past. What are the real stories? How much was skewed because of my patterns and issues?"

"Denial, silence and secrets," Marvel says.

"True. A few things happened in elementary school that related to the denial, silence and secrets. And there was stuff in high school and college that I really feel messed me up even more."

Stop talking, Dottie.

Marvel chuckles.

"I couldn't say these things in therapy either because I wasn't ready, or they didn't ask the right questions. The two therapists that I did see, the one in college and the one when I was pregnant, felt like I was controlling the sessions. I gave my story of the sexual abuse so openly and then they followed my trend of thought and feelings. They didn't ask the questions that you ask. They didn't stop me in my tracks like you, and tell me I was full of crap and show me a couple different perspectives. So maybe I should start at the beginning and tell you all my secrets and you can guide me through for accuracy. Sounds good?"

"Sounds good!" Marvel chuckles again at my delivery.

"What? Why are you laughing?"

"You just crack me up, that's all."

"Thank you." I say and continue talking.

"Okay, maybe I should bring you back to preschool."

"Hey, we have a long ride." Marvel smirks. "Talk, I like listening to you."

"Okay then. Mrs. Pooles Preschool was an experience that I don't believe that I can put into words. The pleasures of what I experienced without doing it an injustice. It was more like a feeling, rather than what we actually played or learned there. The love and the safety was present for learning about people, socializing, and the beginning of academics. I remember the excitement that I felt when preparing myself for the first grade."

"Well said, Cavarelli. Are you taking your Adderall today?"

"Actually, no. It hasn't really been working lately," I answer. "Before when I took Adderall, it would calm me down. Supposedly, something in the drug would activate the dopamine in my prefrontal cortex to assist me in focusing. Something about balancing out my speediness. But now, when I take it, it makes me jittery. Feels like I am speeding. I guess my dopamine is working now. Ha?"

Marvel laughs and says, "Yeah, maybe. A long time ago they used herbs to assist with illnesses or dysfunctions in the body. Then they realized they could make drugs and the drugs were intended to be something that you temporarily used until you got well. But then drugs became big business, a billion-dollar industry, and the focus went from healing to monetary gain. They deliberately create an image that drugs are the answer and that many diseases that could be cured, are now permanent lifelong diseases."

I nod. "Interesting."

"So, you are evidence of what happens when a person gets well and no longer needs the drugs. What actually happens is that when you heal the source of the illness, or the problem, your body chemistry changes and the drugs become ineffective, or they become harmful, maybe addictive."

I nod again.

"This is not to say that medication is not beneficial, but it must be used in an ethical and logical way; with education, along with a greater awareness of what the root cause of illness is. Unfortunately, there are very few people who understand this."

"Yep," I say.

"So, what were you saying about your first-grade year in the Catholic school," Marvel inquires.

"Well, unfortunately, the Catholic school was a complete disappointment. Structure, sitting up straight, you know the deal, Marvel. Although, you didn't do that! Maybe that is why I liked your class."

"Wait," Marvel replies. "So you liked my class, ay?"

"I didn't like you, but I liked the material you were teaching." I smile.

I slap him on the leg, feeling much more comfortable with him in so many ways. I can act like myself — like with the football guys. No flirting because he wouldn't even recognize it, or even care.

He is now just a person who is simply witnessing my growth, as if I am talking to myself. I will trust him and question everything he says and feel if it is right for me. I now realize that I have nothing to risk except the discovery of self. I am finally in a safe place.

"And then remember when I told you that my second-grade teacher placed our desks up against the wall. I still will never understand that."

"Oh, yes, with Leo, Brian and Tim? That's right."

"What kind of teacher does this?"

"Well, maybe a teacher that couldn't handle you. You were probably spinning like a maniac and she didn't know what to do with you," Marvel says. "I don't know why the boys were there. Well, Leo, I could understand. But Brian and Tim — not so much. I can only make up a story of why. And besides, you should be thanking this teacher."

"Why?"

"Isn't that when you formed your team?" Marvel says, "Wait, maybe, I should be the one thanking her. Hah."

I smile at him.

Marvel laughs. "Okay, Dottie, what else ya got?"

"Well, I was thinking about my grandmom the other day. She was a 'take action' kind of lady. In like 1938, she left my grandpop."

"Wow," Marvel says. "That didn't happen much in 1938."

"It was only for two weeks, but she made a statement. I remember my mom telling me that story so many times. That her mom refused to stay in her house unless her mother-in-law left. When she told my grandpop this, nothing happened. Her mother-in-law didn't leave, and so my grandmom left, although her mother-in-law went up there two weeks later to convince her mom to come back home. It was good for her mom because her mom spoke up. I would imagine that those behaviors changed her life!"

"Yep."

"It's funny, because that was the one thing that my mom would say to me and what she learned from my mom that she spoke up and went after what she wanted."

Marvel nods.

"But it wasn't good for my mom."

"Why is that?"

"Well, for those two weeks, her pop-pop sexually abused my mom. And my mom always resented her dad for not coming to get her. She blamed him. I remember my mom saying, 'My dad waited until his mother came to get us. She was the one who saved me from that terrible situation.'"

"And the patterns begin," Marvel says.

I look up at Marvel.

"I remember what you told me about what your mom would say. 'Only women can get things done. Men are wimps, men sexually abuse, men don't follow through, and more importantly, DON'T trust them.'"

"Exactly! Oh, Jesus!" I say putting my hand on my forehead. "And that is what we were taught! Not directly but indirectly."

"Yep!"

"And not all men are wimps, sexually abuse and don't follow through. That is just an example of a belief that may be lodged into a person."

"Yep!"

280

"So, when my grandmom returned home, she told my grandpop, that the only way that she would stay with him would be if he sent her to school."

"Really, in 1938?"

"Yep. So, Grandpop sent his wife to massage school," I inform.

"Really?" Marvel says. "Massage school, how cool is that, in 1938?"

"Yes. She worked at this fancy hair, nail and massage place. Supposedly, she became well-known and was wanted for her great healing hands. And believe me, her hands rocked. She would grab a hold of you and you could feel the healing. Well, I could. My family would not label it healing hands. One time I was sleeping over at her house. I was probably about ten or eleven. My neck was completely stiff. I came down for breakfast and my head was turned to the right and I couldn't move it. It was completely stuck. I was crying. She says, 'Come here, sweetie.' She basically moved my head and neck like a chiropractor would. I remember the feeling of it. It was exactly like a chiropractor. It scared the crap out of me!"

Marvel laughs.

"But I was normal again, and I don't know how she did it! She then massaged my head and I felt something go through her hands. It was incredible."

"Well, you are always talking about wanting to be normal."

"Ha! I do say that a lot, don't I?"

"Yes, you do. Well, I hate to break it to you, but you're still not normal, Cavarelli!"

I give him another smack on the knee.

"Ya know, my mom told me that a couple of movie stars would request her for massages."

"That's funny."

"But more importantly, the mother-in-law immediately moved out of their house to her dad's sister's place."

"So, your mother gained some knowledge and saw that when things weren't right, you could change them," Marvel says. "That's one good thing that came out of it."

"Yes, now that I think about it, there was another time that I was impressed with my grandmom. I was in grade school. I was very upset because I had ordered a year subscription of the *Sassy* magazine. Only one magazine arrived. *Sassy* went out of business and I never received another, but I paid for the year. So, my grandmom got on the phone and I watched her talk to customer service. Oh, my. Kindly, yet persuasively she demanded our money back or to be sent old subscriptions. Well, I did receive my money back. And it changed something in me. It showed me that I could have a voice and ask for what I wanted."

"So anyway, in theory, it sounds good, and yes, did Grandmom rub off on you in some aspects of your life? Yes, she did. You could speak up as long as what? Can you answer that question?" Marvel asks.

"If I didn't bring up things that disturbed the rest of the family, like secrets."

"Yep."

"Ha, too funny, but very true. I can speak up outside of the family. Like for instance, when I was in the sixth grade, the bus stop was located down at the end of the block. Everyone who rode that bus lived on the other end of the neighborhood. I was the only one close to the bus stop. 'Why?' I used to say to the bus driver. The bus stop should be closer to everyone's house, so everyone didn't have to walk so far. I explained my idea to the bus driver, and she agreed just like that. 'You are right. That does make sense, Dorothy. So, we will change it.' This was the same bus driver who allowed me to eat my breakfast toast on the bus every morning, regardless of the sign that read, 'No food or drink on bus.' In fact, I use to make toast and butter for her as well. It didn't make sense that if I was making one piece of toast for myself and there were two slots in the toaster, why wouldn't I make a buttered toast for a person who commented how yummy my breakfast looked every morning. Why wouldn't I make her one? Logical, reasonable and rational, wouldn't you say?"

Marvel grins at the mentioning of one of his concepts.

"Yep. That sounds about right." Marvel laughs. "Stop chasing for approval and love, Dottie. You are allowed to care and have your own opinion. Speak so others will understand. You no longer have to give up your soul, power or whatever you would like to call it."

Marvel smiles. I smile back. A connection is made. There's a moment of silence.

Marvel looks at me feeling my mind to start again. "Yes? Ya got some more?"

"I was just thinking that I really worked hard at mastering those relationships with males so there were no surprises."

"What relationships?"

"Oops, sorry, relationships in general. Like men. Sorry, I was referring to what my mom taught me about men."

"Okay, so, you should think about a transitional statement before you start another topic. You do this often."

I nod and say, "Am I annoying you?"

"No, but it could get to be a problem."

"Okay." I smile, a little embarrassed.

"No need to be embarrassed or whatever you are feeling. I am just telling you. I would expect you to tell me about my behaviors as well."

"Thanks. Okay."

"So back to relationships, Dottie."

"Well, I kept them at arm's length. I had a certain way that I communicated with them, so there weren't any misunderstandings. This is where I stand. I'm sure I seemed a bit bossy at times. I know I did, but that was the only way I knew how to behave with them," I say.

"Well, remember, men were wimps. You could control them."

"Oh, yeah, I didn't think of that. Oh, I did manipulate them. And I tended to hang with boys that were a little wimpy. Oh, geez." I put my head down feeling kind of bad.

"Remember, these are patterns that you were unaware of," Marvel says. "Now that you are aware, you can change your behaviors. For some, it's hard to continue the same patterns when you are aware of them, for others, not so much."

Marvel chuckles.

"Well, then in fifth or sixth grade, things changed; I stopped being bossy with the boys. I no longer wanted to play football with the boys. I don't know what happened. I started kissing them and the tables turned. I no longer was in charge, because this was something I was uncomfortable with and I allowed things to happen. Maybe it was the influence of the other girls, the way they looked, the clothes that they wore. I wanted to fit in. I went from sweats to girl clothes. Why do we change like this? You can say puberty, but I don't think so."

Marvel chuckles again.

"With this behavior change, came the guilt, the feeling dirty and the feeling of 'I just was used.' I did not feel good about any of it, but I kept doing it. Each encounter was worse than the time before. It felt awful.

"And then in February, of my seventh-grade year, my father was dead. And then you know the story. It devastated me, Marvel. As a child, I remember thinking, 'I was bad. I am doing bad things, and now, my dad is watching me.'

"I loved my dad and I hated my dad. I hated him because he made me nervous because he would lose his temper by yelling at me to calm down. I loved him, but knew that I was always in his way and I drove him crazy. Now if I would have known the secret that he was on chemotherapy and that living in his body was completely and utterly hell, I would have had the chance to understand his perspective. Instead, I hated that he didn't love me. So now he was dead, and I felt so guilty — more guilt, more pushing down feelings," I say. "Geez, I am a mess."

"Dottie, he didn't hate you. He probably hated your behaviors."

"Oh, yes, that computes."

"Sounds like you were a little like your mom, a little spinning, yes?"

"I guess she was but I didn't notice because I was on the fast train with her."

Marvel laughs.

"What about your dad, Marvel?" I ask.

"My dad?"

"Yeah."

"That was a tough one for me. My human had to adjust to that loss. Our relationship was a bit rocky growing up but back then I didn't quite understand all the ins and outs of family patterning. My mother was a little imbalanced. I began my self-discovery at a very early age. I really had no choice. I couldn't help but feel everything. I was quite sensitive like you, as you probably can gather. My mom and dad gave me some pretty good twisted up family dysfunctional material to work with in regard to the work I do today."

I smile.

There was silence in the car. And then more silence.

"Well, I have to say that things really did change for me after my dad died. I was looking through life in a new way then. Not only was I kissing boys, I added a little drinking and smoking pot to the equation so I didn't have to feel the pain. I felt guilty that I probably killed him. That was a tough time, Marvel. I really did believe that he was watching me after he died. This added to the guilt."

"Ha, that's funny."

"No seriously, that is the Catholic stuff. There is someone always watching you."

"Well, he probably did see you. But I don't believe in the way you think he saw you, and he certainly wasn't judging you."

I nod.

"So, you believed that he could see all the bad things that you had done and what you were doing?" Marvel asks.

"The rest of my seventh-grade year, I became more and more paranoid. I felt things like I'd never felt before. And each time I felt, I would self-medicate with alcohol, marijuana, and by the time I reached high school, I added other substances to the mix — really anything that I could get my hands on."

"In seventh grade?"

"Yep!"

"I was bad, but I was known as a good girl."

"Deception."

"Yes, I was deceiving myself," I say.

"I played sports and went to the prom and acted like a puppet. I knew how to blend and be a chameleon. I mastered it, so I wouldn't be found out. Kept it hidden — kept it silent. Never tell," I add.

"One time I was sitting in sociology class, pretty hung over after prom. My teacher, who had been a chaperone at the prom, says to me, in front of everyone, 'Hey, Cavarelli, how are you feeling in that body of yours, Miss Most Valuable Player of the year?' She widened her eyes and smiles. I just couldn't believe it. She knew it. She was younger than most and more aware than all of them. I was so embarrassed. I knew my fake image was over. I really liked her. I disappointed her."

"Marvel, that is pretty messed up."

"Yep," Marvel agrees.

"Messed up that I felt that I had to hold up an image. And messed up that I had to numb myself."

"Yep. It was."

"But I feel I lived two different lives," I add, "Every once in a while, I felt this feeling that came over me — this feeling of great wisdom. It would typically be when someone would ask me for advice. It would be a feeling that I knew would help — that my words would change things. I don't know what this feeling did to people, but I could feel it help them in some way. I could feel this invisible thing being transferred to a person when I was helping them. It was weird, like all the fear, guilt and pain would disappear when I was in this state of being. Kind of like how I can see that someone was sexually abused, prior to them telling me. This was probably another image that I held for myself. That's messed up."

"Yep!" Marvel says. "And yes, Dottie, your words and the energy behind your words, changed things. You don't need to figure it out in your mind all the time. Breathe Dottie!"

I take a deep breath.

I smile at Marvel, thanking him for the confirmation and the adjustment of the words that I needed to hear.

I start to continue my story and Marvel stops me.

"Wait; let that one sink in a bit." Marvel instructs, "Again, receive information."

Marvel's brows rise up and turns to me. "Okay?"

"Okay," I say and look up, noticing that we are stopped at a traffic light.

We are off the highway and driving through the town. I didn't even notice.

I wait for a sec and take another deep breath. A couple moments pass. I glance over at Marvel.

"What else?" Marvel says.

"It seems that I am going to tell you all of my sad moments, huh?"

"It seems."

"Well, let's see. It was sophomore year, one day after basketball practice; I called home for a ride. Didn't have my license yet. My brother answered the phone. 'I can pick you up,' he says. I was confused why mom couldn't pick me up.

"Grandmom Lulu had a heart attack."

"Is she okay?" I asked.

"I can just pick you up."

"Is she okay?" I asked again.

No answer.

He picked me up and in the car told me that my grandmom Lulu had died. The way he told me was in a caring way.

"Are you okay? I didn't want to tell you over the phone."

"Hey, in a way it felt better than a neighbor telling me, or telling me to go play and pretend it didn't happen. Hey, at least a family member told me; although he did show me, or we will say confirm to me that a substance like alcohol was the answer to not feel pain.

"We got home and went down to the bar in the basement and he said, 'Want a drink? I am having one.' I refused, of course, I wasn't stupid. Never would I have a drink near home. Hey, but at least he wasn't a hypocrite. He wasn't hiding the truth and keeping it a secret. He drank right in front of me. I watched him pound down a couple until the rest of the family got home."

"Yep, that was truthful," Marvel says.

I nod.

"Alcohol is one way not to feel the pain, although, it's so temporary. And then how you feel in the morning, sometimes, not so good."

"What else do you have stored in there?" Marvel asks as he pulls into the gas station. He turns in his seat to listen.

"Did I ever tell you about my professor at the University in the summer after high school?"

"No, I don't believe so," Marvel says. "Please tell me that it wasn't something that you regretted."

"No, not at all. I was staying away from any kind of relationship at this point."

"Okay, then shoot," Marvel says smiling at me.

"Well, it was my first semester at the University. I attended in June. It all started when this professor handed back our first tests in my Western Civilization class. He expressed that he was disappointed and couldn't believe that everyone in the class had failed the test. Obviously, he never taught in the June — January program before. It was a program for students that had some difficulties in school. If you received three Bs in June, then you were eligible to return in the fall. If not, you could return in January," I explain.

"So, I thought 'Didn't this professor understand that these students had challenges that you can't quite see?' I studied the professor more closely, using my intuitive skills, and I realized that he didn't get it. So, at that point, I had about enough. I would tell him the truth. After class I went to his office and explained to him about these types of students. I had been observing students in school for years. That's just what I did. I knew the different types. I explained how most of them weren't following him because he was going too fast. He needed to write some kind of outline on the board. But most importantly, he needed to slow down. I finished my monologue with an attitude of 'You gotta get this, it's important and I know what I am observing and saying is correct.'

This was not my usual method of using my bubbly personality in a school setting. I looked at this gray-haired man sitting in his office chair with a blank look on his face, and he said, 'I will make a note of it.' I nodded, said thanks and quietly walked out of his office."

I continue, "I thought, oh damn, what did I just do? I shuffled into class the following Monday, after the professor had plenty of time over the weekend to laugh over beers with his fellow professors at the freshman who told him how to teach. What would he do? Would he make it even more difficult for us? Did he listen? Did he even understand? Would he completely ignore me? My life would change at that moment. I waited in anticipation, a little embarrassed, a little excited. Was my college life over before it began?

"The professor walked in the room and picked up a piece of chalk. 'A little bird told me,' he said as he winked at me, "that I was going too fast and that I need to slow down and write an outline on the board, so here goes.' He turned his back towards the board, with chalk in hand, and started to teach. I received a score of 88 on the second test. Before the third test, I went to his office before class. As soon as he saw me, he said with a chuckle, 'What did I do now? Am I teaching okay?' I said, 'No, you are teaching fine. I just want to know if I could take that test in a quiet room to eliminate distractions and all.' He said yes, of course. I received a score of 92 on that test.

"What the professor did may not seem profound to the average person who has typical learning patterns, but to me, it meant everything. His words warmed my heart, bringing a smile to my face, heart and head. At that moment, I knew that I could do this college thing — that I could do anything. That revealed that being honest, speaking your truth and asking for what you need, is how you can not only get by, but create what you want here on earth. Because he listened to me, and really heard me, it showed that I could make a difference in the world, in *my* world, with *my* creations."

"That was a good memory for you, Dottie!" Marvel says smiling.

"It really was," I answer.

"In the fall, I decided to go to Europe with my soccer club team instead of the University. School could wait until January. After Europe, everything opened up for me in every way. I came back different and I felt this sort of freedom that was difficult to explain. Were my issues gone as a result of this freedom?"

Marvel smiles. "Nope."

"Nope. Still there and still going strong," I agree.

We both laugh.

Silence again.

Still in the car at the gas station, I look around to see if anyone is noticing us. I continue. "I attended the local community college where I felt more focused. As I said before, I wasn't interested in guys, especially my age, so I decided to play volleyball with a bunch of thirty-year-olds."

"Oh, no." Marvel jokes.

"No. This is another good memory!

"I hung with a bunch of older people who were already in their careers. I found them fascinating and interesting to watch them interact. They played their share of games, and I don't mean volleyball, but what I did like about them was that they said what was on their minds.

"My mom was a little skeptical at first, when they would pick me up, especially on a school night. They had a way of talking to her that made her feel at ease.

"'Mrs. Cavarelli, we need Dorothy to 'set' tonight. We need her for the volleyball game. We will have her back by 10pm.' They always kept their promise. The guys would take care of me. If anyone messed with me, they had my back. I am just realizing now that they played the same role as my football buddies back in grade school."

"Sounds great," Marvel says.

"Yes, it was. I went back to the University in the spring, and I tried being very selective in who I hung out with. I tried dating a couple of guys, but it was never fulfilling. I never felt the happiness I was seeking."

"Dottie, you were, and still are, seeking someone else to provide you with the love you must find inside yourself. Unfortunately, society directly teaches that sex is a way to get a mate or to have someone love you. This is especially true for women. Women are taught, through the media and family beliefs, that their lady parts are the key to love, and then it is often used as power, or given away to see who will love them," Marvel says.

"I was with more guys than I feel I should have been before my ex-husband," I admit. "I met Don my last year at the University."

"How many women were you with, Marvel?" I ask.

"Are you seriously asking me this?" Marvel smiles "You don't want to know."

"How many Marvel?" I say, already knowing the answer.

"Two," Marvel says.

I put my head down again.

"Typically, when people engage in this type of behavior, their worth and value and self-love are not present. So, they looked outside themselves to fill that emptiness. They must understand that their heart is sensory. Their soul is sensory. They confuse sensate love with sex, although love is sensory. They seek this sensory part, by having sex, through other people to fill the emptiness, which will never fulfill you or give you what you seek.

"What they do not realize is sex does not equal love or being loved. Nor does it eliminate the feeling of worthlessness within. Sex can be a beautiful thing when you are connected to someone, but it can never connect you with someone. It can create the illusion of being connected, but that's it. And that is all in your mind.

"After a sexual experience, because of their beliefs and patterns, people typically go to their head. They judge it as bad, or that they were taken advantage of. Because they went into the experience wanting something or believing they would gain something. They had a feeling like they had value, that the person will now pay attention to them, as opposed to just wanting to have the experience for themselves.

"Sometimes they do it out of peer pressure, because everyone else is doing it. Then other times, they may use it to control others, get what they want, or because the sensory feeling was like getting high and they could temporarily forget their feelings which may become an addiction to forget. The judgment of having sex may now compound the worthlessness issue, because they see themselves as dirty, bad, wrong or worse. Now that puts a double lock down on the heart; therefore, turning off the sensate body and the heart. They yearn for feeling this love, and the sex is tempting because they can feel again. You must understand we are talking about how sex for unhealthy reasons creates these problems. Sex, in its higher form is beautiful and magnificent. But rarely are people ready for the higher form; especially, when they are young.

"The negative part about sex comes when people are not making a conscious, neutral decision to be intimate with someone. Their intentions are to get something from it, however unconscious it may be. When they return to the mind, they typically go into autopilot to protect the heart. This shuts down the heart, and they return to the emptiness. This is not what everyone does, but it is the majority, especially for women.

"So, what you have to learn here is that the heart is sensual and that it is the source of sensuality. When one touches the physical through sex and sexual relations, they're also connecting with the sensual body or what we have called the sensate body. If one lives through the mind, the sensate body is not awakened, nor is it deliberately put to sleep to avoid feeling. That's because when one feels, it brings up memories in this and other experiences. The sensual body is often confused with the sensate body. The heart must be open to connect with the sensate body. Even if the heart is not open, and you have not accessed the sensate body, you will feel sensuality. That is because the physical body is sensual in nature.

"When the heart is perceived as empty, it's because it is detached from their own essence, or inner self for multiple reasons. Manifested as outside programming — focused on others to give their love. They were taught that you get it from others, or you must give it to others, to get it, which is totally absurd.

"Typically, when people look to the sexual area to stimulate temporary fulfillment, they seek the stimulation of the sensate body in order to stimulate the heart. So, when the body is physically aroused, the heart chakra is stimulated, and they temporarily feel the love and value. When they come back from that experience, they tend to go to the mind, and then the heart goes empty again, and they may constantly seek the sexual experience to stimulate the heart.

"Again, all too often people confuse sensual, sensate and sex. One reason is that sex stimulates the physical body, and at some level, the heart which is then interpreted as love and that it comes from sex or another person. What they don't realize is it is stimulating the memory of self-love.

"It is a false addiction to experience self-love and value. They may have those moments where they don't care about the human results of sleeping around because the feeling and sense of worth and value is more important at that moment. Typically, when they come back from the experience again. The mind turns on and shuts off the feelings, and then they go back to worthlessness and whatever guilt or shame for having sex.

"In the long run, they may feel it is worth it, because they have no other way to find that solace of self-love and worth. Everyone should know that they are the love itself, and need it from no one. They may share their love if they choose."

I glance up at Marvel and nod.

"Too much?"

I shrug my shoulders. "Yes, too much."

I smile at him.

We arrive at our destination. After we check into the hotel, he hands me my room key.

"Hey! It's about 4pm now, so I was thinking we could go grab a bite to eat first." Marvel motions to the restaurant across the street. "Then turn in. We have to be at the campus pretty early tomorrow morning."

"Sure," I tell him.

At dinner, we start to talk, again about everything but us.

"When was your first experience with the paranormal?" I inquire.

"Really?" he asks. "That's what you want to ask me?"

"Yep!"

"I would say, hmmm, it was 1961 when I was about six years old."

"And?"

"And what?"

"Continue. Marvel, you have to learn to share."

"Maybe you're right." He smiles at me and begins to talk. "You might need to remind me time and time again.

"I was in my bed and having difficulty sleeping. So, I rolled over and looked on the floor next to my bed. There was a *Look* magazine. I don't know if you remember the *Look* magazine."

"Nope."

"Well, to my surprise, the woman on the cover began to come off the page. In sheer terror, I hid under the covers, and for quite some time I never looked at a magazine before going to sleep. After that, I seemed to have the uncanny ability to often know people's real intentions and the meaning behind their words. I felt I had this ability earlier, but had no conscious memory of it. Although my perceptions were often denied validity by my parents, they felt right to me. After being told I was wrong for many years, I began to believe my parents, only to find out, around thirteen, that I had often been correct. This angered me. It created resentment and issues about not being heard, which I have had to work through. It seems that sometimes adults are caught up in their world and do not truly listen to their children."

"So, do you remember telling our seventh-grade class about that Terry guy from England? You said you travelled with him, or something. You implied that he saw things. You didn't really tell us much more than that. But I did always wonder."

"Oh, you did, did you?" Marvel says.

I smile.

"Yeah, I miss that guy," Marvel says with a sigh. "He died in the 90s. He actually said to me right before he stepped on the airplane, for a visit back to England, 'Michael, you have enough.' I never understood what he meant. That was the last day that I saw him."

"Wow, really?"

"He realized that he was a healer at a very young age. When he was a young boy, when the soldiers came home from World War II in England, his father would take him to the boat to see the soldiers return. One of these times, Terry walked up to one of the soldiers in a wheel chair, having just come off the boat, and remembers laying his hands on his legs and the soldier got up and walked. That was one of the first times that he knew he was different and had healing abilities.

"Also, during the war, when the Germans were bombing England, his father told him that he heard an inner voice that their farm would be protected and not to move the family. And sure enough, all the farms were hit by some sort of bombing, except theirs. His father was also a well-known healer, and herbalist in the surrounding towns."

"That's pretty cool." I smile.

"Anyway, Terry taught me a lot. He really understood the sensate body," Marvel adds.

"What is the sensate body?" I ask.

"Really? Do you really want to know?" Marvel asks as he takes a bite of his broccoli.

Finally, something else other than an omelet and chocolate bar.

"Yes," I say.

"The sensate body is the energetic, invisible aspect of a person that determines their sensate experience — this includes their emotions. This is the system of sentience, sensuality and sensing. It is through the sensate body that the five physical senses are activated. This system is connected to, but not governed by, the mental body or the mind," Marvel says as he puts down the fork and taps the side of my head.

I stare at Marvel.

"Dottie, are you there?"

"Ya know, I was just thinking. Were you really that Herman guy? Mr. Einstein's colleague, from a past life. What do you think about that? Wait, don't tell me, Marvel. Why does it matter?"

"Exactly, why does it matter?" Marvel laughs. "The point being that I am here now."

And I am thrilled to be with you... here, now.

Silence.

"Hello, Dottie. Are you there?"

"Oh, Jesus, Marvel. I am here."

"What's he got to do with this?"

"Okay, let's talk about that. Do you know him?"

"We talk from time to time. Well, not in this time," Marvel chuckles.

I look at him, not too sure if he is being serious or not.

Marvel stops and stares at me. He finally initiates it.

"What do you suppose we do about 'us'?" Marvel asks.

Hearing the word "us" feels natural.

"I need to tell you, and ask you some things before we start this. You need to love yourself enough that you always come first. I come first with me. That makes a great relationship. And what I mean by that is, you must check with you first, not make decisions based on someone else, like me."

Not a typical first date.

"You need to be able to identify when something comes up for you — like for example when I trigger you. You have to be able to communicate and work through it together."

Definitely not a typical first date.

"I won't settle for anything that is not this. In other words, I am not willing to settle for anything that is not completely about our growth. I would rather live alone for the rest of my life, than have to struggle unnecessarily."

Okay. Let's get started.

"There is so much more that you need to learn. Does that make sense?"

What makes more sense is learning as I go, sweetie.

"Yes," I say and decide to say what I am thinking, too. "But what makes more sense is learning as I go. Applying what I have learned so far."

"It's not as easy as it sounds," Marvel says. "You have to be willing to stop and look at yourself when you are in the middle of your issue — when your patterns kick in. I guarantee you that I will trigger you. Do you think that you can do that?"

Of course, my love. Everything will be okay.

"Of course," I respond.

"You crack me up, Cavarelli."

"Why?"

"Because of your optimism."

"You crack me up, Michael."

"Finally! We are on a first name basis!"

"Well, I couldn't be calling you Marvel if we are going to do this, could I?"

Marvel smiles.

"I never planned on doing this ever again — I mean being with anyone else. It was just too difficult."

Me either. Our eyes lock again.

"Okay, it's my turn," I announce. "You know when you said that a new relationship may look different, but patterns will be the same. You are different than any other guy I know."

"No, I must be like someone. Who am I like in your family?"

"No one. Every guy I have gone out with up until now was like my brother. I didn't really know my dad."

"What little did you know about your dad?"

"He was cranky, but sweet and witty at times. He seemed to make everyone laugh, except me. I guess I was too young to understand his jokes. He insulted me a lot. Is that what you plan on doing?"

"Of course not, well maybe," he jokes.

"I am sure you picked up something about him, making you believe something about the male partner. I remember my mom and dad fighting a lot. But then they stopped. I believe that is when he was sick. She didn't want to upset him, ever. My mom and I were sweet to him when we would go out to dinner. I do remember if he was feeling happy then Mom felt better. That's really all I can remember."

"Hmmm," Marvel contemplates. "What attracts you to me?"

"You are darling, and when I look in your eyes, I see you, your beautiful soul. That is all I see. It's something in your eyes. It's actually pretty cool."

"Oh," Marvel takes a breath.

I stare at him wanting to melt right into him; become transparent and merging right in with him.

We continue eating and don't really say much more about the subject. We walk back to the hotel.

"Okay," Marvel says, "I guess we should turn in for the night, yes?"

"Okay, sure." *I want to kiss him.*

"Okay, then," he says.

"Okay," I turn towards the door with my room key in hand. "Have a good night, then."

"Good night, Dottie," Marvel says and smiles, his eyes sparkle.

The next morning I open my hotel room door to find Marvel just ready to knock on it.

"Hey you," he says.

I say, "Hey. Good morning."

"Breakfast?" Marvel asks motioning me to lead the way to the lobby.

"Yep. I am almost done. Come in."

"Okay." Marvel steps through the door, looks around, and then slides into the chair.

I go to the mirror and finish putting on my mascara.

I can feel him staring. I turn around. "What? I told you, Marvel, I am not giving up mascara!"

"You feel nice today or..." Marvel stops. "You look nice today."

"Thank you."

"Are you ready?"

"Yes."

We leave the room. Eat breakfast and didn't talk much. Marvel pays at the register as I check out the desserts in the case. I can feel him watching me as I turn and smile at him.

"What?" I say.

"Oh, nothing. You're sweet."

The day is over before we know it. His last meeting is with the head counselors. I watch him how he transitions his language to the different levels of staff. He is amazing as usual.

In the car, heading towards home, I sit closer to him this time. He looks at me and smiles. He turns back towards the steering wheel. We ride not saying much. I have this feeling of love that is indescribable. I look at him again.

Oh my. I love him. I love him for who he is. I love him from another place and time. I know this love. I feel my pulse and racing heart.

This feeling stays with me for quite some time. He pulls up to my house, I reach for my bags. "Okay, Marvel, Michael, whoever you are," I smile. "That was fun!"

I kiss him on the cheek and feel the pulse again.

"Dottie, I need to know if you are serious," Marvel says.

Serious?
I answer, "What do you mean?"

"I don't want to go any further with you if you are not serious."

I stare at Marvel.

Not too sure what he means by serious.

"Yes. That was fun this weekend. I just need to know. Do you really want to do this?" There was something different in his eyes.

"Do what?"

He continues, "I don't want to go any further, if you are not serious."

My anxieties replace the feelings that I just had minutes ago.

I don't know.

"Can I have the weekend to think about it?"

Did I just say that? Ugh. That didn't come out right.

"What I meant to say is, I need the weekend to feel this."

"Okay," he answers smiling. "You feel it, and then let me know."

I get out of the car. Open the door to the back seat and grab my bag. Michael looks back at me with his beautiful brown eyes. He touches my hand gently. "Have a good night, Dottie."

"You, too." I stop to notice his eyes, lovely and bright as ever. "See ya."

I walk towards the house. My heart beats fast. I don't know why I am surprised. Marvel doesn't do anything half-assed. Completely upfront.

"Holy crap!"

CHAPTER 22

Over The Rainbow

I wake up fresh. I text the kids from my bed — although I don't know why. I can smell the aroma of pancakes which tells me they have arrived home. They are already here from their dad's house. Christopher would be cooking, Kacey in her room, and Megan floating about the house.

I quickly change and then take a deep breath, which forces the excitement into my lungs. I smile thinking that I will see their faces soon. I walk to the top of the stairs, where I find Megan looking up at me from the bottom.

"Hey, you," I say.

"Hi. I was just coming up to get you. We made breakfast for you."

"You did? What did ya make me? I hope something good."

"Your favorite," Megan exclaims.

"Yessss!" I say scrunching my fist with excitement.

"Raisin Bran with soy milk. I don't get how you like that crap, Mom." Megan's language is changing each day she completes another day at middle school.

"What else are you making down there? I can smell something else. Is Chris —

Megan interrupts, a familiar pattern. "Dad gave us the rest of his chocolate chips. And yes, Chris is making chocolate chip pancakes!"

I sigh. "And Kacey?"

"Where do you think? Duh… Mom," Megan again sharing her new language.

"In her room?" I ask.

"Yes, and probably sorting out her sodas," Megan says sarcastically.

"Let me go check on her." I walk to the bottom of the stairs, give Megan a hug, and walk back upstairs towards Kacey's room. Megan follows me up the stairs but goes towards her bedroom.

I knock, touching the door lightly. "Kacey?"

"Come in, Mom." Kacey says, on her knees with her hands in the mini-fridge.

"Why didn't you come in and wake me?" I inquire.

"Chris told me not to."

"Since when do you listen to Chris?" I wonder.

"He told me that he wouldn't put chocolate chips in my pancakes if I woke you."

"Smart," I say referring to Chris.

"How many do you got there?" I point to the six-pack of soda in the fridge that she bought for $2.95. She sells soda to her brother and sister for a dollar.

"Did you make any sales, today?" I tease.

"No, because Chris said that he wouldn't make me any pancakes at all if I charged him today."

"Oh, really?" I answer with my palm in front of my face so she wouldn't see me smiling. "So, missy," I spread myself out on her bed, "how ya doing? Did you have a good time at Dad's?"

"Yes." Kacey moves to her feet to talk to me. "So, what did you do?"

"I went with Marvel upstate to help him with a workshop."

"Upstate?" Kacey asks. She always wants to know everything down to the very little detail.

"Upstate means the upper part of Pennsylvania."

"How long did it take you to get there?" she inquires.

"Like three hours."

"Wow, did you have fun?"

"Yes, it was fun."

No more questions from Kacey. Her focus is more on the soda now. She places the last one in, shuts the door, and then jumps up on the bed with me.

"So," I say.

"So," Kat copies my hands gestures that are tucked under my chin; her eye's bright blue staring directly into mine.

"So, I was thinking," I say as I have Kacey's full attention, "that I might go on a date with that Mr. Marvel guy this week. What do you think about that?"

"Who? Michael?"

"Yeah, Michael," I say covering my smile once again.

"Well, he is a nice guy, and you get along with him. And you like working together and you have fun with him. Where will you go?" she says with excitement. "Can I come?!"

"No, honey. You can't come." Again, I hold up my hand to hide my smile. "But I will let you know if I have fun. And maybe you can come the next time."

"I think you definitely should go on a date with him, Mom," Kacey says as she gets up, grabs a soda from the fridge and heads towards the door. She stops and turns around and says excitedly, "Those pancakes smell good. Don't they?!"

I nod as I watch her leave for some pancakes.

I sit in her room, still on the bed, but now rolled over on my back. "She thinks I should," I say out loud. I smile and spread my arms out.

Megan walks by the entrance. "She thinks that you should do what?"

"Kacey thinks I should go out on a date with Marvel."

"Who? Michael?"

"Yes, Michael," I answer laughing at the fact that my kids call him Michael and I still don't.

"Yeah, where ya gonna go?"

"I don't know yet."

"You should," she says and gives me a thumbs-up. She walks towards the chocolate scent.

I jump up and race Megan down the stairs as she holds herself firm to not let me pass. This is a game that we have been playing since she was little — one of the few games that she still doesn't think is too old for her.

"Hey, Mom. We should play soccer outside in the yard sometime. We haven't done that in a while?" When she was little, I would dribble the soccer ball around the yard, in between her legs. I kept the ball away from her, which brought her a lot of frustration — until she caught on. When she learned to hold her own, there were times that I couldn't get it away from her. I loved those times. This was when she was a part of me, and I was a part of her.

We have a great day catching up and sharing our stories. We enjoy ourselves at the park. At one point, I stop and reflect. If I move forward with Marvel, and it becomes something more, it will change the dynamic for the four of us. The thought of this causes some anxiety, working its way through my system, like lava does thru the earth's surface.

At least it's not a tornado.

Thoughts begin to race in, seeing clearly that I am considering this. The transition feels a little scary. A part of me wants to retreat back and stay in my own world — where it's safe. But I want it more than being in a safe comfortable place. I want him next to me. I want to grow old together, side by side. How can I know this? Why is this so clear, yet so scary at the same time?

I look up at Christopher as he pushes Kacey on the merry-go-round.

"Guess what, Chris. Mom is going on a date with Michael!" Kacey blabs.

Chris stops what he's doing and looks at me with curious eyes. "Seriously?"

I say, "Yeah, well maybe."

"Maybe or not really, or probably not?" Christopher starts to sound like the guys. 'Be direct, Cavarelli,' they would tease.

"Well, yes. What do you think?"

"Are you nervous or something?" he says not answering my question.

"Well, no... why?"

"Because this is how you feel when you are nervous. In fact, you are not really direct when you're nervous."

"How did you get so smart, Christopher?" I tease him, pushing his hair out of his face.

"Yes, Mom, I think that you should go out with him," he says giving Kacey another push.

Why are the kids fine with this, but I am a big bag of nerves? I was fine before the 'are you serious' question was asked. I smile thinking about Marvel and his face. I love him. I know what I want. I know what I will do.

I try to stay present the rest of the day. I enjoy the rest of the night with the munchkins and my alone time before falling asleep.

DREAM:

The same bear from last night's dream appears. "Whatcha got there?"

"Nothing," I say as the Bird.

"It's something."

"I can't show you now. I have a question for you. If I come with you, will you have to see everything about me?"

"Why wouldn't I want to see everything, and why wouldn't you want to show me everything?"

"All my secrets? What's really inside?"

"Don't you think I know everything anyway?" the Bear chuckles.

I fly around the room. "There's more, ya know?"

"The only one who will be judging is you."

I fly away as I hear a Billy Joel song playing. "Don't you ever let your lover see the stranger in yourself."

305

I fly out of the cave into a tornado. It swirls down into a garden of poppy seeds. At first, they make me sleepy and then the sun beats down removing all the poppies. The Bird turns into me. The Bear turns into Marvel.

I have this incredible feeling inside of me. I have white clothing on and feel a peace that I have never felt before.

Glenda appears and says, "A Bear and a Bird? Living together, hmmm! They may love each another, but can they live together?"

My eyes open. I want to be back there — back in the dream state. I want to feel the grass and the sun again. I want to feel the bear again. I want to be with the bear, even though I am a bird. I don't even know what I am saying. Am I still dreaming? I turn towards the window. I try closing my eyes again, but it fails. I continue to lay there and try to imagine the grass and sun and that peaceful feeling. Perhaps I can try to create this same dream-like feeling here in my awakening.

Can I make this wonderful feeling a reality for me here on earth?

I want to be with the Bear?

I sit up; *I want to be with the Bear!* I reach over to grab my phone. Move to text mode and write:

Me: wanna talk

My heart races.

Marvel: sure

He answers so quickly, like he was right next to me. I can feel him. Feeling him allows my heart to relax. Knowing him makes me smile. Another text appears.

Marvel: wanna meet today?

I smile. I feel excitement and nervousness at the same time.

Me: sure!

I make my way down the stairs. Of course the kids are up. I have breakfast with them, and then help them gather their belongings to go back to their dad's again, although there is not much to gather these day because they have duplicates at both homes. They are pretty self-sufficient too. They always have been. They were taught to be accountable for their own lives. They were taught to get stuff done, make stuff happen. That is where happiness lies, through the mind, through thought, by thinking things out, and being one step ahead of everyone else. You can say that they are all mentalists, like me. Control your surroundings so you will feel safe. Be ahead of everyone else, no surprises.

Are my children really these things, or are they just copying my behaviors? Am I just seeing them through my own distorted filters? Not sure. I don't know where Chris comes from. He seems to live his life through feeling and intuition. He feels more like Marvel.

Oh, Jesus. Stop the thoughts, Dottie, and feel?

I have this feeling that our lives are about to change.

Oh my, I am actually considering this!

Just the fact that I am considering this makes my heart race again.

I shut the door behind them, turn around, and lean back against the curtains. "I can do this!"

I run upstairs to my phone to invite Marvel over here for the first time.

Two hours later, Marvel arrives at my house. He hesitantly walks into my house, noticing all the antiques in my home.

"Yeah, what?"

"Just noticing the antiques."

"I see that," I say. "What about them?"

"Nothing."

"Again, if we are going to do this, you will have to share more, ya know."

"Again, you my dear, might have to help me with that one."

"Sometimes I don't know what's going on in that brain of yours."

"Maybe nothing," Marvel says. "And do you mean my mind? Because my brain is just physical matter. It's my consciousness that holds the answers — my answers."

"You know what I mean."

"Then say what you mean."

"Are you trying to avoid the question?"

"No, not at all. Just be clear."

I smile at his preciseness.

"What?" he says.

"Nothing, I still think it's funny that you said that I wasn't well."

"I can't believe that you said that and you hadn't seen me in over twenty years."

"Well, it was true. Come on, you have to agree."

"True!" I say. "And I am so very thankful, sweetie."

I just called him 'sweetie!' I see his directness as kind of cute now — at least for the moment. What I hated was now I find it cute. I will probably find irritating once again if my patterns start kicking in again. Oh, I have a lot to learn about this kind of relationship.

"Hello, are you there, Dottie?"

"Yes."

"I believe the reason why I don't share everything, like you do, dear," Marvel says and chuckles at his implication that I share everything, "is because I was just used to processing things myself because no one understood. Nobody got it and nobody cared."

"Well I care!" I say. "So you better get used to this sharing stuff, okay?"

"Okay!" Marvel says with a smile. "And you sweetie, will learn how to communicate clearer. Remember what I told you about those patterns. They can sneak up on you."

I nod. "But let's take a break from patterning today. Let's say we just —"

Marvel interrupts my words by pressing his mouth to my lips.

My heart races.

I kiss him back. He looks into my eyes — it's as if I can see right into his soul. Eyes that I want to crawl into and see more. Lips that are sensual, not creepy, and not manipulative. But eyes that are kind — a kindness from some other place.

He grabs my face firmly and gives me a kiss that makes that love from some other place turn into love right here and now — right down through my body. He picks me up and places me gently on the couch. He looks at me again. No words from him.

Of course, I have lots of thoughts. I already knew that I loved him from that other place, but didn't know that he had it in him to make me pulsate. He is making my heart race, and every other part of my body. What is this feeling? It is a feeling in my body and my heart.

Stop the thoughts, Dottie.

As he continues to kiss me, I feel myself melting into the couch. He comes up for air and smiles at me. He then rests his head on my heart. I close my eyes …

DREAM:

"There is plenty more, ya know!" Glenda lightly touches me with her wand. "Touch, feelings, love, sex, intimacy, and more importantly, there is so much more to Marvel. You and Marvel! There is so much more on the other side of the rainbow."

I smile at her. Is this real life, Glenda? Or is this whole thing a dream?

A blending of realities take place. I see that I am in my living room. I know that I am on the couch.

"Do you believe it's real?" Glenda asks.

I open my eyes. My heart races.

Where am I? Breathe, Dottie.

Was this whole thing a dream?

309

I look around. My eyes search for something familiar.

I am on the couch in my living room, alone. Then my eyebrows raise up and I jump off the couch, and yell, "Where's Marvel?"

"I'm in here, love." Marvel gently responds appearing in the doorway of my kitchen, holding two glasses of water.

I smile at his words. "Hello, sweetie!" I answer. I sit back down on the couch.

"Welcome back," he says.

I sit up, still smiling.

Marvel sits down next to me placing the two glasses on the end table. "I didn't want to wake you. You felt so peaceful. No thoughts," he chuckles.

"Well, there were plenty of thoughts... in my dreams," I answer.

"Like what?"

"Glenda always has plenty to say."

"She does, does she?"

"Yes! Do you believe she is real outside of your dreams?" I smile. "Are dreams real. What the hell are dreams anyway?"

"Dreamland is in fact, 'The Land of Oz,' don't you see? The book *The Wonderful Wizard of Oz* is just a way to explain two different realities. Earth is Dorothy's life on the farm and the Land of Oz is Dorothy's inner life — her imagination and soul. But what you should understand, Dottie, is that dreamland is just a word that we use to understand things that are not seen.

"For the question becomes, which is the dreamland — your earth-life or dreamland. Dreamland becomes the ultimate reality. There is no ride inside a bubble, like in the movie. It's just your own bubble of consciousness. Some people call it teleportation, yet it's more than that. Some people call it the relocation of consciousness. So, Dottie, be in your own bubble, for Oz sake," he teases.

I laugh.

310

"You see, what they don't tell you in the book, is that the house didn't really knock Dorothy out, it woke her ass up. It didn't put her to sleep. It woke her up from the dreamland she was living in."

I move myself over on Marvel's lap, straddling him to give him a bear hug.

"It woke her ass up! That's funny." Marvel laughs hysterically repeating his words and seems to not even notice or care that I am not joining in.

"We have access to everything. We can create anything here. You must be in a dream-like experience to believe that you are, let's say not good enough. If you believe you are not good enough, then you're not good enough. And the problem with dreams is that when you are not conscious, you believe that the dreams are real. This traps you in the dream, and all of its limitations."

I smile. *My man is on a roll.*

"This actually goes back to the ancient traditions that this world is an illusion. And we all have to remember that we are the wizards of our own life."

I kiss his neck. *He is so very cute.*

"Do you want to dream or do you want to live your dreams. Do you want to consciously create your own dreams or do you want to be a victim to your dreams? How do you want to dream this dream you are dreaming? What do you want to experience? Do you want to wake up and become the dreamer who is creating the dream? Or do you want to wake up and be the creator creating the dream, or while dreaming the dream knowing that you are dreaming and creating? That's called conscious or awakened dreaming. So, what would you like to do? What would you like to be, my love, the creator or the dreamer?"

"Shh, Marvel," I whisper as I touch his lips with my finger. "Let's pretend I didn't just ask that dream question."

I lean back so I can see his beautiful face and say, "Marvel, you are here now and I love you. I want to experience you. I want to dream with you. I want to create with you. And of course, create with you issue free and pattern free." I add smiling, "What do you say?"

Marvel looks deep into my eyes, places his hand on my heart, and says, "Okay, love!"

We start to kiss.

Suddenly, Glenda appears and lightly touches me on my shoulder with her wand.

I wave Glenda away. I then continue kissing Marvel. I close my eyes.

"Dorothy, Dorothy! There is so much more over the rainbow," she says with a smile moving around behind Marvel, facing me. "There is plenty more to come! Okay, I can see you are busy now. See ya the next time."

I open my eyes.

We want to hear from you

Adele Saccarelli-Cavallaro
215.680.2351

Michael Cavallaro
267.421.6667

adeleandmichaelllc@gmail.com
www.adeleandmichael.com

@dottieandmarvel
dottieandmarvel@gmail.com

Made in the USA
Middletown, DE
30 September 2017